Mrs. William Simpson Standardsville

Jan. 1, 1924

Jan 1, 1924

Heavens Fold, Glacier National Park, Mont. From forest to peak 2000 feet. (U. S. Senate Report No. 580.)

HIGH SCHOOL

GEOGRAPHY

PHYSICAL, ECONOMIC, AND REGIONAL

BY

CHARLES REDWAY DRYER, F.G.S.A., F.R.G.S.
FORMERLY PROFESSOR OF GEOGRAPHY AND GEOLOGY
INDIANA STATE NORMAL SCHOOL
AUTHOR OF "LESSONS IN PHYSICAL GEOGRAPHY"

REVISED EDITION

AMERICAN BOOK COMPANY
NEW YORK CINCINNATI CHICAGO BOSTON ATLANTA

Dr. H. S. Geog.

E–P 13

PREFACE

THAT the better part of geography is to be found in a study of relationships is the conviction of all geographers. Only by such study can an affirmative answer be given to Jowett's question, "Can geography be used to make students think?" There is no subject which presents a greater number and variety of relationships than geography. It leaves hardly any field of human knowledge untouched, and is the mutual debtor and creditor of all. It is capable of yielding a purely scientific discipline "uncontaminated with the worship of usefulness," and it can be made as baldly "practical" as the commercial spirit requires. The higher interests of education demand a judicious combination of pure and applied science.

The most important thing about the earth is the fact that it is a human planet, that men not only live upon it, but make, somehow, a living out of it. The earth as a planet, a machine which "goes" and "works," an organism which has grown and developed in the past and will continue to do so in the future, has never been so thoroughly studied and understood as it is to-day. The main result of such study, under the name of physical geography, has been a favorite subject in secondary schools. Some special phases of human activity, more or less closely related to the earth, such as products, manufactures, trade, races, customs, language, religion, and government, are everywhere taught under the names of commercial and political geography. But these different kinds of geography are seldom brought closely together, and the crowning relationship of all geographic science, the relation of the human species to its natural environment, is generally missed or but dimly seen.

To get a view of the earth, not only as the home of man, but as the garden in which he has grown, the school in which he has been educated and civilized, the environment in which still higher ideals may be attained, is the object of modern geographical study. This can be accomplished only by taking an economic standpoint, from which the dependence of human life upon natural conditions and the influence of those conditions upon human life can be most clearly seen. This book is an attempt to present such a view and to treat the leading facts and principles of geography as factors in the human struggle for a better living, that is, for the highest possible civilization. Physical geography, a view of the earth as it would be if no man had ever lived upon it, forms the necessary basis. The first part of this book is called physical geography because the principal subject discussed in it is the natural earth, but the treatment is more brief than in many recent textbooks. Many topics of great interest to the student of pure science are omitted or lightly touched, preference being given to those features and processes which have directly "helped or hindered man in his progress." The fact is constantly kept in mind that man is himself a part of nature and the picture is painted from the beginning against a strong background of human life.

The second part is called economic geography because the point of view is reversed, and the outlines of household management practiced by the great human family in its terrestrial home are presented against the background of the natural earth already shown. It is hoped that by this method of treatment the peculiar interest and value of physical geography will not be lost, while its use as a foundation for economic geography will give added attraction and stability to both. Parts I and II are planned to furnish as much material as can be used in a high school course of five or six months.

For those schools which devote a longer period to the study of geography, Part III furnishes a more detailed, intimate, and graphic study of the same theme. The natural earth is still the basis and is divided into natural provinces arranged in a few groups, forming typical environments in which the economic adaptations of human life must be broadly similar, varying only with the stage of civilization of the inhabitants. Where the civilization of a natural environment is not native, but has been introduced from some other more favorable environment, interesting contrasts appear; but in every case the possibilities are strictly limited by natural conditions. North America is found to present all the typical natural environments of the world except the strictly equatorial. A detailed discussion of these with references, more or less extended, to similar environments in other parts of the world, serves to bring out all the principal kinds of adaptation to natural environment which the human race has achieved, and gives a bird's-eye view of world economies. This part of the book comes near to being a concrete example of a recent definition of economic geography as "the study of the different types of environments in the relations they bear to the activities of human life."

The treatment by natural rather than by political and, consequently, artificial divisions is attended by no serious difficulty except in the handling of statistics, which are always compiled according to political units. The result is some slight want of exactness in figures, but as these are constantly changing, the defect is not great. The author recognizes the fact that such treatment is an innovation in some degree revolutionary; but he believes that the advantage it gives in showing the essential relationships of geography more than compensates for all difficulties, and that when once understood it will be accepted and welcomed.

Reports of committees of the National Education Association and of the Association of American Geographers have recently outlined in some detail courses in geography for secondary schools. While this book has not been written on the plan of conforming to the requirements of either, it will be found to cover substantially the ground of both.

An unusual number and variety of maps have been introduced in the hope of leading teachers and students to a better appreciation and use of this unrivaled method of geographical expression.

TABLE OF CONTENTS

PART I. PHYSICAL GEOGRAPHY

PART II. ECONOMIC GEOGRAPHY

PART III. REGIONAL GEOGRAPHY

PART I. PHYSICAL GEOGRAPHY

CHAPTER I

EARTH, SUN, AND MOON

The Earth is a globular mass of rock, water, and air, tied to the sun by gravitation and revolving around it at a distance of about 93,000,000 miles. The core or central body of the earth is probably a solid ball of hot nickel-iron, with an outer crust largely composed of oxygen and silicon combined with other elements to form various kinds of rocks. The whole solid earth may be called the *rock sphere* (*lithosphere*). The depressions in the crust are occupied by a thin sheet of water which covers nearly three fourths of its surface and constitutes the *water sphere* (*hydrosphere*). The rock and water spheres are surrounded and inclosed by an *atmosphere* of nitrogen, oxygen, and other gases, the extent of which is not definitely known.

Fig. 1. — Section of part of the earth.

The atmosphere is as truly a part of the earth as the rock, but this fact is often disregarded and the word *earth* is used to mean only the solid and liquid mass. In this sense the earth is a slightly compressed spheroid, its polar diameter being 7,899.6 miles, its equatorial diameter 7,926.6 miles, and its circumference about 24,900 miles.

Men do not live upon the surface of the earth, which is the outer surface of the atmosphere, but hundreds of miles below, on or near the surface of the rock and water spheres, which is commonly called *the face* of the earth.

The Sun is a bright star, about 110 times the diameter of the earth. The body of the sun is surrounded by an atmosphere consisting of white-hot vapors of various metals, which radiate heat and light in every direction. The heat and light from the sun penetrate the earth's atmosphere and reach the land and water. The earth rotates on its shortest axis once in 24 hours, thus exposing different sides to the sun and causing an alternation of sunlight and shadow, or day and night. The rotation of the earth is clearly shown by the apparent movement of the stars from east to west.

Latitude and Longitude. — The earth's rotation not only divides time into short periods of light and darkness, but also furnishes fixed points from which to measure distances and fix locations.

If a mark is made upon the surface of a smooth, uniformly colored ball, it is impossible to describe its position for want of other points of reference. If the ball is set to spinning like a top, the rotation establishes an axis and two poles at opposite ends of it. A line may be drawn around the ball midway between the poles which will be an *equator*, or divider of the surface into two equal parts. A line may also be drawn from pole to pole at right angles to the equator. Then the position of any point on the ball may be determined and described by its angular distance from each of these lines. This is the meaning and purpose of latitude and longitude.

Latitude (breadth) is angular distance from the equator toward each pole and is measured in degrees up to 90 degrees. *Longitude* (length) is angular distance from a line arbitrarily fixed at right angles to the equator, each way around to the opposite side of the earth, and is measured in degrees up to 180 degrees. For convenience a set of lines is imagined or drawn parallel with the equator, called *parallels*, and another set at right angles to the equator, called *meridians*. These lines form a network, which divides the face of the earth into quadrangles indispensable in surveying and mapping.

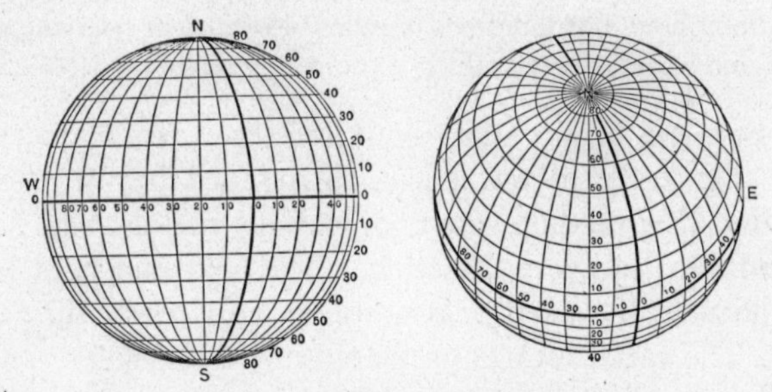

Fig. 2. — Parallels and meridians.

The number of parallels and meridians is unlimited. Portions of some of them are surveyed and located on the ground and form boundaries of states, counties, townships, and sections. They are drawn upon a map at any convenient distance apart, and the network is used to locate the desired features. The meridian passing through Greenwich, near London, is now used as a base line or prime meridian throughout the world. The axis of the earth always maintains the same direction in space, the north end of it looking toward a point in the heavens near the star Polaris, "the north star." To an observer at the equator Polaris is on the northern horizon (Fig. 3); but if he travels northward the star rises higher above the horizon until at the north pole it is directly overhead. Hence directions and latitude may be determined by observing the stars.

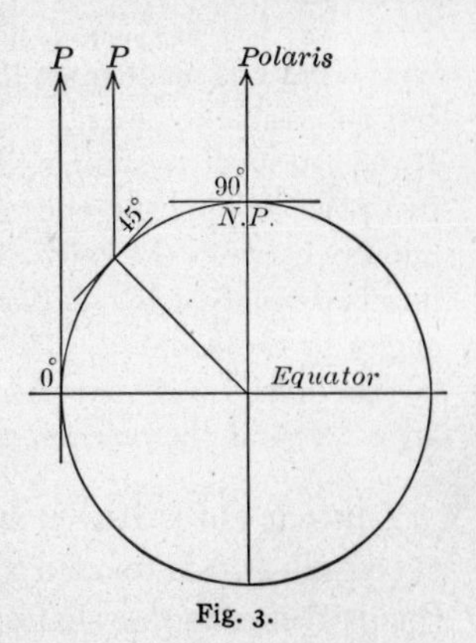

Fig. 3.

The Seasons. — The earth revolves around the sun in a nearly circular orbit, requiring a little more than 365 days to complete one revolution. The revolution of the earth may be seen by noticing that the groups of stars visible at any given hour of the night change from week to week, and month to month. If the axis of the earth were perpendicular to the plane of its orbit, its revolution would bring no change except in the appearance of the heavens at night, and would be of little importance; for in that case the line dividing the lighted side of the earth from the dark side would always pass through the poles, half of the

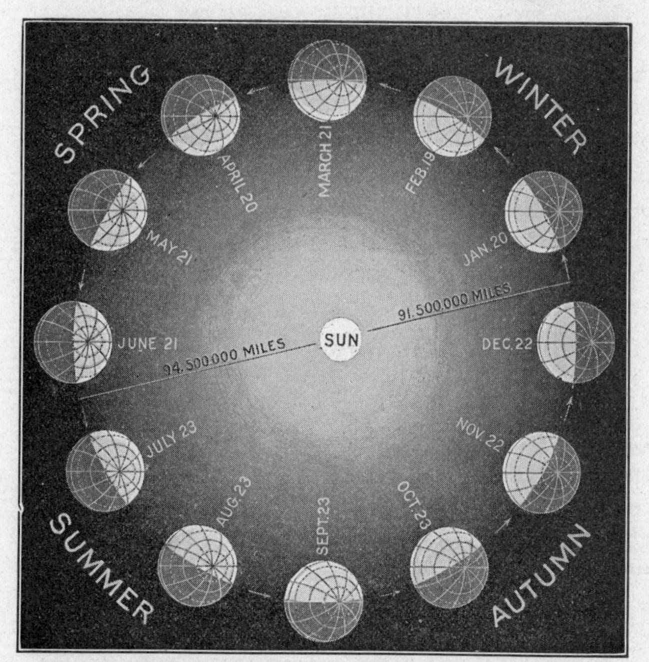

Fig. 4. — Position of the northern hemisphere throughout the year.

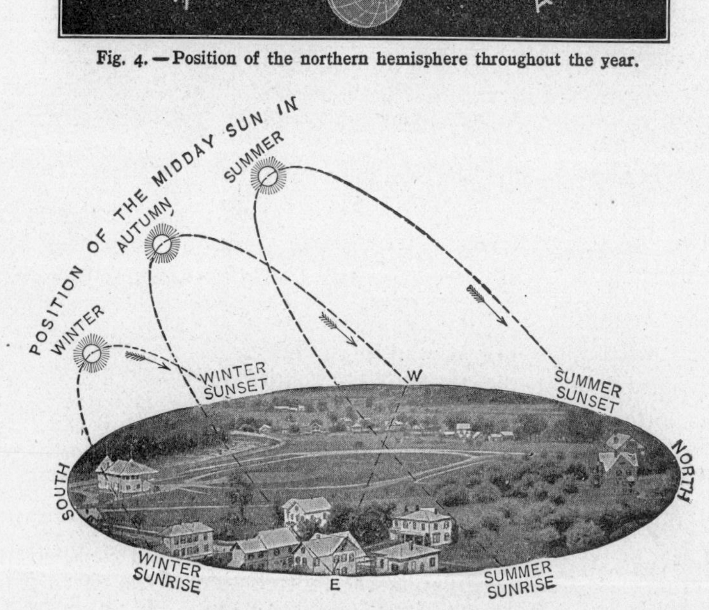

Fig. 5. — (From Todd's New Astronomy.)

northern and half of the southern hemisphere would always be in the light, and day and night would be everywhere and always of equal length, as in Fig. 6 *B*. But the earth's axis is inclined about 23° 30′ from a perpendicular to the plane of its orbit, and always in the same direction. As the earth moves around the sun, the northern and southern hemispheres are turned toward the sun alternately and each in turn receives more than an equal share of sunlight, as in Fig. 6 *A* and *C*. When either hemisphere is turned toward the sun, every place in it is in sunlight more than half the time, and the days are longer than the nights. When it is turned away from the sun the reverse is true.

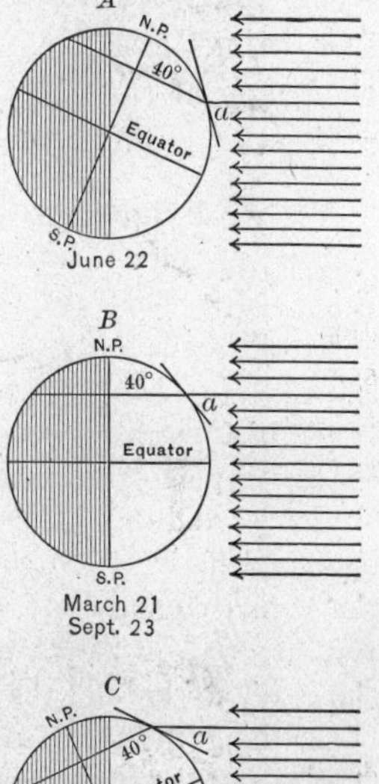

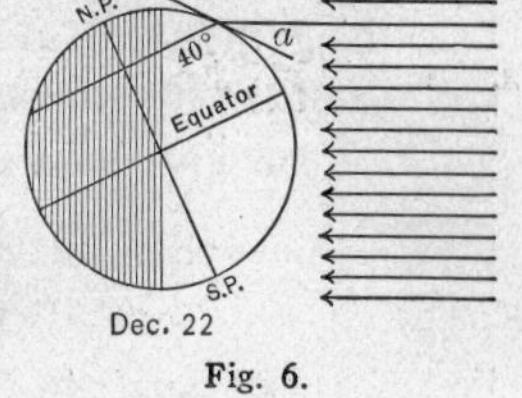

Fig. 6.

Fig. 4 shows the conditions in the northern hemisphere for each month of the year. Fig. 5 shows the apparent path of the sun in the heavens at different seasons in middle northern latitudes. The long path of the sun above the horizon in summer brings long days and a warm season; the short path in winter brings short days and a cold season.

The sun's rays have greater heating power at noon than in the morning or evening because they then pass through less air,

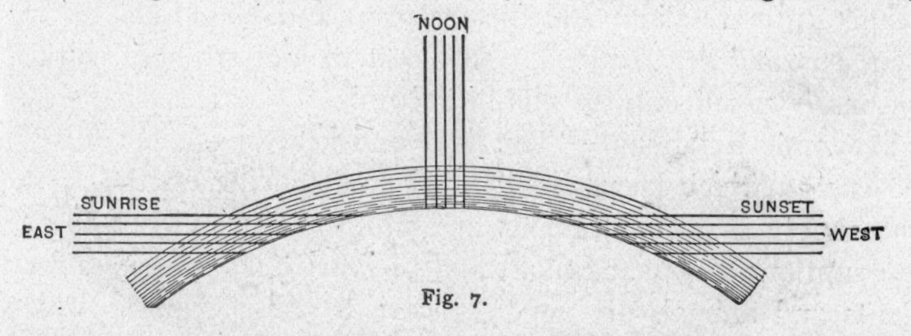

Fig. 7.

strike the earth more nearly at right angles, and are spread over less surface (Fig. 7). When the days are long the sun's rays are more nearly direct and their heating power is greater than when the days are short. Thus the inclination of the earth's axis brings about a variation in the length of the day and in the angle of the sun's rays, and these changes work together to make the months successively warmer or colder.

The most important points in this cycle of changes are: (1) *The vernal equinox*, March 21, when the sun is vertical at the equator and shines to either pole. The days and nights are everywhere of equal length and the angle of the sun's rays is the same at corresponding latitudes in both hemispheres. (2) *The summer solstice*, June 22, when the sun is vertical at the tropic of Cancer, 23° 30′ north of the equator, and shines 23° 30′ beyond the north pole to the Arctic circle. In the northern hemisphere the days are longer and the sun's rays more direct than at any other date. (3) *The autumnal equinox*, September 23, when the conditions are the same as at the vernal equinox; (4) *The winter solstice*, December 22, when the sun's rays are vertical at the tropic of Capricorn, 23° 30′ south of the equator, shine 23° 30′ beyond the south pole to the Antarctic circle, and fall short of reaching the north pole. In the northern hemisphere the days are shorter and the sun's rays are more slanting than at any other date. The change of conditions from one of these dates to the next is gradual.

The inequality of day and night and the variation in the angle of the sun's rays increase toward the poles; therefore the contrast between summer and winter increases in the same direction. The presence of permanent ice and snow in the polar regions renders the seasonal differences there less than they otherwise would be. Between the tropics the differences of temperature are slight and the seasons are distinguished as wet (summer) and dry (winter). The year of four strongly marked seasons is found only in middle latitudes.

Economic Relations. — The light and heat of the sun furnish the energy which keeps things alive and moving on the earth. The supply is not continuous and uniform, but subject to the interruptions of day and night and the variations of the seasons. Plants and animals are very sensitive to these changes, which impose upon them alternating periods of activity and rest. Outside the polar regions, every space of 24 hours is divided into a period of daylight and a period of darkness. In daylight plants and animals, including man, are generally active in obtaining food and acquiring whatever is necessary or desired for subsistence. Darkness is generally a period of rest during which they assimilate food, build up tissue, repair waste, and renew strength. For men the regular and frequent recurrence of periods of sleep, preferably during the hours of darkness, is absolutely necessary to health and efficiency.

The influence of change of seasons upon plants is very great. In equatorial regions vegetation is luxuriant at all times, but alternations of wet and dry periods induce some variation in the rate of growth. Where the contrast of seasons is strong, more than half the plants pass the cold or dry season in the form of seed, and more than half the animals live less than a year. Many animals live over the winter by migrating to a warmer region, by using the food stored during the summer, or by lying torpid. Men whose occupation is directly dependent upon plants, as farmers and gardeners, do little through the winter, or change their work.

Solar and Civil Days. — The rotation and revolution of the earth furnish two units for reckoning time, the day and the year. The period from the moment when the sun reaches his highest point in the heavens and is on the meridian, to the moment when he next reaches the same point, varies from day to day. The average length of this period is divided into the hours, minutes, and seconds shown by ordinary clocks and watches. For convenience the ordinary or civil day is made to begin and end at midnight, and is of the same length in every part of the world. Inside the polar circles the civil day does not always correspond to actual day and night, since the time from sunrise to sunset varies from a few minutes to six months.

If the earth's face were plane, sunrise, noon, and sunset would each occur over every part of it at the same moment, but as the spheroidal earth rotates, sunrise, noon, and sunset travel continuously westward at the rate of 15 degrees of longitude every hour. When it is noon at Greenwich it is about 7.00 A.M. at New York, 6.00 at St. Louis, 5.00 at Denver, and 4.00 at San Francisco. So each meridian has its own sun time, slower and earlier than the meridians east of it, faster and later than those west of it. The longitude of any place may be measured by the difference of time between it and Greenwich, one degree for every four minutes.

Standard Time. — For people who stay at home their own local mean sun time is the most convenient; but for travelers, and especially for railroad companies, it is advantageous to

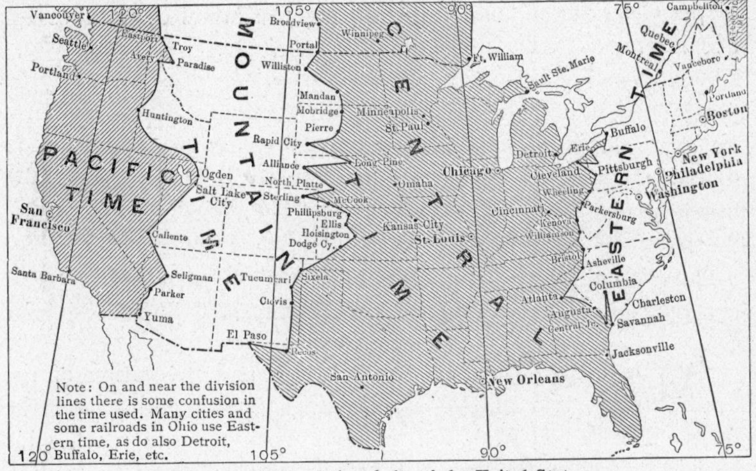

Fig. 8. — Standard time belts of the United States.

adopt standard meridians 15°, or one hour, apart, and to use the time of each meridian over a certain area on each side of it. In North America five standard time belts are in use: Atlantic or 60th meridian time (four hours slower than Greenwich time), Eastern or 75th meridian time, Central or 90th meridian time, Mountain or 105th meridian time, and Pacific or 120th meridian time. The boundaries of these belts are irregular. When a traveler crosses the boundary of a time belt, he sets his watch forward, or back, one hour. Nearly all civilized countries have adopted standard time meridians.

International Date Line. — If one travels westward, sun time becomes slower at the rate of one hour for every 15 degrees of longitude, and in going around the earth a watch must be set back, in all, 24 hours, which would cause the traveler to lose one day from his calendar. If he travels eastward, sun time grows faster at the same rate, and a watch must be set ahead to correspond. Thus one would add a day to his calendar. Hence it is found necessary to fix upon an arbitrary line for the correction of the calendar. This is called the international date line, and for all vessels is the meridian of 180°. Whenever a ship crosses this line to the westward, a day is added to the reckoning, but if to the eastward, a day is dropped from it.

The Calendar. — The calendar now in use in most of the civilized world was adopted by Pope Gregory XIII in 1582. The earth completes one revolution around the sun in 365 d. 5 h. 48 m. 46 s. The calendar is made to agree approximately with the solar year by having three successive years of 365 days each and then a leap year of 366 days. An extra day added every fourth year is a little too much, and therefore century years, like 1900 and 2000, are leap years only when divisible by 400.

The Moon, Month, and Week. — The division of the year into months and weeks was originally suggested by the changes

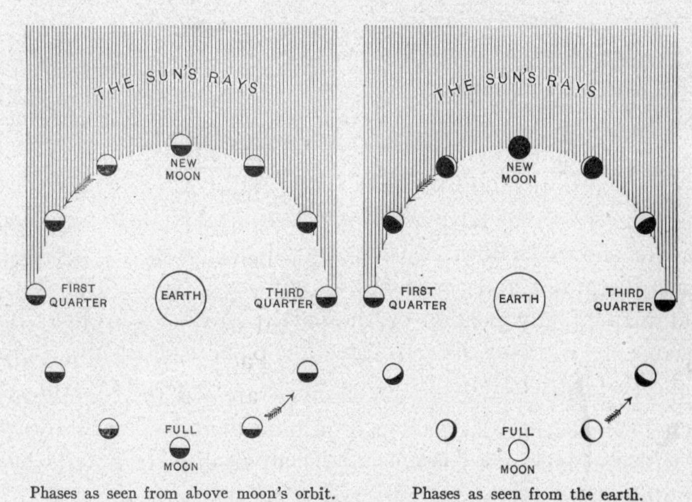

Phases as seen from above moon's orbit. Phases as seen from the earth.

Fig. 9.

of the moon. The moon revolves around the earth from west to east in about $29\frac{1}{2}$ days. When it is between the earth and the sun the dark side is turned toward us and is called new moon (Fig. 9). About a week later half of the lighted side is visible and is called first quarter. When the moon is on the opposite side of the earth from the sun its lighted side is turned toward us and is called full moon. Then again, about a week later, half the lighted side is visible and is called last quarter. The intervals between these changes are variable, but average about seven days. The calendar weeks and months do not coincide with the periods or phases of the moon, and the number of days in successive months varies in an arbitrary and irregular manner.

The year is naturally divided by the solstices and equinoxes into four seasons: spring, March 21 to June 22, 93 days; summer, June 22 to September 23, 93 days; autumn, September 23 to December 22, 90 days; winter, December 22 to March 21, 89 or 90 days. Although the Gregorian calendar is imperfectly adjusted to the natural time periods of day, week, month, and year, any change in it would cause so much disturbance and confusion as to make it undesirable, if not impossible.

Maps and Map Projections. — The special means of expression in geography is the map, because a map shows the facts of distribution better than anything else can. A map is a drawing which shows the position, direction, distance, and area of objects upon a horizontal plane, as though a portion of the earth's surface were stripped off, spread out flat, and reduced in size. The one thing essential for a good map is that the position of every feature shown be located correctly; if this is done, the directions, distances, and areas will be correct. No absolutely correct map of any portion of the earth's surface can be drawn, because it is impossible to flatten a spherical surface into a plane surface without distorting it.

The indispensable basis and guide in the construction of a map is the network of parallels and meridians. Numerous projections or plans for drawing the parallels and meridians are in common use. Some show the forms more correctly than others, some distort forms for the sake of showing areas correctly, while others are very erroneous as to forms and areas but correct as to directions. The best maps for common use are designed to show forms, areas, and directions with as little error as possible.

The *orthographic* projection (Fig. 10) is a picture of a globe as it appears from a distance many times its diameter. Straight parallel lines, projected through the parallels and meridians of the globe upon a plane surface perpendicular to them, locate the network of the map. Such a map is correct near the center, but around the edges the areas are greatly reduced.

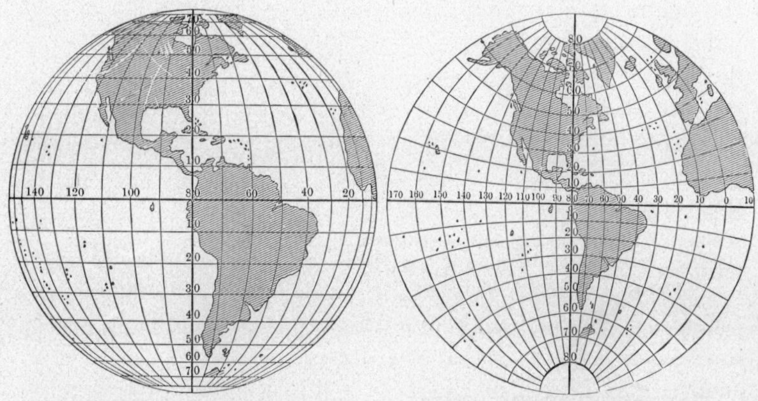

Fig. 10.—Orthographic projection.

Fig. 11.—Stereographic projection.

The *stereographic* projection (Fig. 11) is a picture of a transparent hemisphere as it would appear to the eye placed at the middle point of the surface of the opposite hemisphere. In this map the areas are reduced near the center and enlarged toward the edges.

The *globular* projection (Fig. 12) is a picture of a transparent hemisphere as it would appear to the eye placed at a distance 1.707 times the radius of the sphere from its center. In this map the parallels along any meridian and the meridians along any parallel are very nearly equidistant. It shows

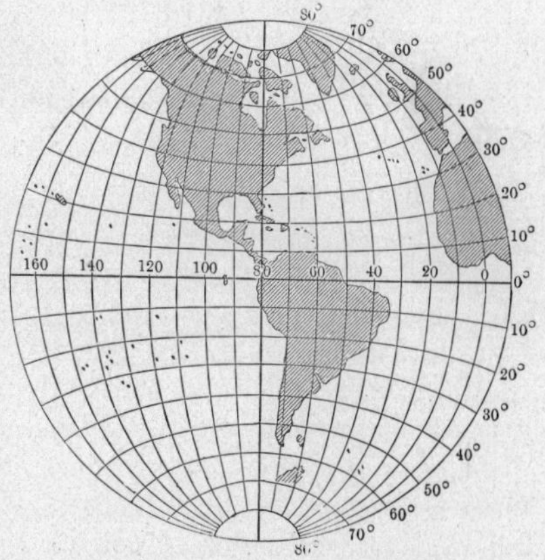

Fig. 12.—Globular projection.

both form and area with less error than any other projection, and is especially advantageous for maps of the hemispheres used in teaching.

In the *cylindrical* projection the surface of the sphere is conceived to be that of a cylinder of the same diameter, cut lengthwise and flattened out. The meridians are straight, parallel, and equidistant. If the parallels are projected stereographically, the length of the cylinder is twice the diameter of the sphere (Fig. 13 *A*), and areas are increasingly exaggerated toward the poles.

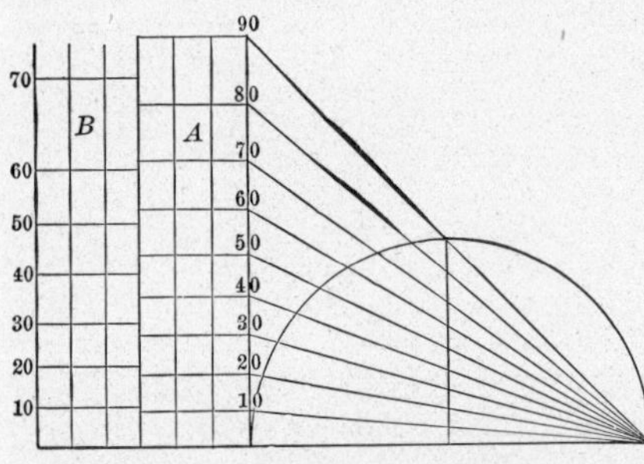

Fig. 13. — Cylindrical projections.

Mercator's projection (Figs. 13 *B* and 14) is cylindrical, but the parallels are so spaced that the degrees of latitude are proportional to the degrees of longitude. It is the only projection on which directions are absolutely correct, and hence it is much used by sailors. It is the best for maps of winds and ocean currents in which true directions are required. Cylindrical projections have the advantage of showing all the more important parts of the earth upon one continuous sheet, but on account of the enormous exaggeration and distortion of areas in the higher latitudes, they should never be used in teaching children and should always be corrected by reference to a globe.

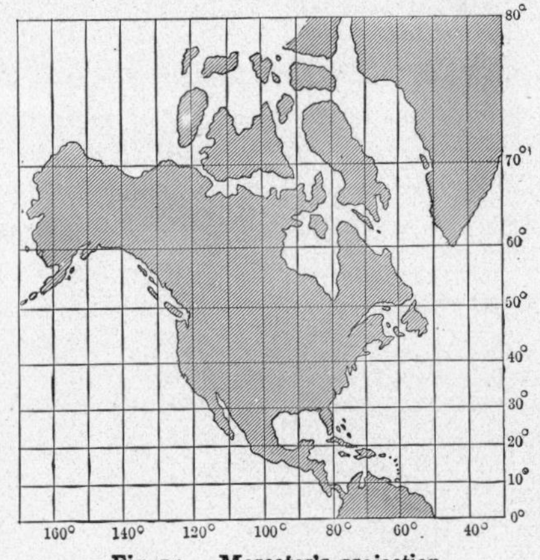

Fig. 14.— Mercator's projection.

Mollweide's equal-area projection (Fig. 16) shows the whole face of the earth upon one continuous sheet, one hemisphere in the center and half of the other on each side. Near the center forms are but slightly distorted and distances are nearly correct. In the marginal portions distortion is considerable, and north-south distances are exaggerated; but this projection has the advantage of showing areas correctly. Hence it is used for maps in which a comparison of areas is important.

In the *conical* projection (Fig. 15) the surface represented is conceived to be that of a cone cut lengthwise and flattened out. The parallels are arcs of equidistant, concentric circles, and the meridians are radiating straight lines intersecting the parallels at right angles. For areas of no great extent in latitude, such as the United States, a map on this projection is very nearly correct.

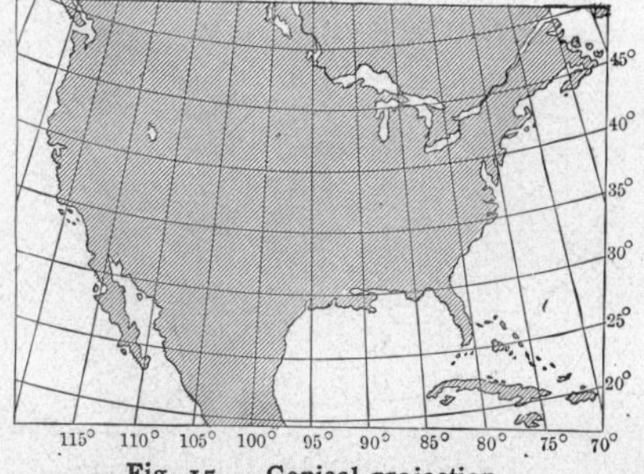

Fig. 15. — Conical projection.

Map Scales. — The scale of a map is the ratio which distances and areas on the map bear to the actual distances and areas on the earth. Scales are expressed by ratios, as 1 : 1,000,000, which means that one inch on the map corresponds to one million inches on the earth; or in linear units, as 1 inch = 1 mile; or by graduated lines. For small areas the scale may be large, one foot or more to the mile; for large areas it must be small. On maps of large areas no uniform scale can apply exactly to all parts.

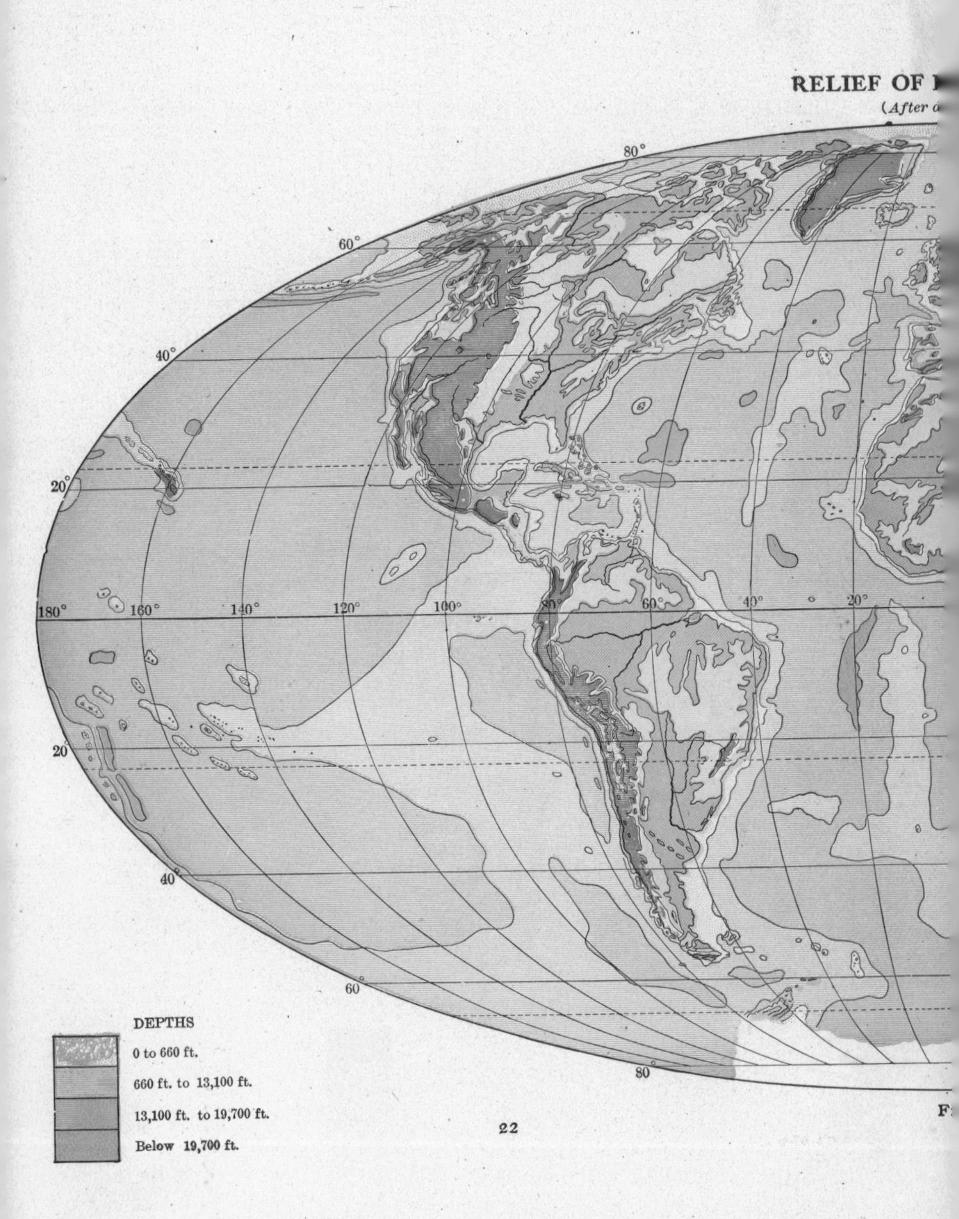
RELIEF OF
(After
DEPTHS
0 to 660 ft.
660 ft. to 13,100 ft.
13,100 ft. to 19,700 ft.
Below 19,700 ft.
80°
60°
40°
20°
180°
160°
140°
120°
100°
80°
60°
40°
20°
20°
40
60
80

RTH CRUST

ırtonne)

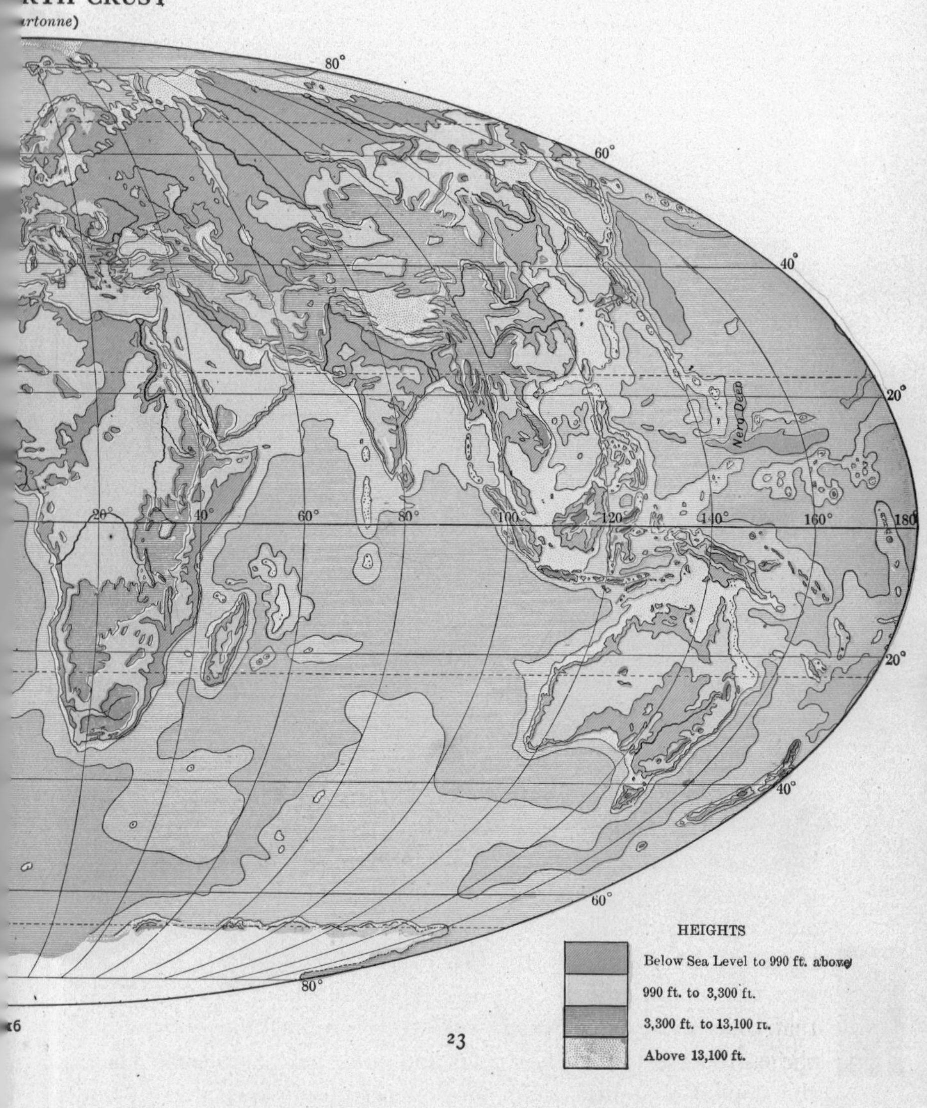

HEIGHTS

Below Sea Level to 990 ft. above

990 ft. to 3,300 ft.

3,300 ft. to 13,100 ft.

Above 13,100 ft.

CHAPTER II

THE PLAN OF THE EARTH

The Earth Crust. — If the water were out of the way so that the whole surface of the earth crust could be seen, two contrasted areas would appear. One third of it is a broad, irregular, elevated table or platform, roughened by mountains, plateaus, hills, and valleys. The rest of it is a steep-sided, smooth-bottomed depression, lying about $2\frac{2}{3}$ miles below the elevated surface. The elevated area is the *continental platform,* and the depressed area is the *oceanic basin.* The highest point known (Mt. Everest in central Asia) is 29,000 feet above sea level, and the lowest point known (Planet Deep, near the Philippine Islands, western Pacific Ocean) is 32,078 feet below sea level. The difference or range of elevation is about $11\frac{1}{2}$ miles.

This is only one seven-hundredth part of the diameter of the solid earth, and if represented upon a globe seven feet in diameter would be about one eighth of an inch. The earth crust is much smoother in proportion to its size than the skin of an orange.

The Margin of the Continental Platform. — The sea water not only fills the oceanic basin full, but also spreads out over the lower part of the continental platform until the outer edge of the platform is about 660 feet under water. The continents and large islands all stand upon the platform and are bordered by a belt of shallow water (Fig. 16). The lowlands less than 660 feet above water, and the adjacent *continental shelf* less than 660 feet under water, constitute an unstable portion of the earth crust which has risen and sunk many times. Where the slope is so gentle, slight movements up or down make great changes in the outlines and area of the land.

If the crust should rise 660 feet, the shore line would recede to the outer edge of the shelf and the total land area would be increased about 20 per cent. If the crust should sink 660 feet, the shore line would advance upon the land and about 30 per cent of the present land area would be flooded by the sea. Much greater up-and-down movements than these have occurred in the past. Rivers carry down the waste of the land and deposit it upon the continental shelf, spreading out material for the rock strata of new lands which may sometime rise from the sea. The shallow waters of the shelf are the home of abundant plant and animal life, and the site of the great fishing grounds of the world. Because of the shallowness tides rise higher along the shores than they do in deep water, and make it possible for large ships to reach ports like Montreal, Glasgow, and London, situated far up the bays and rivers. The relations of the continental shelf to the land and its inhabitants are far closer than those of the deep ocean basins.

Arrangement of the Great Crust Features. — The continental platform which supports the great land masses forms a nearly continuous belt around the earth at about 70° N. Lat. (Fig. 16). From this belt three arms extend southward, the American to about 57° S. Lat., the Eurafrican to about 37° S. Lat., and the Asia-Australian to about 45° S. Lat. An Antarctic continent of undefined extent surrounds the south pole. The oceanic basin forms a continuous belt around the earth at about 60° S. Lat., from which three arms extend northward, interlocking with the continental arms. Of these the Pacific basin is roughly circular in outline, the Atlantic arm is long, narrow, and S-shaped, while the Indian arm is short and broadly triangular. The Arctic basin occupies an area around the north pole, the limits of which are not accurately known. Each continental arm is broken nearly midway of its length by a cross projection of the oceanic basin, the American by the Gulf of Mexico and Caribbean Sea, the Eurafrican by the Mediterranean Sea, and the Asia-Australian by the straits of the Indian archipelago.

Land and Water Hemispheres. — About 70 per cent of the land lies north of the equator and about 58 per cent of the sea lies south of it. If a map of a hemisphere is drawn with London as a center, it will include about 82.5 per cent of all the land, and the opposite hemisphere with its center near New Zealand will include about 63 per cent of all the sea. The land hemisphere thus drawn is 46.7 per cent land, and the water hemisphere is 90 per cent sea (Figs. 17 and 18).

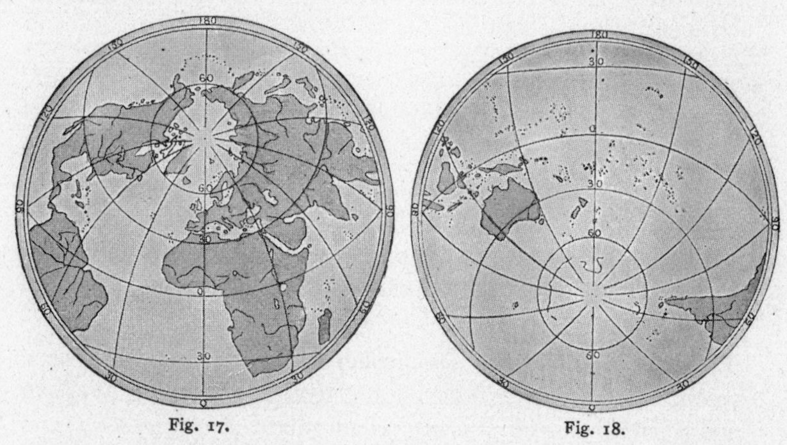

Fig. 17. Fig. 18.

The Arrangement of Land Masses. — The continental land masses conform roughly to the position and shape of the continental platform and are thus divided into seven continents, Europe, Asia, and North America lying close together in the northern hemisphere; South America, Africa, Australia, and Antarctica lying wholly or partly in the southern hemisphere, and more widely separated from one another.

Fig. 19.

If a globe is viewed in such a position that the center of Asia (E. Long. 90°, N. Lat. 50°) is the center of the visible hemisphere (Fig. 19), it will be seen that the other continents are arranged around Asia with some approach to symmetry. Europe is but a large peninsula projecting westward. Africa lies close against the southwestern shores of Eurasia, and

is tied to it by the Isthmus of Suez and the shelf at the mouth of the Red Sea. Directly northward of Asia, across the narrow polar basin, lies North America, connected by the shelf of Bering Sea and Strait. To the east of south the submarine platform of the Malay archipelago stretches away to Australia. In past ages America and Australia have been connected with Asia, and Africa with Europe, by land bridges, and to-day every part of the continental lands except Antarctica can be reached from Asia without crossing a strait more than 250 miles wide. The central position of Asia and the continuity of the radiating arms of the continental platform, furnishing easy routes of travel to nearly all habitable lands, have been of great importance in controlling the migration and dispersal of plants, animals, and men. There would be no insuperable difficulty in building a continuous railroad from Cape Horn to the Cape of Good Hope, with branch lines to Liverpool and Lisbon, while Australia could be connected with the system by a short ocean ferry.

Eastern and Western Hemispheres. — The earth has been somewhat arbitrarily divided into an Eastern and a Western Hemisphere. In the Eastern Hemisphere Europe, Asia, and Africa compose the "Old World"; in the Western Hemisphere North and South America are called the "New World." There is no reason to think that any part of the land of the Old World is actually older than some parts of the New World. The human species probably originated in Asia, and the earliest records of human history are found in Asia and Africa, but Australia was not discovered by Europeans until 100 years after the discovery of America by Columbus. Asia and Europe form physically one continuous land mass and are often treated as one continent under the name of Eurasia, but for historic reasons geographers usually regard them as distinct.

Northern and Southern Continents. — The continents naturally fall into two groups which are strongly contrasted in physical characters, in their relations to plant and animal life, and in the part they play in human history. About four fifths of the area of the northern continents lies in those temperate latitudes which are most favorable for the development of human faculties; while about four fifths of the area of the southern continents lies in the hot belts, between the parallels of latitude 30° north

and south, where the climate is oppressive and plants and animals are either absent on account of aridity, or are able on account of humidity to compete successfully with man in the struggle for possession. The southern continents are isolated from the northern and from one another and are relatively inaccessible. They contain less than one eighth of the world's population. Consequently they are in their human relations, as well as in their physical conditions. subordinate appendages of the great northern land masses.

Asia. — The central and largest continent spreads a vast expanse from the equator far into the polar regions, too shapeless to suggest any geometrical figure. The eastern side presents to the Pacific a belt of mountainous peninsulas and off-shore islands, which border the shelf for 6,000 miles. The southern margin is cut by deep notches into three massive peninsulas. On the west it is imperfectly separated from Europe by the Black and Caspian basins, and other depressions which once connected them with the Arctic Ocean. On the north low plains slope gently to the icy sea. The body of the continent consists of a mass of plateaus and mountains, the loftiest in the world, the culminating core of which is Tibet.

From the Tibetan center, highlands trend southeastward toward Australia, northeastward toward America, westward into Europe, and southwestward into Africa. The average elevation of Asia is 3,120 feet, 25 per cent of it is below 660 feet, and 14 per cent is above 6,600 feet. Asia contains 30 per cent of all the land and more than half of all the people on the globe.

Europe, a westward projection from Asia between the Arctic Ocean and the Mediterranean Sea, is characterized by many peninsulas and inclosed seas, which penetrate far into the interior. These give it the longest coast line in proportion to its area of all the continents, and furnish unequaled facilities for travel and trade by water. The highlands of Asia are prolonged through southern Europe by less lofty ranges of folded mountains to the shores of the Atlantic. These are flanked by

plateaus and lesser ranges of moderate height. In the northwest the rugged peninsula of Scandinavia presents a bold front to the sea. The body of the continent is a low plain, no point of which is as much as 1,000 miles from the sea.

The mean height of Europe is 990 feet, 57 per cent of it is below 660 feet, and less than 2 per cent is above 6,600 feet. Although it contains only 6.7 per cent of the land, favorable conditions have made it the home of one fourth of the human race, and the dominant influence in modern civilization.

North America is built on the triangular plan, with its longest side next to the Pacific, extending in a double curve more than 6,000 miles, and bordered by the lofty Cordilleras. The continental limits are extended far northward by the half-drowned, ragged land patches of the Arctic archipelago, to which is attached the largest of islands, Greenland. The southeastern side is paralleled for about half its length by the low Appalachian highland. The southern extremity tapers off into the crooked Isthmus of Panama, which connects it with South America. The body of the continent is made up of the largest continuous low plain in the world. It resembles Eurasia as the left hand resembles the right, presenting to the Atlantic a low and broken coast, penetrated on the south by the Mexican and Caribbean mediterranean, on the north by Hudson Bay, and between the two by drowned river valleys, all of which give access to the interior plains.

Lying on the opposite side of the north Atlantic from Europe, and 2,000 to 3,000 miles distant, North America has felt the influence of European civilization more strongly than any other land. Like Eurasia, it faces the Atlantic and presents to the Pacific a high and forbidding back. Its average elevation is 2,300 feet, 33 per cent of it is below 660 feet, and 6 per cent is above 6,600 feet. Its area is 16 per cent of the land, and its population 7.5 per cent of the inhabitants of the world.

South America is a simplified copy of North America, resembling it in triangular form tapering southward, and in having a high western margin, low interior plains, and for the most part a low Atlantic coast. It is characterized by the smoothness of

its coast line and the magnitude of its rivers, of which the Amazon is, in area of basin and volume of discharge, the largest in the world.

Settlers have found it much more difficult to penetrate and occupy than North America, and its inhabitants, still largely of native Indian blood, are on the whole much less advanced in civilization. Its average elevation is 1,900 feet, 43 per cent is below 660 feet, and 9 per cent is above 6,600 feet. It contains 11 per cent of the land, and 2.4 per cent of the people of the world.

Africa resembles the Americas in triangular outline, but is the most compact and unbroken of the continents. About 70 per cent of its surface is a plateau with steep margins. Although its northern coasts are in close touch with Eurasia and have shared in its history and civilization, the great desert of Sahara has been an almost impassable barrier to penetration from that side. On the east and west, deserts, dense forests, rapids and falls in the rivers, and an unhealthful climate, have combined to prevent occupation and to retard progress in culture.

Its native peoples have remained for thousands of years in a condition of savagery which justifies the name of "the dark continent." Nearly every square mile of it is now under the influence and partial control of European people, and its future seems hopeful. Its average elevation is 2,130 feet, 15.4 per cent is below 660 feet, and 2.4 per cent is above 6,600 feet. It contains 20 per cent of the land area, and 8.6 per cent of the population of the world.

Australia, including New Guinea and Tasmania, is a simplified copy of Africa, with the southern extension greatly reduced in size. Its surface is largely a dry plateau, with folded mountains on the east and north (in New Guinea).

Isolated and cut off from the great centers of plant and animal life since early geologic times, all its indigenous inhabitants are of a very primitive type. On this account they offered little resistance to European colonists, who within the last century have taken complete possession of the habitable parts of the mainland. Its average elevation is 1,150 feet, 36 per cent is below 660 feet, and less than one per cent is above 6,600 feet. It now supports, on 6 per cent of the land area, one third of one per cent of the population of the world.

Antarctica. — That there is an area of continental land around the south pole, about half as large again as Europe, seems now to be definitely settled, but it is so deeply buried in snow and ice that its outlines and surface are imperfectly known. Its average elevation is twice as great as that of any other continent. It is now in the twentieth century becoming a field for systematic exploration. On account of severity of climate and difficulty of approach, sojourn, and travel, the progress of discovery will be slow and costly. It contains no permanent human inhabitants, and little life of any kind, except sea birds which nest and breed upon its coasts.

Islands. — Nearly all the large islands and many small ones stand upon the continental shelf and are therefore *continental*. Greenland, the Arctic archipelago, Newfoundland, and the Greater Antilles belong to North America; the British and Mediterranean islands to Europe; New Guinea and Tasmania to Australia; Ceylon, the Malay archipelago, the Philippines, Japan, Sakhalin, and Nova Zembla to Asia. Madagascar, New Zealand, Iceland, and perhaps Spitzbergen and Franz Josef Land occupy detached portions of the continental platform. The numerous small islands of the Pacific and some in other parts of the sea are the tops of submerged mountain ranges or volcanic peaks which rise from the deep sea floor, and are therefore *oceanic*.

Oceanic islands are of small area, isolated by wide stretches of deep water, and have little variety of resources. Consequently, they constitute an environment unfavorable for the development of the higher animals, including man. The part which they have played, or ever will play, in the life history of the globe is very small.

Summary. — The principal features of the land relief of the globe consist of a nearly continuous belt of highland near the shores of the Pacific and Indian oceans, and wide areas of lowland bordering the Atlantic and Arctic oceans. Consequently nearly all the large rivers flow into the Atlantic and Arctic, Asia only contributing streams of the first class to the Pacific and Indian drainage. These facts account for the greater importance, in modern times, of the Atlantic and of the lands bordering upon it.

CHAPTER III

WORLD ECONOMY

The earth is a sort of organism of which all the parts work together harmoniously like those of a plant or animal. No part of the earth is dead, but like a tree it is most active on the outside. Everything that goes on in the world is made possible by a multitude of conditions which probably do not exist in the same combination upon any other planet.

The position of the earth — its distance from the sun — determines the amount of heat which it receives. This is sufficient to maintain at all places upon the face of the earth a temperature which never falls lower than about 120 degrees below the freezing point of water (– 88° F.), and never rises higher than about 120 degrees above the freezing point (152° F.). This makes it possible for large quantities of water to exist in each of three forms — solid ice, liquid water, and gaseous vapor.

The form of the earth determines the angle at which the nearly parallel rays of the sun strike its face at different latitudes, and consequently the amount of heat received per square mile. This gives a variety of temperatures, ranging from the torrid to the frigid.

The attitude of the earth, or the inclination of its axis, in combination with its daily and yearly motions, determines a change of seasons, or variation of temperature, at all latitudes, and prevents both the constancy which would exist if the earth's axis were perpendicular to the plane of its orbit, and the excessive variation which would result if the axis were nearly parallel to that plane.

The revolution of the earth around the sun at a nearly uniform speed in an orbit which is nearly circular brings about the regular

succession of seasons and years, each of which is of moderate length. The succession of warm and cool, or wet and dry, seasons gives to plants and animals alternating periods of comparative rest and activity.

The rotation of the earth upon its axis exposes the greater part of its face to alternations of heat and cold, light and darkness, at short intervals, and imposes upon living beings correspondingly short and frequent periods of activity and rest. It also enables men to look out at night into space, see the moon and stars, and learn something of the universe of which the planet earth forms an insignificant part.

The structure of the earth includes solid, liquid, and gaseous spheres. The size and weight of the solid sphere largely determine the force of gravity, which is sufficient to prevent the atmosphere from escaping into space and to give it such composition and density as to support plant and animal life. The attraction of the earth also determines the weight of every object upon its face, and the strength or rigidity of plants and the muscular power of animals are nicely adapted to support or to move their own and other weights. The earth crust gives a firm support for all creatures which live upon the land, and to plants soil for anchorage and a storehouse of available food. The depressions in it form basins which hold most of the water and prevent it from covering the crust completely. Although the form and surface of the crust are continually changing, the changes are slow, and the crust is relatively the most fixed and stable part of the earth outside the core.

Circulating Systems. — In contrast with the rigidity of the crust, the fluid masses of water and air are very mobile and make it possible for extensive systems of currents to circulate in the atmosphere, in the sea, and on the land.

The air is seldom, if ever, perfectly still. Driven by the heat of the sun, it is rising, or settling, or moving horizontally in broad streams which cover thousands of miles and extend around the earth. The whole mass is whirling in great spirals from equator to poles and back again, forming a planetary wind system, analogous to the circulation of blood in animals. Driven by the winds, the surface waters of the ocean are in perpetual motion, drifting around and across the basins. The water of the sea evaporates, mingles with the air, spreads over the land, falls as rain or snow, and runs back again into the sea, completing a third circuit. The land is attacked by the air, worn away by the water, and carried into the sea. The water penetrates the earth crust and, circulating through it, dissolves, deposits, and concentrates metallic ores and other minerals, sometimes bringing them to the surface in mineral springs and geysers. Thus the earth has four great circulatory systems, active in its solid as well as its fluid parts, which keep its materials in motion and make its face to undergo perpetual change.

The water supplies plants and animals with food and also with a circulating fluid which distributes new material to their tissues and brings away waste. The air supplies plants with carbon which forms the bulk of their food, and both plants and animals with oxygen which they breathe and by which they maintain the chemical changes upon which life depends. The air penetrates to the bottom of the sea and makes the whole mass of water habitable by millions of living forms.

Solar Energy. — The sun shines down through the atmosphere and into the water, and its light, heat, and chemical rays furnish the power or energy which keeps things moving and alive upon the face of the earth.

The air and water absorb and retain the heat of the sun, tempering its intensity by day, preventing its too rapid escape by night, and maintaining over nearly the whole face of the earth such a temperature as plants and animals require. Not far below lies the fervent heat of the interior, and not far above, the intense cold of stellar space.

The Plan of the earth presents a vast expanse of water broken at intervals by large and small masses of land. While the land masses predominate in the northern hemisphere, their longer axes extend north and south through so many degrees of latitude as to traverse all the zones of climate. This variety is made still greater by diversities of elevation, relief, and distance from the sea. The number and variety of living forms probably decrease from near sea level downward to the deep sea floor and upward to the mountain tops, but the great expanse of sea surface and the low average elevation of the land make a very large proportion of the face of the earth available for a dense population of some kind. The arrangement and variety of situation, relief, soil, and climate have brought about a corresponding variety of living forms, each adapted to the peculiar set of conditions under which it lives. Probably no large part of the sea or land is entirely devoid of life; but the sphere of life is strictly confined to the thin shell of the earth where land, water, and air intermingle.

Human Life. — The most important and interesting thing about the earth is the fact that men live upon it. So far as we know this is the only human planet. Man was originally a land animal, and upon the land a large majority of human beings will always live. But using the land as a base, man has extended his field of activity over the sea and into the lower atmosphere.

He requires a constant supply of oxygen from the air, and a supply of food at short intervals, which he gets from plants, animals, and water. He must also maintain his body at a constant temperature, which he does by the consumption of food on the inside and the use of clothing, shelter, and artificial heat on the outside. For clothing, building materials, and fuel he is again dependent upon plants, animals, and rocks. He could not live many minutes upon the moon, which has no soil, water, air, or vegetation. From the natural resources of the earth he has learned to obtain much more than the bare necessities of life, which he shares with other animals. He has learned to satisfy his ever-growing wants for safety, comfort, and luxury, and to gratify his hunger for knowledge, his taste for beauty, his love of social enjoyment, and his longing for the things which he finds most valuable.

Geography has something to say about all these things, and seeks to understand how they have come to be where and what they are. It studies the world organism and tries to discover how men can live in it and lead so many different kinds of life as they do in different parts of it, what natural conditions help or hinder them, and how they may use the organism to better advantage in the future.

CHAPTER IV

THE LAND

Structure. — The ground upon which we stand, walk, and work is a part of the earth crust, the outer shell or layer of the rock sphere. The crust contains hundreds of species of minerals, mixed together in different combinations to form rocks. A large mass of any solid mineral or mixture of minerals is called *rock*. Almost everywhere, except upon very steep slopes, the ground is composed of loose, incoherent material, commonly called earth or soil, and distinguished as clay, sand, gravel, pebbles, boulders, or mixtures of them. They are all fragments of older rocks which have been broken up and decomposed. This sheet of loose, fragmentary material may be hundreds of feet thick, and is called *mantle rock*, because it overlies and covers the other rock. The upper foot or two of mantle rock is generally mixed with *humus*, or decayed vegetable matter, and constitutes *the soil*, in the strict, or agricultural, sense of the word.

Fig. 20. — Stratified sand and gravel, Terre Haute, Ind.

Bed Rock. — If a boring is made anywhere down through

the mantle rock, it will be found to be underlain by *bed rock*, a compact, coherent mass, which is not easily broken up or removed. Bed rock often projects through the cover of mantle rock and is exposed to view upon a hillside, in the face of a cliff, or along the bed and banks of a stream. Such an exposure of bed rock on the surface is called an *outcrop*. In most places the upper part of the bed rock is stratified, that is, it lies in distinct sheets or layers called *strata* (singular *stratum*). The common

Fig. 21.—Stratified bed and mantle rock, Erie County, N. Y.

kinds of stratified bed rock are shale, sandstone, conglomerate, and limestone. They are also called *aqueous* or *sedimentary* rocks, because they have been formed by the accumulation of sediment in bodies of water.

In some places immediately beneath the mantle rock, and everywhere beneath the stratified bed rock, lies a mass of unstratified rock, which owes its form and structure to cooling from a plastic or molten condition.

Melted rock has risen from great depths and has cooled in the cracks and between the layers of stratified rock, or has escaped to the surface and spread out over the country. Rocks which have solidified from a molten

Fig. 22. — **Unstratified igneous rock, Hoboken, N. J.** (N.Y. Geol. Surv.)

state are called *igneous*. Lava, of which there are many varieties, is a common form of igneous rock. Some rocks which were originally sedimentary, have been changed by heat and pressure, but have not been melted, and

Fig. 23. — **Contorted gneiss, a metamorphic rock, near Hudson Bay.** (Can. Geol. Surv.)

are called *metamorphic* or altered rocks. Igneous and metamorphic rocks are often distinguished as *crystalline*, because they are mainly or wholly composed of crystals, which are often conspicuous from their shape, color, and sparkling luster. Granite is a good example of crystalline rock.

Economic Relations. — The surface, soil, vegetation, and value of a region depend largely upon the kind of rock which underlies it. The common kinds of both mantle and bed rock are dug or quarried for use in constructing roads, streets, bridges, houses, and public buildings, while the finer kinds, like marble and granite, furnish beautiful material for buildings, monuments, and statues. All the useful minerals, such as coal and the ores of the metals, are obtained from the earth crust, generally from the bed rock by *mining*. Thus the agricultural and mineral wealth of a country depends upon the structure of the earth crust.

Relief Maps. — Many devices are in use for showing elevation and form, or *relief*, upon a map. One of the most common and generally useful is by "overlaying" with different colors to show successive stages of height and depth, as on the map, Fig. 16. Such a map shows general elevation within certain limits, but fails to show the details of form. Each boundary line of a color or shade is level, or everywhere at the same distance, 990 feet, 3,300 feet, etc., above or below sea level, measured vertically. These lines of equal elevation upon a map are called *contour lines*, or simply *contours*. By drawing contours at small intervals relief may be shown with any desired degree of precision, and colors become unnecessary.

The United States Geological Survey is making a topographic atlas of the United States, of which about two fifths is now completed. The contoured maps in this book, Figs. 28, 30, 31, 35, etc., are taken from it. They show the relief, drainage, and *culture* or human features, such as towns, houses, and roads, with great detail and precision. It is worth while to learn to use these maps, which are among the best made of any country in the world.

Fig. 24 shows a sketch or picture of a landscape, and Fig. 25 a contoured map of the same region. In the foreground is a portion of the sea, the shore line of which forms the basal or zero contour. Contours are drawn upon the map at intervals of fifty feet *measured vertically* from the sea level, and they mark the lines where the seashore would be if the sea should rise fifty, one hundred, etc., feet. Where the slope is steep, one would have to travel only a short distance to rise fifty feet; hence the contours are close together. Where the slope is gentle, one would have to travel far to rise fifty feet; hence the contours are farther apart. By shortening the contour interval to ten or five feet, as may be done upon a large-scale map, the elevation of every point may be shown very precisely. For showing

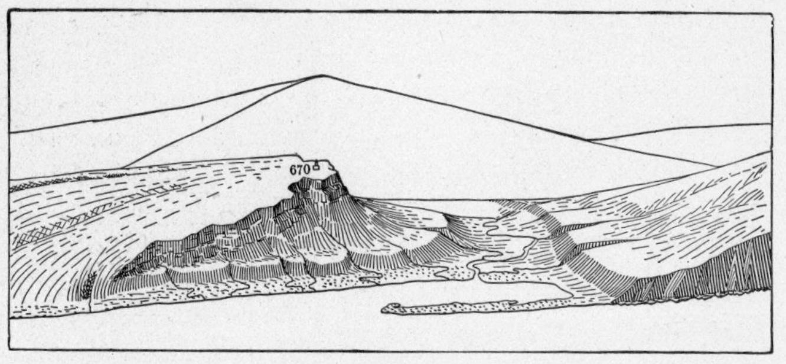

Fig. 24.

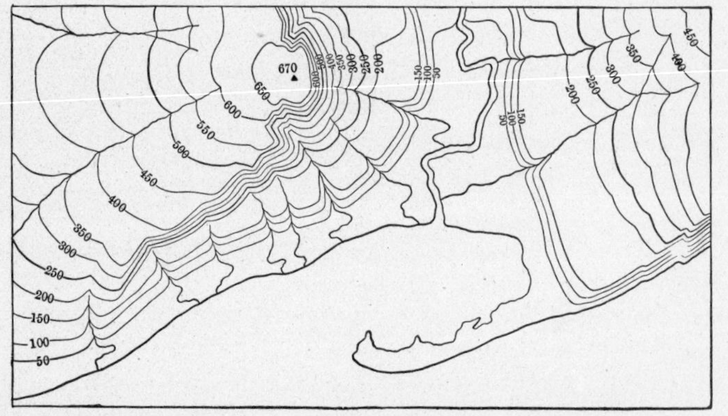

Fig. 25.

exact elevation no device is equal to the contoured map; but it has the disadvantage of not being *graphic*, that is, of not being understood by everybody at a glance.

A very common device for showing relief upon a map is the use of *hachures*, or fine lines running up and down the slopes, and so drawn as to show the steepness of the slope by the depth of shading. Hachured maps may be made very graphic and almost equal to a picture. Figs. 26 and 27 show the relation between contoured and hachured maps of the same area. A combination of the two is the best possible method of showing relief upon a map.

Fig. 26. — Contoured map.

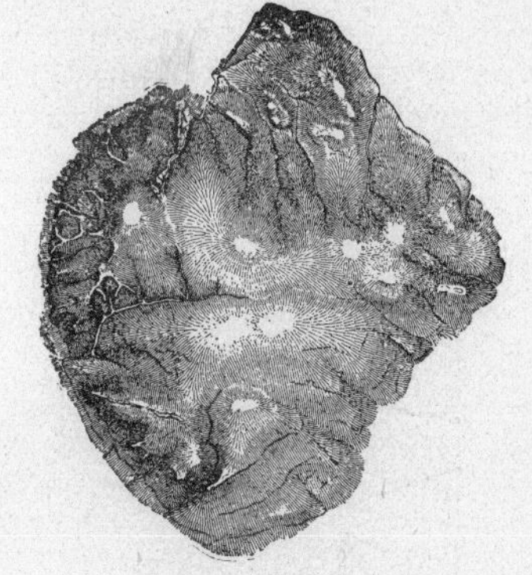

Fig. 27. — Hachured map.

Land Forms. — The surface of the land presents a variety of forms which differ widely in outline, elevation, slope, mass, and structure. The inequalities of surface found in any region constitute its vertical *relief*. A smooth, level plain might be said to have in itself no relief, but if it stands at a higher level than some adjoining land or water surface, it would have relief in relation to the lower surface.

The design upon a coin stands out in relief above the general surface of the metal. If the elevations are low and the depressions shallow, the surface has low relief; if the elevations are high and the depressions deep, the surface has high or strong relief. In common speech the roughness of the country means about the same as relief.

The large and controlling features of land relief are plains, plateaus, mountains, hills, and valleys. The internal forces of the earth have raised some portions of the land and depressed other portions, producing plains, plateaus, and mountains which mark the main features of the design. External forces, acting chiefly through air and water, have roughened a large part of the surface into an intricate pattern of smaller features, including ridges, valleys, hills, hollows, mesas, and basins.

Plains. — Plains, or lowlands, are broad, smooth, gently sloping tracts of land not far above sea level. The borders of a plain may be sharply defined by the abrupt slopes of a mountain

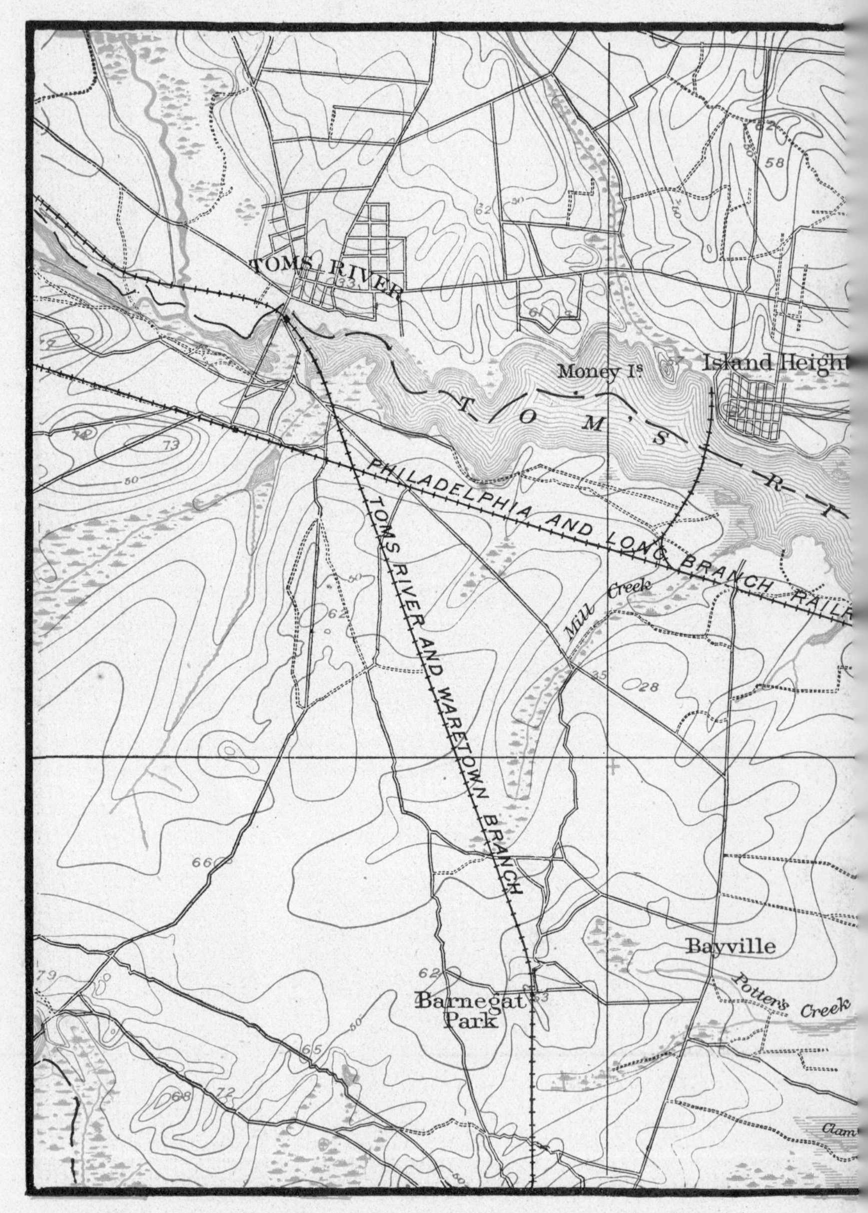

Fig. 28. — Coastal plain, drowned valley, barrier beach, and lagoon, New Jersey.

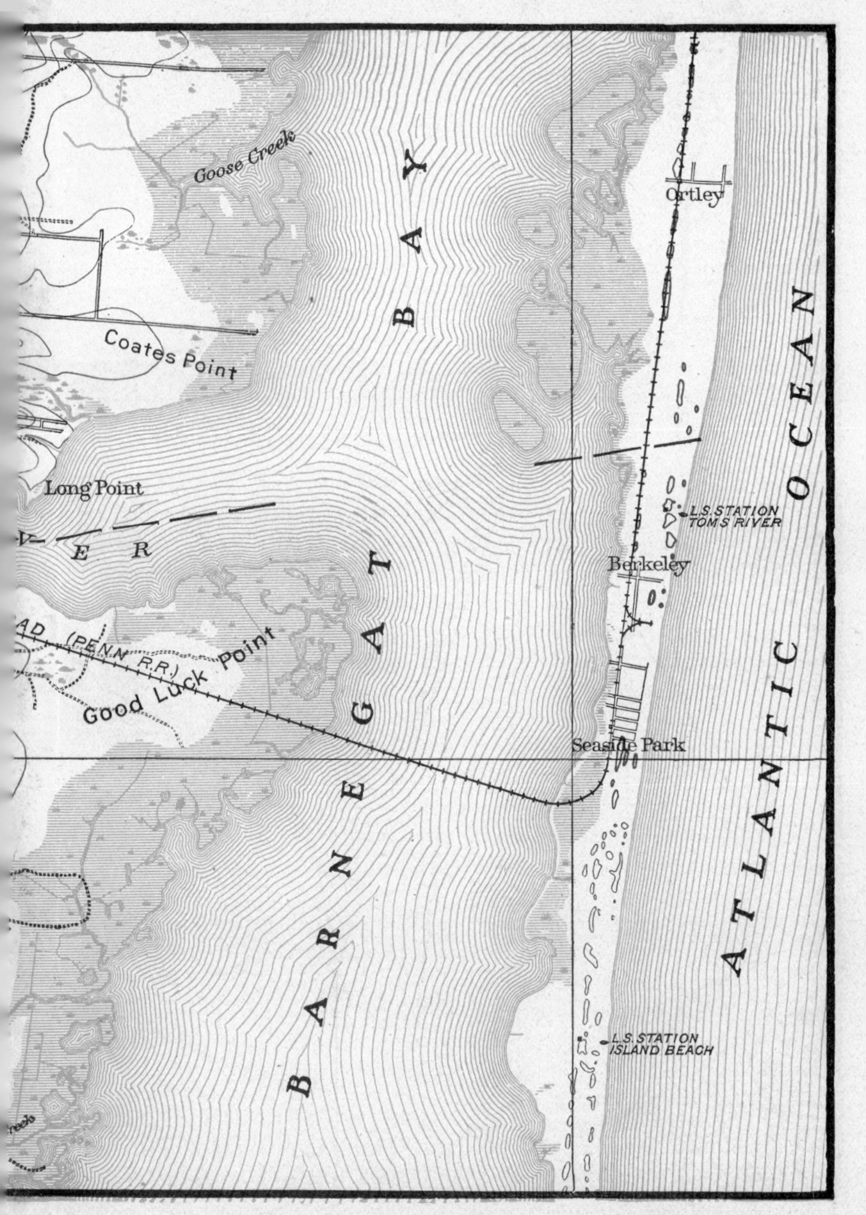

Scale about 1 mile per inch. Contour interval 10 feet. (Barnegat Sheet, U.S.G.S.)

range, or they may rise by an almost imperceptible grade to the height of a plateau, or slope gently to and beneath the waters of the sea. Plains are generally overspread with a deep layer of mantle rock brought down from higher land by streams, glaciers, and winds, or produced by the decay of the bed rock underneath.

Structural Plains. — The flatness of the great low plains of the world is due to various causes. Most plains are underlain by sedimentary rocks, the strata of which have not been much disturbed from their originally horizontal position. The surface is flat because the strata beneath it lie flat. When the surface thus conforms to the structure of the earth crust, the plain is called *structural*. It is like the cover of a closed book (Fig. 36).

The best examples of the structural plain are found in the lowlands which border the coasts of the continents, and are called *coastal plains* (Fig. 28). They are generally narrow, but sometimes, as in the case of the plains along the Atlantic and Gulf coasts of the United States, they stretch back hundreds of miles to the plateau or mountains which lie behind them. Coastal plains are formed by the slow rising of the sea bottom until it emerges from the water. They are covered with layers of imperfectly consolidated sediment which has been brought down in previous ages from older lands and deposited offshore. They are continuous with the submerged plain of the continental shelf. They are usually the latest additions to the continent and are composed of materials recently deposited; hence such lands are young in every sense. Old coastal plains sometimes occur in the interior of the continents, far from the sea. They were formed in the same way as the others, along the shore of a sea which has long since disappeared, and are now far inland because other plains and even mountains have risen between them and the present coast line. A strip of country extending from Wisconsin to New York along the south side of the Great Lakes is an old coastal plain. The most extensive plains in the world occur in the interior of continents, as in North America, South America, and Eurasia. These are for the most part structural plains, underlain by nearly horizontal strata.

Worn-down Plains. — Some large plains owe their flatness and low elevation to erosion. Once high and rough, they have been worn down by weathering and the work of streams and glaciers to a nearly even surface not far above sea level. Such plains are seldom as smooth as coastal plains, but are studded with low, rounded hills, composed of materials less easily eroded than the rest. They are called *worn-down plains*, *peneplains*, or *plains of degradation* (Figs. 29, 30).

A large U-shaped area surrounding Hudson Bay, from Labrador to the Arctic Ocean, was once occupied by a mountain range which has been worn down to its very roots. It is composed largely of igneous and metamorphic rocks which must have been formed originally far below the

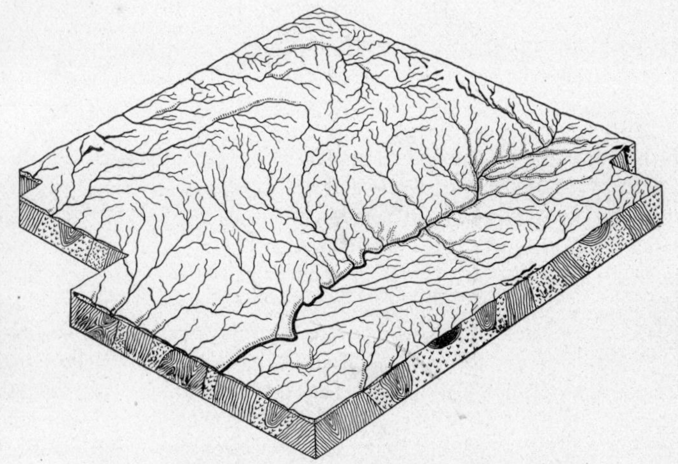

Fig. 29. — Stereogram of a worn-down plain. (Wis. Geol. Surv.)
Complex structure shown in section on the edges.

surface, and have been exposed by the removal of the rocks which once covered them (Figs. 23, 111). The structure is complex, that is, masses of different kinds of rock lie mingled together in almost every possible shape and position, and the present surface cuts across them without any conformity to their shapes and positions. This region is called the Laurentian peneplain. A similar plain in northern Europe occupies Finland, Lapland, and Sweden. Such plains are among the oldest lands on the globe, because it has required millions of years to wear them down to their present form and height.

Alluvial Plains. — Many plains, usually of less extent than those already described, have been formed by the spreading out of sheets of mantle rock over a surface previously more or less

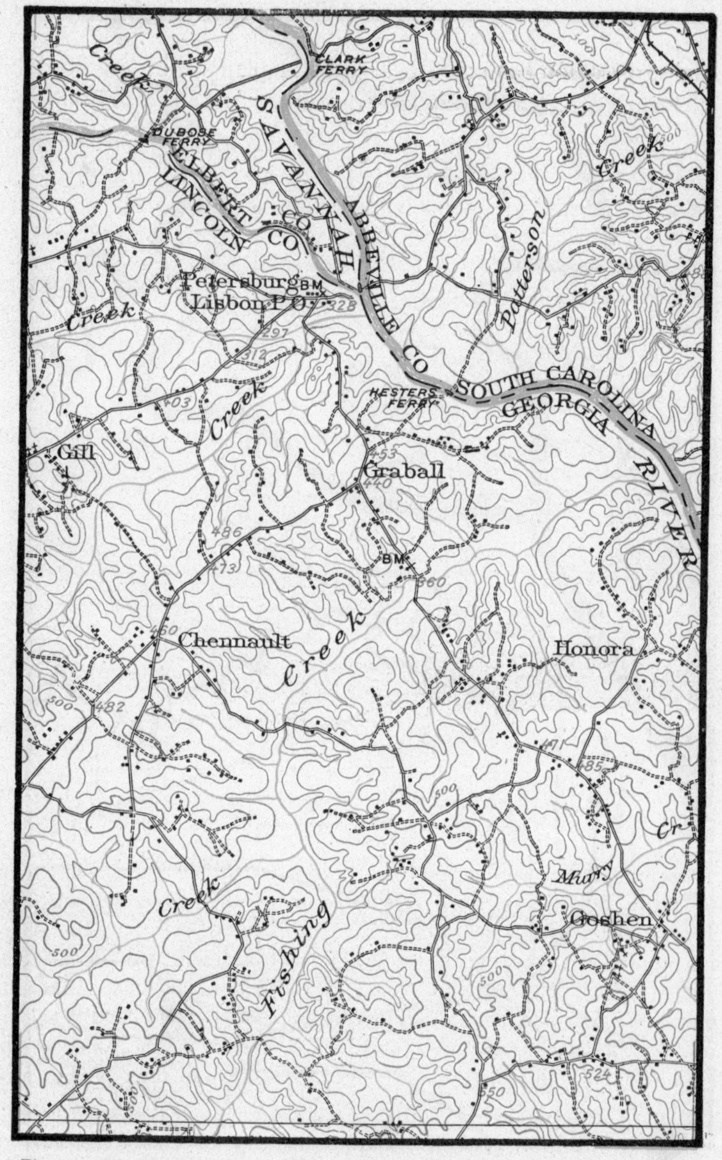

Fig. 30.—Worn-down plain, Georgia and South Carolina. Scale about 2 miles per inch. Contour interval 50 feet. (Crawfordville Sheet, U.S.G.S.)

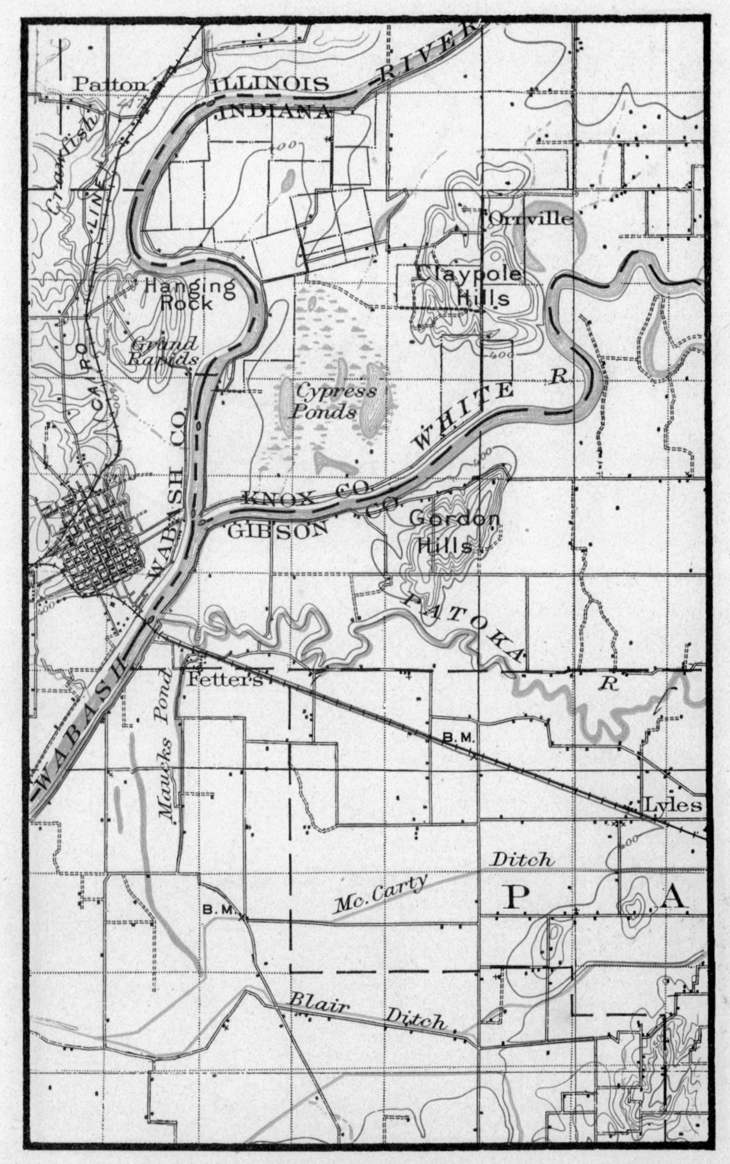

Fig. 31. —**Alluvial plain, Wabash River, Indiana and Illinois.** Scale about 2 miles per inch. Contour interval 20 feet. (Patoka Sheet, U.S.G.S.)

Fig. 32. — Alluvial plain, Wabash River, near Terre Haute, Ind.

uneven. A large river, more or less along its whole course, but especially toward its mouth, gets out of its banks in times of high water, spreads over the adjoining country, and deposits a coat of mud or sand, thus building up a smooth surface known

Fig. 33. — Lake plain, Clearwater, Minn. Outlet in the distance.

as a *flood plain* (Figs. 31, 32, 75, 76). When it enters the sea all its remaining load of sediment is dropped and the flood plain is built out into the water, forming a *delta* (Fig. 69). Plains thus made by the accumulation of river sediment are called *alluvial*. The alluvial plains of the Mississippi, Amazon, Ganges, Nile, and Hoang are among the largest in the world.

Lake Plains. — All streams which flow into a lake carry and deposit sediment until in time the lake basin may be filled up and converted into an almost perfectly level *lake plain* or *lacustrine plain* (Fig. 33). The famous wheat-growing district of Minnesota, North Dakota, and Manitoba is the bed of an old glacial lake.

Glacial Plains. — In North America and Europe millions of square miles have been covered by moving ice sheets, which, as

Fig. 34. — Glacial plain, Laporte County, Ind.

they melted, deposited vast sheets of mantle rock called *glacial drift*, of such thickness as to fill up, bury, and smooth over the irregularities of the bed-rock surface. The nearly level surface thus produced is called a *glacial plain* (Figs. 34, 35).

Alluvial, glacial, and lacustrine plains may be grouped together as plains of *accumulation* or *aggradation*.

Eolian Plains. — In regions of small rainfall and scant vegetation the loose mantle rock is lifted and drifted about by the winds, and some of it is carried entirely out of the region and

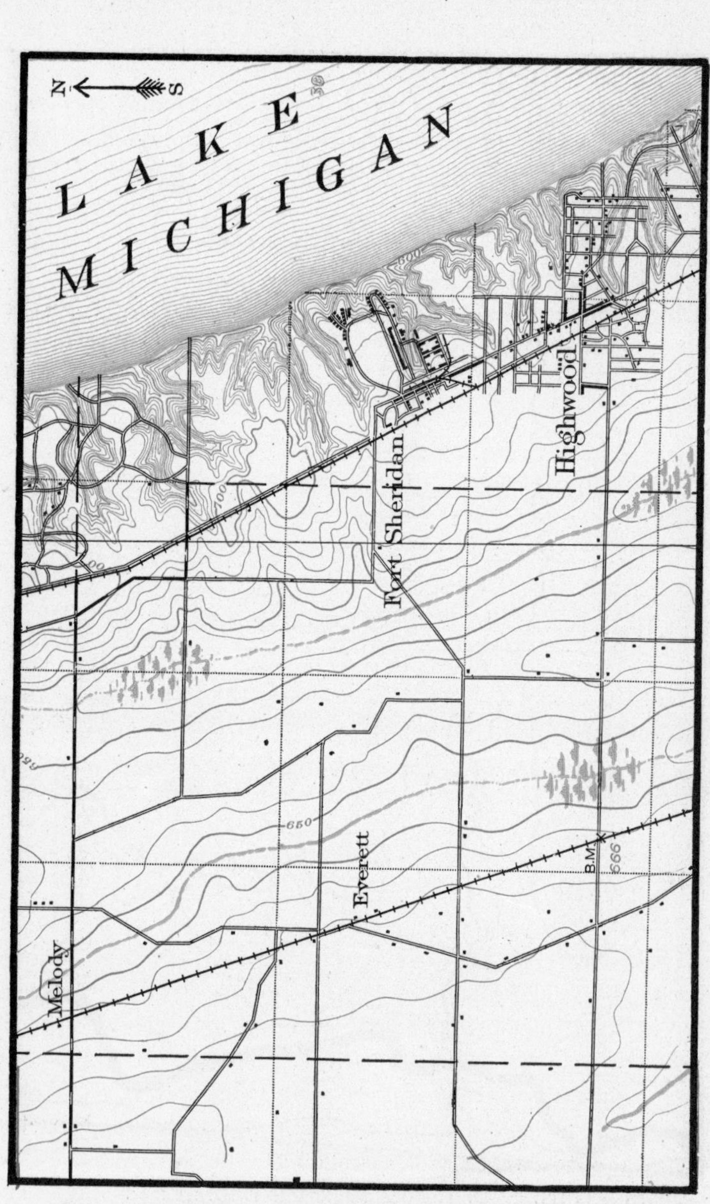

Fig. 35. — Glacial plain and cliff coast, Illinois. Scale about 1 mile per inch. Contour interval 10 feet. (Highwood Sheet, U.S.G.S.)

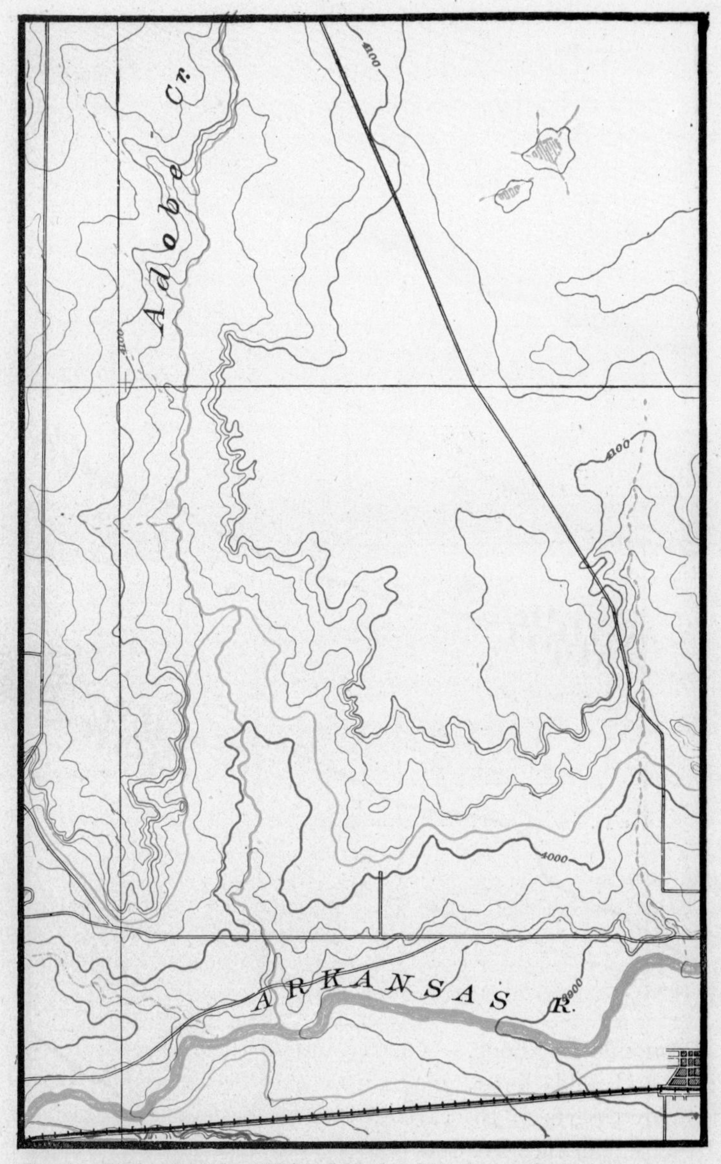

Fig. 36. — **Portion of the Great Plains, Colorado.** Scale about 2 miles per inch. Contour interval 25 feet. Irrigation canal near 4000 foot contour. (Las Animas Sheet, U.S.G.S.)

deposited over neighboring lands or in the sea. This process, long continued, produces a worn-down plain, studded with knobs of resistant rock, and its level may be degraded even below that of the sea.

The Kalahari desert in South Africa owes its relief to this cause, and may be called a *wind-worn plain*. The material carried away from a wind-worn plain may accumulate upon neighboring lands in such quan-

Fig. 37. — Wind-worn plain, Algerian Sahara. (Schimper, *Plant-Geography*.)

tities as to bury them hundreds of feet deep under a mantle of fine dust. In China thousands of square miles are covered with a material called *loess*, which has been blown from the dry plateaus of central Asia. Both the wind-worn plains and those made by the deposition of wind-blown dust are called *eolian plains* (Figs. 37, 141, 142).

Economic Relations. — On account of their accessibility, fertility, and mild climate, plains have ever been the most densely populated parts of the earth. It is probable that 75 per cent of the human race live less than 1,000 feet above the sea. The wealthiest and most highly civilized peoples of the world live on the plains, and there nearly all the great cities have sprung up. The most favored countries are those which possess broad plains traversed by great rivers and bordering upon the sea.

Alluvial, glacial, and lacustrine plains, on account of depth and fertility of soil, are the best agricultural regions in the world. Coastal plains are usually less productive. Worn-down plains are often infertile on account of lack of soil, but they sometimes support forests which yield valuable timber and swarm with fur-bearing animals, as in the Laurentian region of Canada. They are apt to be rich in mineral wealth, because long-continued erosion has laid bare veins of ore once deeply buried. The iron and copper mines of the Lake Superior region, the silver, cobalt, and nickel mines north of Lake Huron, and the diamond deposits of South Africa occur in worn-down plains. Eolian plains are generally deserts, not on account of poor soil, but because they occur only in regions where the rainfall is very scanty.

Plateaus. — Plateaus are broad masses of elevated land. They are high plains, and there is no fixed and definite line of demarcation between plains and plateaus. It is sometimes convenient to use 660 feet (200 meters), 1,000 feet, or even 2,000 feet above the sea to limit the height of plains.

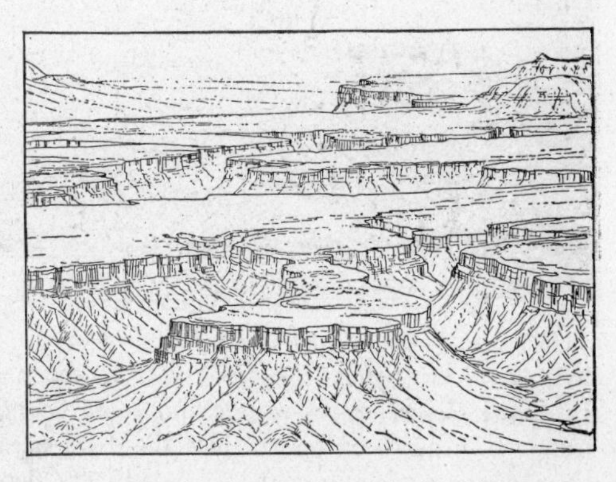

Fig. 38. — A plateau: Mesa Verde, Colorado.

In a region of low relief, a broad, massive elevation above 1,000 feet may be called a plateau, while in a region of high relief the name would be given only to a similar area above 2,000 feet. Plateaus may be as smooth and level as plains, as in the case of the Great Plains east of the Rocky Mountains, but are generally more broken (Figs. 36, 38). They are often bordered or traversed by mountain ranges. Low plateaus may be called *uplands*, and high plateaus *highlands*.

Economic Relations. — On account of rougher surface, poorer soil, and colder and drier climate, plateaus are generally less favorable for human occupation than plains. In middle latitudes, plateaus of moderate height, such as the Great Plains of the United States, and some of the plateaus of central Asia, constitute a region of *steppes*, covered with patches of grass, over which the people wander with their herds of horses, cattle, and sheep in search of pasture. Very high plateaus, such as Tibet, have an Arctic climate, and are almost uninhabitable. In tropical regions, plateaus such as those of Mexico, Peru, the Dekkan, and central Africa have a temperate climate, and are better homes for men than the hot and unhealthful plains which border them.

Mountains. — Mountain ranges are long, narrow ridges of great height. They are usually due to the folding, crumpling, and breaking of the earth crust along lines of weakness (Figs. 39, 41, and frontispiece). They are characterized by complex structure, steep slopes, and sharp crests. The crest is cut by notches, or passes, into a series of peaks, which from a distance look like the teeth of a saw. The notches seldom extend halfway down to the base. Mountain ranges seldom occur singly, but usually many ranges extending in the same general direction form a mountain system. All mountains owe their height to upheaval of the earth crust by internal forces, but their forms are due chiefly to erosion (Figs. 40, 44, 58, 60, 102, 103, 104, 105, 106, 109).

Fig. 39. — Fold in the Jura Mountains. (Robin, *La Terre*.)

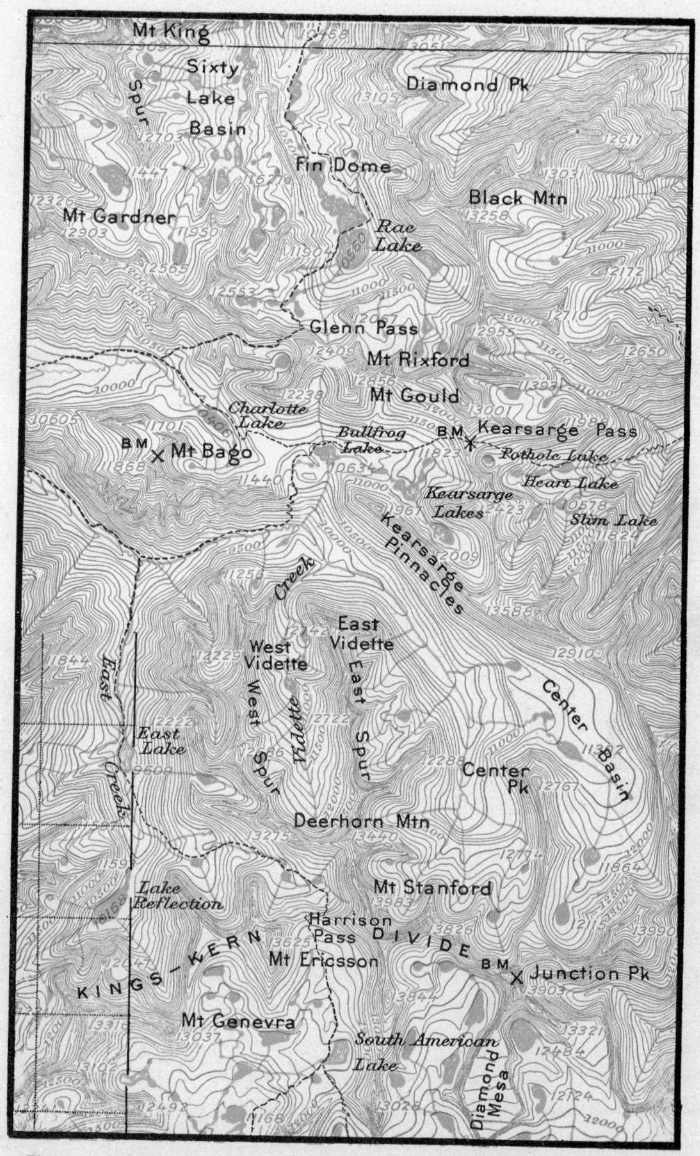

Fig. 40. — A portion of the Sierra Nevada, with glacial cirques and lakes, California. Scale about 2 miles per inch. Contour interval 100 feet. (Mt. Whitney Sheet, U.S.G.S.)

Fig. 41.—Folded rocks, Turkestan. (Carnegie Institution, *Explorations in Turkestan.*)

Fig. 42.—Dissected plateau, Toe River, North Carolina. (U. S. G. S.)

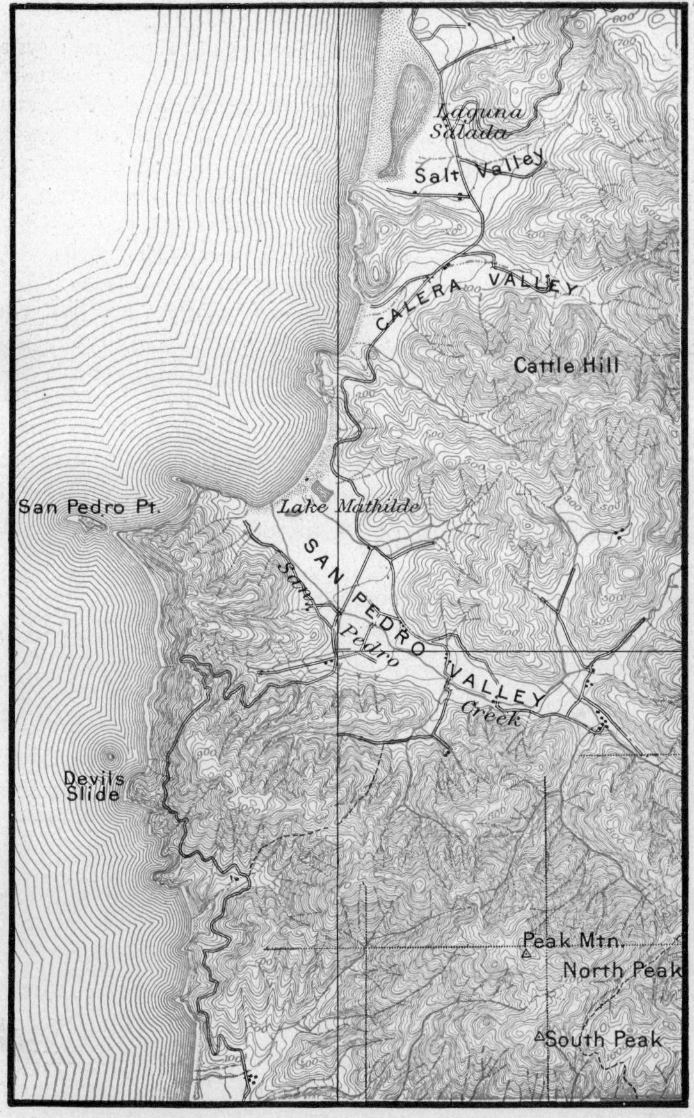

Fig. 43. — Dissected plateau and cliff coast, California. Scale about 1 mile per inch. Contour interval 25 feet. (San Mateo Sheet, U.S.G.S.)

Plateaus are sometimes dissected by a network of valleys into a system of sharp ridges and peaks which resemble in form "a sea of mountains," and are not improperly called mountains, although *dissected plateau* would be a more exact descriptive name (Figs. 42, 43, 73). The elevations left on worn-down plains or plateaus, projecting like nail heads or knots in an old floor, may be of mountainous size, like the White Mountains of New Hampshire. Isolated mountains or peaks, not forming a part of a range, are always remnants left by erosion, or of volcanic origin. Some of the most famous mountains of the world belong to the latter class, as Vesuvius and Etna in Europe, Kilimanjaro and Kenia in Africa, and Shasta and Orizaba in North America (Figs. 51, 52, 53, 54).

Economic Relations. — Mountains are difficult to penetrate, to cross, or to live on. They are formidable barriers to the migration of plants, animals, and men, and the inhabitants upon opposite sides of a mountain range are often very unlike. The vertical height and steepness of mountains render travel and transportation among them costly in effort and limited in amount. The use of vehicles is often impossible, and neither man nor beast can climb up and down with a heavy load. The soil upon mountain slopes is thin and poor, and there are large areas of bare rock. The climate of mountains is severe in proportion to their height, and the higher summits are covered with snow and ice. Agriculture is impossible except in the valleys. Mountains act as condensers of water vapor and have a heavier rainfall than the adjacent lowlands. Most mountains are forested up to a certain height called the *timber line*. Where the forests have been burned or cut grasses flourish. Hence mountaineers are usually lumbermen or herdsmen. The upheaval of a mountain range breaks up the earth crust and produces many cracks in which the ores of metals may be deposited by deeply circulating waters. The rapid erosion of mountains removes the cover and exposes the veins of ore upon the surface. Therefore many of the richest mines of gold, silver, copper, lead, and other minerals occur in mountainous regions. The permanent population of mountains is sparse. The people are rude, hardy, and active, because only such can make a living there, and luxuries are few.

They are free and liberty-loving because they can easily defend themselves against invaders. Conquered peoples may take refuge in the mountains, leaving the lowlands to be occupied by their more numerous conquerors. Towns and cities, such as Leadville and Cripple Creek in Colorado, sometimes spring up around a rich mine above the timber line, but the citizens are dependent upon the lowlands for everything they use. Mountain scenery is grand and picturesque, and the air is pure, invigorating, and in summer agreeable. Hence mountains are pleasure and health resorts for the people of the lowlands.

The Alps have become the playground of Europe, and are visited by about a million people every season. Railroads, coach roads (Fig. 295), and hotels are constructed for their accommodation, and the inhabitants reap a rich harvest from their guests.

Mountain streams have a rapid fall and constant volume which make them especially valuable for water power. As coal becomes more scarce and costly, manufacturers will seek water power to run their machinery, and mountainous countries, such as Switzerland, Italy, and Norway, may become great manufacturing countries.

Mountains are great soil factories, where bed rock is rapidly broken up and carried away by streams to be deposited in their lower valleys. The rich and populous plains of the Po, the Rhone, the Rhine, and the Danube have been built up by the waste of the Alps. The soil of the alluvial plains of the Mississippi, the Amazon, the Ganges, and the Hoang has been brought from the mountains in which these rivers have their sources.

Hills. — Hills are small elevations, and the distinction between hills and mountains is indefinite. In a region of moderate relief, like Pennsylvania, ridges 1,000 feet high are called mountains, while in a region of great relief, like Colorado, ridges 2,000 feet high are called hills.

While all great mountain ranges owe their origin to disturbance and upheaval of the earth crust, most hills are due either to the cutting out of the valleys between them, or to the heaping up of mantle rock by glaciers, ice sheets, and winds. Hence hills are of two classes, — **hills of *erosion*** and **hills of *accumulation*.**

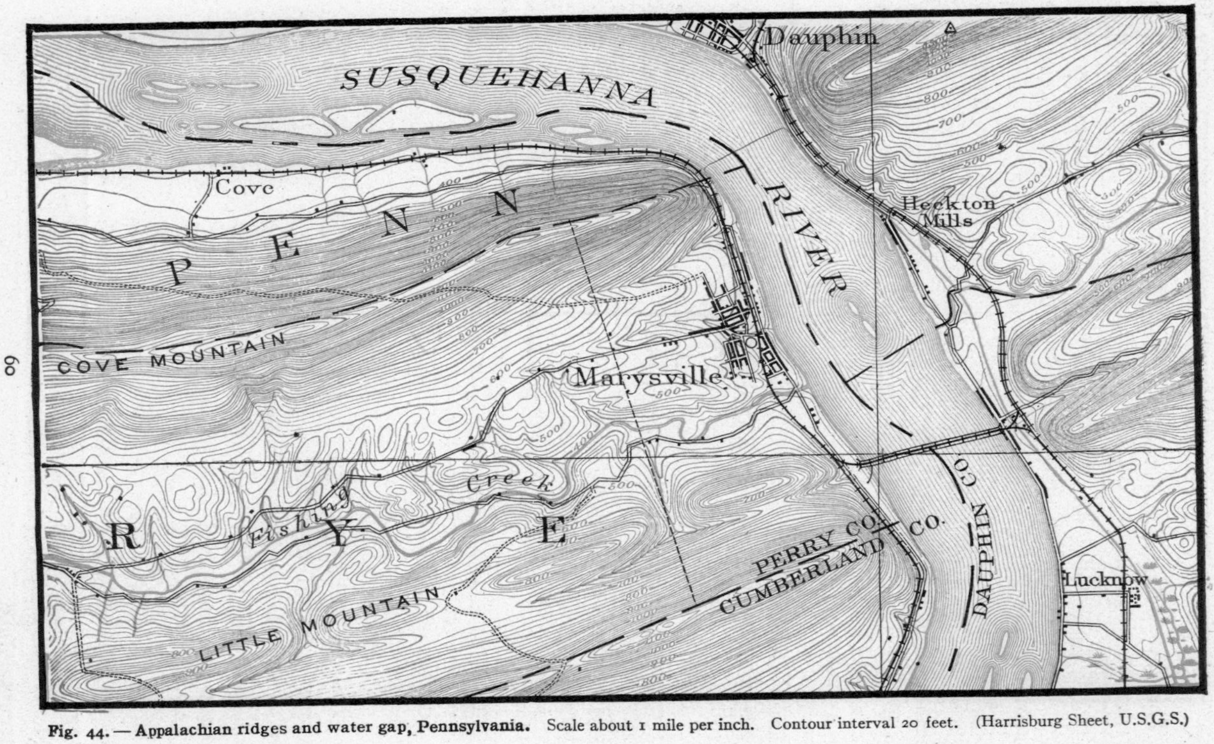

Fig. 44.— Appalachian ridges and water gap, Pennsylvania. Scale about 1 mile per inch. Contour interval 20 feet. (Harrisburg Sheet, U.S.G.S.)

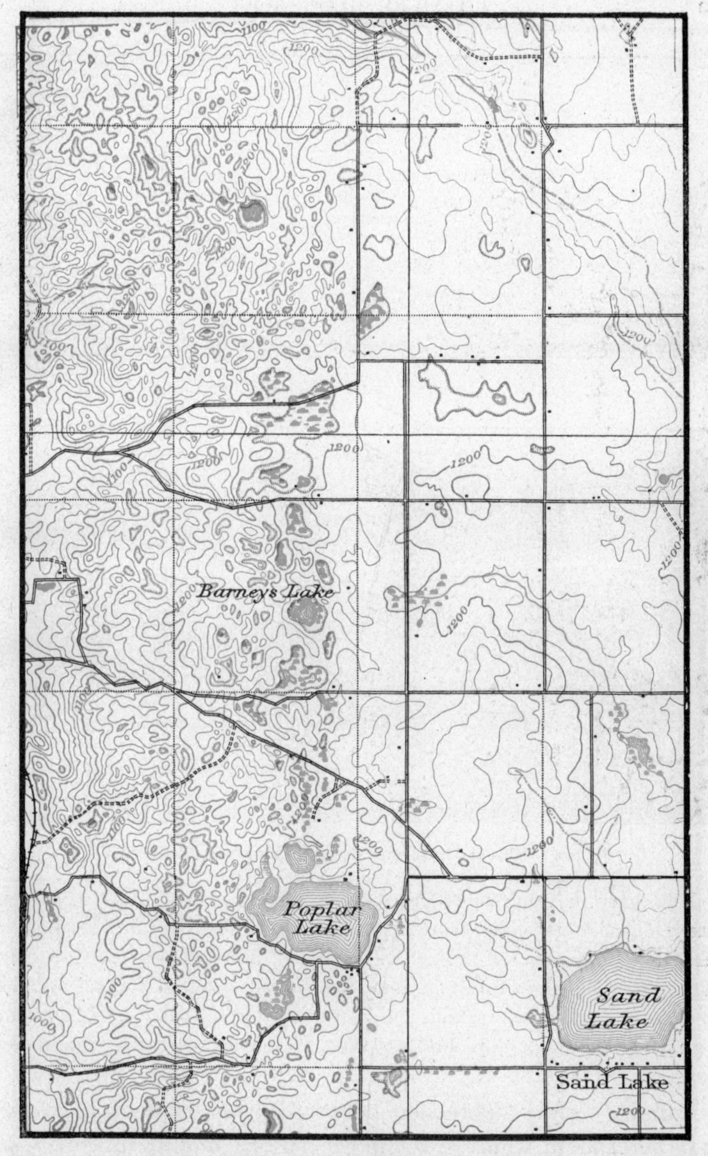

Fig. 45. — Hills of accumulation, with basins, Wisconsin. Scale about 1 mile per inch. Contour interval 20 feet. (St. Croix Dalles Sheet, U.S.G.S.)

Fig. 46. — Hills of erosion: Jacalitos Hills, California. (U.S.G.S.)

Fig. 47. — Hills and hollows of glacial accumulation, Victor, N. Y.

Hills vary in value according to their structure, size, and ruggedness. Sand hills are generally worthless, and if wind-drifted are destructive. Glacial hills may be as productive as plains, although less easy to cultivate. Some hills are forested, and some furnish good pasturage. A hilly country is always picturesque and attractive for its beauty. It presents a pleasing variety of slope and situation in contrast with the monotonous sameness of the plains.

Valleys. — Any depression between higher land on each side may be called a valley. Wherever parallel mountain ranges are upheaved, the corresponding depression between them is called an *intermont* valley. The Valley of California is an intermont

Fig. 48. — Kettlehole basins, Naples, N. Y.

valley between the Sierra Nevada on the east and the Coast Ranges on the west. Most valleys are long and narrow, but between hills and upon plains and plateaus there are many broad depressions, often occupied by lakes, which should be called *hollows* or *basins*.

Fig. 49. — Faults. (U.S.G.S.)
Block between faults has dropped down.

Valleys are the most common of all relief forms, and most of them have been made wholly or partly by running water. That is a long story which will be told in some of the following chapters.

Broken Block Lands. — Some regions resemble in relief a poorly laid pavement in which some of the bricks or tiles stand above or below the others. The earth crust has been broken by nearly vertical cracks into blocks which have been displaced, some upward and some downward, or tilted to one side. The cracks are called *faults*, and the process of displacement is *faulting*. The elevated blocks may form steep-sided table-lands, or, if tilted, sharp-crested ridges. The depressed blocks may form basins or *rift valleys*, according to their shape.

An area in Europe extending from central France to Hungary has been broken into many pieces, and faulted into a complex set of tables, ridges, and basins. The Mediterranean region is faulted on a very large scale. The Sierra Nevada of California is a faulted block, the eastern edge of which has been tilted up to form a very steep slope. Many of the mountain ranges of the Great Basin are tilted blocks.

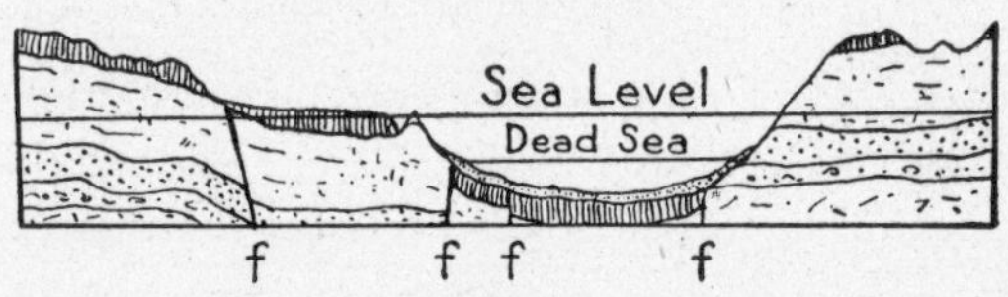

Fig. 50. — Cross section of rift valley. (Blackwelder and Barrows, *Elements of Geology*.)

The subsidence of a long, narrow block between two parallel faults produces a *rift valley*, of which the valley of the Rhine from Basel to Bingen is a good example. A rift valley on a grand scale extends from lakes Nyassa and Tanganyika, in Africa, through the Red Sea to the valley of the Dead Sea and the Jordan River in Asia, a distance of about 4,000 miles (Fig. 118).

Volcanic Lands. — Cracks in the earth crust often permit the escape of melted rock, steam, and hot gases from the interior. When this takes place with violent explosions and a brilliant display of fireworks the event is a volcanic eruption. Enormous quantities of lava (melted rock) in the form of dust, sand, and cinders are thrown into the air and spread over the surrounding country. Streams of liquid lava flow from the vent and, gradually cooling and stiffening, help to build up a volcanic cone or mountain to a height, in some cases, of three or four miles. The vent of a volcano is called a *pipe* or *chimney*, and there is, usually, a cup-shaped depression, or *crater*, at the top. The immediate cause of an eruption is the sudden expansion of water in the lava into steam. The melted rock comes from great depths and its origin is not fully understood. Volcanic eruptions produce a peculiar relief characterized by conical or domed elevations, standing singly or in groups and lines and

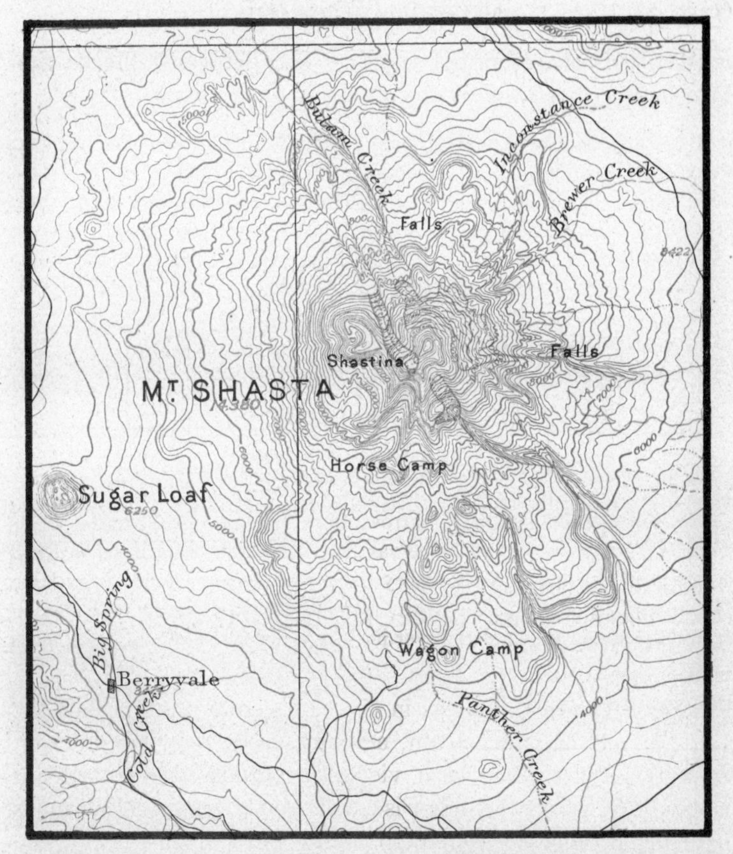

Fig. 51. — A volcanic cone: Mt. Shasta, California. Scale about 4 miles per inch. **Contour interval 200 feet.** (Shasta Sheet, U.S.G.S.)

Fig. 52. — Volcano, New Guinea.

varying in height from a few hundred to many thousand feet (Fig. 53).

Fig. 53. — Volcanic domes: Puys of central France.

Most of the numerous oceanic islands have been built up by volcanic eruptions in the bottom of the sea, and stand in lines along the course of submarine fissures. In India and in the states of Oregon, Idaho, and Washington, lava has flowed quietly from cracks and flooded hundreds of thousands of square miles to the depth of several thousand feet, building up a lava plateau with a smooth surface resembling that of the sea (Fig. 57).

Fig. 54. — Sundance Mountain, Wyoming. A dome of igneous rock.

Economic Relations. — Volcanic eruptions are temporarily destructive to life and property. In 1902 an eruption of Mont Pelée in the island of Martinique, one of the West Indies, utterly destroyed St. Pierre, a city of 30,000 people, with its inhabitants, in a few minutes. Yet volcanic action is on the whole constructive rather than destructive. Vast quantities of water vapor and carbon dioxide are added to the atmosphere, and new supplies of rock material are transferred from the interior to the exterior of the earth. Volcanic dust (so-called ashes) is carried by the wind hundreds of miles and sown broadcast over the land, renewing the soil. Even lava beds, in the course of time, weather and crumble into rich earth and become available for the support of plant and animal life. By the agency of submarine volcanoes new lands are created amid the waste of waters.

Fig. 55. — Results of an earthquake in Japan.

Earthquakes. — Broken block and volcanic lands are especially subject to earthquakes. Volcanic eruptions often cause earthquakes which are locally violent, but affect only a small

VOLCANOES AND EARTHQUAKE AREAS

After de Martonne

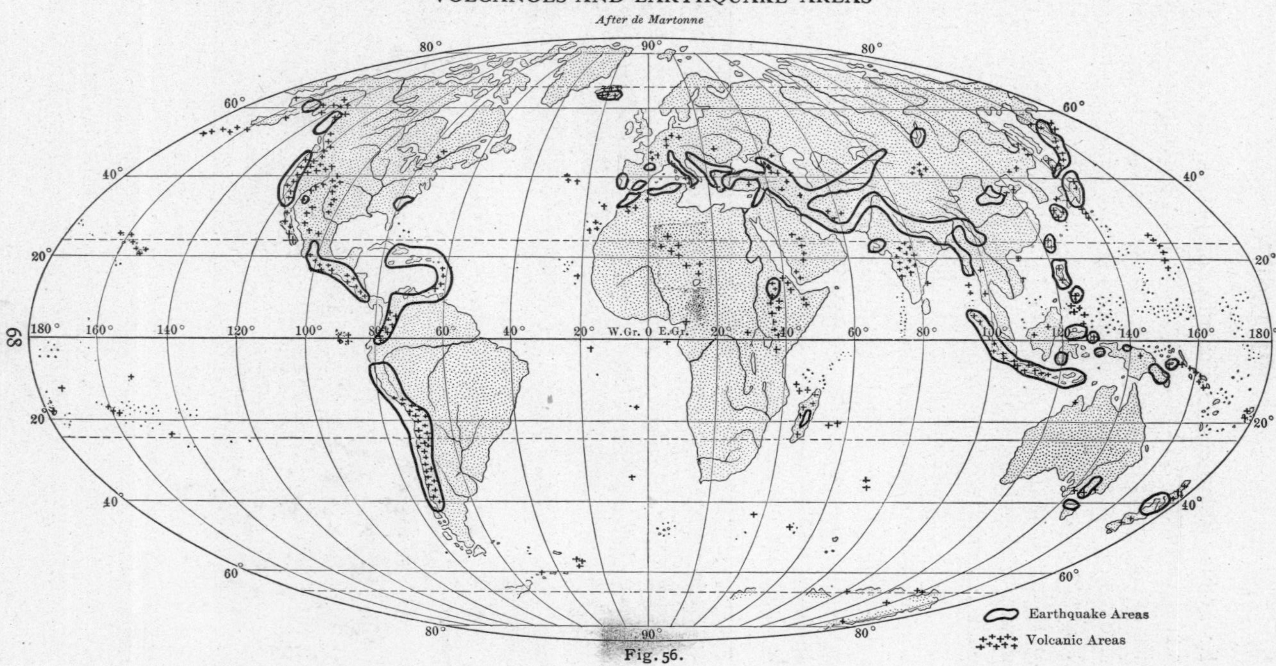

Fig. 56.

area. Great disturbances which shake literally the whole earth are incidents in the process of faulting, and are due to the sudden slipping of the blocks along a crack in the earth crust. The movement of the blocks may be vertical or horizontal, and does not exceed a few feet. The jar travels through and around the earth in every direction, diminishing in intensity as the distance from the center of disturbance increases.

Economic Relations. — Near the center an earthquake is often exceedingly destructive to property and human life. Although the distance through which a building is moved may not exceed a small fraction of an inch, great speed is attained so rapidly that hardly any structure can withstand it. It is as if a railroad train should start from a state of rest and acquire a speed of sixty miles an hour in one second. When an earthquake occurs in the sea bottom or near shore, it produces enormous waves which may be as destructive as the quake itself.

In Japan, where the ground seems to be never completely still, houses are built of very light materials. Structures of steel and concrete upon a solid rock foundation are least liable to injury. Buildings of brick and wood standing upon alluvial or newly made ground are most dangerous. Hundreds of earthquakes occur every year, but most of them are too feeble or too remote from centers of population to do serious damage. The principal areas subject to destructive earthquakes are shown on the map, Fig. 56.

Physiographic Provinces. — Fig. 57 shows the division of the land according to structure, and indicates broadly the causes and character of relief. These divisions constitute the great physiographic provinces of the land. This map should be compared with the relief map, Fig. 16.

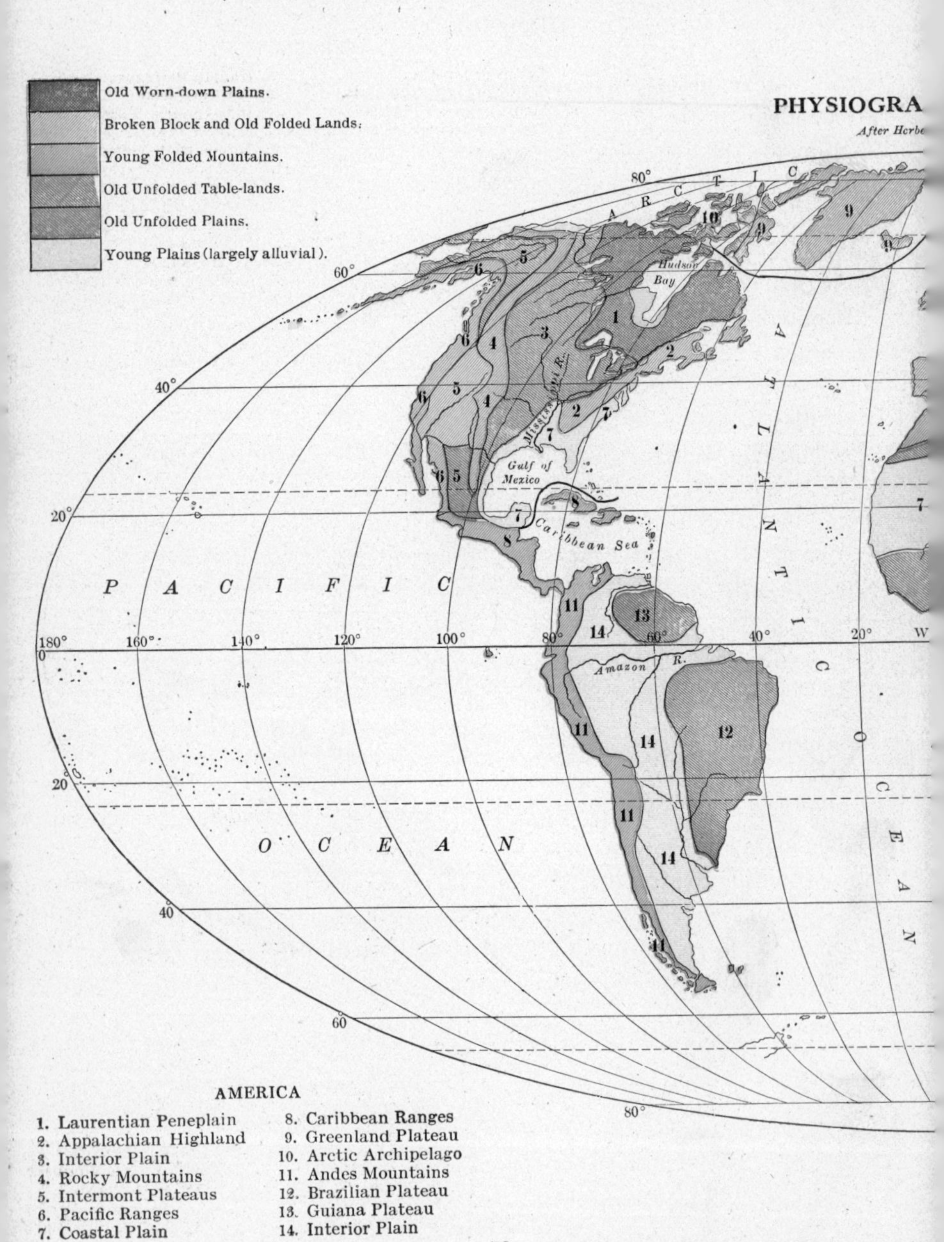
Old Worn-down Plains.
Broken Block and Old Folded Lands.
Young Folded Mountains.
Old Unfolded Table-lands.
Old Unfolded Plains.
Young Plains (largely alluvial).
PHYSIOGRA
After Herbe
A R C T I C
Hudson Bay
A T L A N T I C O C E A N
P A C I F I C O C E A N
Mississippi R.
Gulf of Mexico
Caribbean Sea
Amazon R.
80°
60°
40°
20°
180°
160°
140°
120°
100°
0
W
AMERICA
1. Laurentian Peneplain
2. Appalachian Highland
3. Interior Plain
4. Rocky Mountains
5. Intermont Plateaus
6. Pacific Ranges
7. Coastal Plain
8. Caribbean Ranges
9. Greenland Plateau
10. Arctic Archipelago
11. Andes Mountains
12. Brazilian Plateau
13. Guiana Plateau
14. Interior Plain

PROVINCES

difications

EURASIA

1. Baltic Peneplain
2. Scandinavian Highland
3. Mediterranean Highlands
4. Western Basins and Table-lands
5. Baltic-Black Plain
6. Interior Plain
7. Ural Mountains
8. Iranian Plateaus
9. Mongol-Tibetan Plateaus
10. Indo-Chinese Ranges
11. Chinese Plateau
12. Manchurian Plateau
13. Arabian Plateau
14. Dekkan Plateau
15. Caspian-Ob Plains
16. East Siberian Plain
17. Chinese Plain
18. Indus-Ganges Plain
19. Mesopotamian Plain
20. Malay Archipelago

AFRICA AND AUSTRALIA

1. Atlas Mountains
2. Central African Plateau
3. Saharan Plateau
4. Kong Plateau
5. Cape Plateau
6. Rift Valley
7. Niger-Libyan Plain
8. Australian Plateau
9. Australian Mountains
10. Australian Plain

CHAPTER V

GRADATION BY RUNNING WATER

Gradation. — If a building lot or the site of a town is rough, it is generally graded by cutting down the hills and filling up the hollows. The same process of grading is continually going on all over the surface of the land. The mountains and plateaus are being worn down and the material is carried away to lower levels. Valleys and basins are filled and plains are overspread with the waste of the highlands. The lowest and largest depressions of the earth crust are occupied by the oceans, therefore the process of gradation will not stop until all the land above sea level is carried away and deposited on the sea floor. Thus it happens that even lowlands are being eroded, although more slowly than highlands. Lowering the level of the earth crust by erosion is called *degradation;* raising its level by deposition is called *aggradation;* and the result of the two processes is *gradation.* Gradation is a very complex process carried on by many different agents, the work of each one of which must be studied separately.

Weathering or the Disintegration of Rocks. — Wherever bed rock is exposed to the action of air, water, and sun, it is broken up and decomposed into loose *mantle rock,* or rock waste. The oxygen of the air attacks some rock minerals, especially iron, which rusts and crumbles into powder. The carbon dioxide of the air combines with lime in the rocks to form limestone, which is dissolved away by water. In the daytime bare rocks become heated by the sun and expand; at night they cool rapidly and contract. This change of volume repeated many times causes the rocks to break up and scale off. Water frozen in pores and cracks breaks rock, as it breaks pitchers and pipes in the house.

Fig. 58. — Frost work, Pikes Peak, Colorado.

Mountain peaks, where freezing and thawing take place almost every day, are shivered to pieces and crumble into a heap of ruins. In arid regions sand blown by the wind rapidly wears away the hardest rocks. Unprotected telegraph poles are soon cut down by the sand blast. Unsupported rock masses are broken off and pulled down by gravity, and are reduced to smaller fragments by the fall. The growth of tree roots in cracks and the acids formed by decaying vegetation help on the process of rock destruction, while even burrowing animals contribute something to the result. The whole combination of processes by which massive bed rocks are converted into mantle rock is called *weathering*, and its products are clay, sand, gravel, pebbles, and boulders.

Fig. 59. — Erosion by wind and sand. (The Sphinx, Egypt.)

It is difficult to find an exposed surface of rock anywhere which has not been changed by the weather until it looks quite different from a freshly broken surface. Old monuments in cemeteries show the effects of exposure to air and rain. Buildings built at different times of the same kind of stone often reveal their relative ages by changes in color or surface, and in the course of centuries stone buildings may be badly damaged by the weather.

Movement of Mantle Rock. — Mantle rock sometimes remains in the place where it is formed, and may accumulate to

Fig. 60. — Talus slopes, Tongue River cañon, Wyoming. Note irrigation conduit. (U. S. G. S.)

the depth of many feet. Air and vegetable acids, carried down into the cracks and crevices of bed rock by ground water, extend the weathering process in some cases hundreds of feet below the surface. But mantle rock is always in a condition to be moved by gravity, wind, or water. At the bottom of a steep cliff there is usually a *talus*, or heap of rock fragments fallen from above. On mountain sides enormous masses of rock sometimes slide down at once and bury forests and houses in the valley. Such an event is called a *landslide.* Streams of stones moving slowly but continuously down a steep slope are called *screes.* Even on moderate slopes there is a slow creep of the mantle rock

Fig. 61.—Landslide, Switzerland. (Robin.)

downward. Wherever mantle rock is fine and dry the wind blows it away, drifting sand and dust into dunes and ridges, spreading them over the neighboring country or carrying them out to sea. Glaciers transport rock fragments of all sizes, some as large as a house and some as fine as flour, which are left in a heap when the ice melts.

The most efficient agent in transporting mantle rock is running water. The rain washes dirt into the streams, which buoy up and carry away great quantities of clay, sand, and gravel. The swifter the stream, the coarser the material it can carry. Even large boulders are rolled over one another and along the stream bottom (Fig. 65). Their edges and corners are rounded off and the whole grist is rapidly ground finer. Where the speed of the current is checked a part of the load is dropped, the coarsest first; and gravel or sand bars and mud banks are built up along the stream. If the stream flows into a lake or the sea, its current is stopped completely and all its load of sediment settles to the bottom.

Summary. — Thus, by the various processes of weathering and erosion, important results are accomplished: (1) Soils, composed of various mixtures of clay, sand, gravel, and humus, are provided for the growth of vegetation; (2) the higher places of the earth crust are worn down or *degraded*, and the lower places are filled up or *aggraded;* (3) during this process of gradation the great land features are carved and molded into ever-changing patterns of relief.

Valleys and Streams. — If the course of a stream is followed up, it will be found to be joined at intervals on either side by *tributaries*, each of which flows in a valley usually proportioned to the size of the stream. The main stream and its valley grow smaller above the mouth of each tributary until they are reduced to a tiny rivulet flowing in a furrow, and finally come to an end at a spring, pond, or swamp, or upon the smooth slope of a hillside. If any tributary is followed up, it also is found to divide like the trunk of a tree into smaller branches and rivulets. The surface of the land on either side slopes toward the stream or one of its tributaries, and at the same time there is a continuous slope downstream from the head or tip of every branch.

If the slope is ascended from the stream, at a greater or less distance a point is reached where the surface begins to slope away from that stream toward some other stream. A more or less definite line may be found which marks the junction of the two slopes and separates the water flowing into one stream from that flowing into the other. If this *divide* or water-parting is followed, it is found to pass around the heads of all the tributaries and to inclose the *basin* or area from which water drains into the stream *system.*

Fig. 62. — Divide, Vigo County. Ind.

Run-off. — Some part of the rain falling upon any basin evaporates, a part sinks into the ground, and the remainder, called the *run-off,* flows away on the surface. Some of the water which sinks into the ground comes again to the surface and joins the run-off. The ratio of the run-off to the rainfall varies with the slope, structure, climate, and vegetation of the basin.

At first the run-off forms a thin and scarcely perceptible sheet; but it soon gathers into little rills which join one another and grow larger until they flow into one of the permanent branches of the stream system. The smallest branches flow only while it rains, and their grooves or gullies are dry most of the time. The permanent branches are supplied from ponds, swamps, glaciers, or springs.

Near the sources of the stream the slopes are apt to be steep, the current swift, the channel narrow and deep and perhaps interrupted by rapids and falls. The bed is strewn with boulders, pebbles, or coarse gravel (Figs. 60, 71, 73, 74, 77). Farther down, as the slope becomes more gentle, the bed is smoother, rapids are less frequent and are separated by long reaches of quiet water, and the channel becomes wider, shallower, and more crooked. The loose material is less coarse and consists chiefly of fine gravel and sand. Here the watercourse is likely to become double and to consist of a wide outer *valley* which the stream covers only at high water, and through which the narrower *channel* winds irregularly from side to side. Still farther down, the valley may become very much wider and consist of an extensive *flood*

Fig. 63. — Valley with bluffs, New York.

plain bounded by *bluffs*. Here the ordinary channel follows a meandering course, full of zigzag bends and horseshoe curves. The slope is gentle, the current sluggish, and the bed obstructed by sand bars and mud banks (Figs. 31, 32, 63, 70, 72, 75, 76). The stream finally flows into a larger stream, or into a lake or the sea.

Transportation of Sediment. — A stream of water is also a stream of mantle rock, by which the waste of the land is running away toward the sea. Some streams are clear, but they always contain a small quantity of invisible mineral matter dissolved out of the ground. A turbid or muddy stream is carrying mantle rock in *suspension*, which is kept from sinking by ripples, eddies, and cross currents due to irregularities in the bed. Most rock fragments when immersed in water are buoyed up to the extent of about one third of their weight, and are therefore more easily moved than when out of water. (Lift a stone out of water into the air.) In still water the finer particles of rock settle more slowly than the coarser, and in a current they are carried along more easily. (Shake up clay, sand, and gravel in a bottle of water and let them settle.) *The size of the particles of rock which a stream can carry in suspension increases rapidly as the speed of the current increases.* A current running one third of a mile an hour can carry clay; two thirds of a mile, fine sand; two miles, pebbles as large as cherries; four miles, stones as large as an egg.

A swift stream can carry more sediment of any kind in suspension than a slow one, and a stream of any speed can carry a larger quantity of fine sediment than of coarse; but the quantity of sediment which any stream can carry is limited. A stream which is carrying all the sediment it can is said to be *loaded*, or, less appropriately, *overloaded*. If the speed of a stream carrying a full load is slackened, its carrying capacity diminishes rapidly, and it immediately drops a part of its load, and always the coarsest first. If a current carrying a mixed load of clay, sand, and gravel is gradually brought to a standstill, it drops the coarse gravel first, then fine gravel, then coarse sand, then fine sand, and the clay last of all. Thus running water is the most efficient assorting agent known, and is often

Fig. 64. — Stream bed with banks of gravel dropped by the stream, Parke County, Ind.

used for that purpose. (Put clay, sand, and gravel in a pan of water, and by stirring, rinsing, and pouring wash out the clay first and then the sand.) If some of the sediment is much heavier than the rest, the heavier particles are left behind, while larger and lighter particles are carried away. (Put fine shot and gravel in a pan of water and wash out the gravel.) This is the reason why a miner can "pan out" coarse gravel and have fine gold dust left in his pan. If rock fragments are too large for a stream to buoy up and carry, it may push and roll them along the bottom.

The Speed of Streams. — A stream is swifter on a steep slope than on a gentle one. It is also swifter in the narrow parts of its channel than in the wide parts, because the same quantity of water must pass through both in the same time. Therefore any stream is swifter and more powerful at high water than at

Fig. 65. — Stream bed with boulders.

Fig. 66. — Alluvial cone.

low water. The greater the volume and speed of a stream, the greater the quantity and the coarser the quality of the sediment it can carry.

In times of flood, streams bring down great quantities of coarse material which they are obliged to drop as the flood subsides. When a stream is low in summer, it may not seem to be carrying any sediment at all, but its channel may be strewn with heaps of large stones which it brought down at the last spring flood. If a slow stream is loaded with fine sediment, any obstruction, as a boulder, log, fallen treetop, or even a small stake, may check the current sufficiently to cause a mud or sand bar to be deposited on the downstream side.

Deposition. — All the sediment carried by a stream must, sooner or later, be deposited at lower levels. Wherever the current is checked deposition is apt to occur. A stream flowing down a steep bank rapidly erodes a gully and deposits the material at the bottom of the bank in a conical or fan-shaped

Fig. 67. — Alluvial fan, Switzerland. (Robin.)

heap. Along the foot of a mountain range this process sometimes occurs on a large scale, each mountain stream building a steep *alluvial cone*, or a flat *fan* which may spread out several miles.

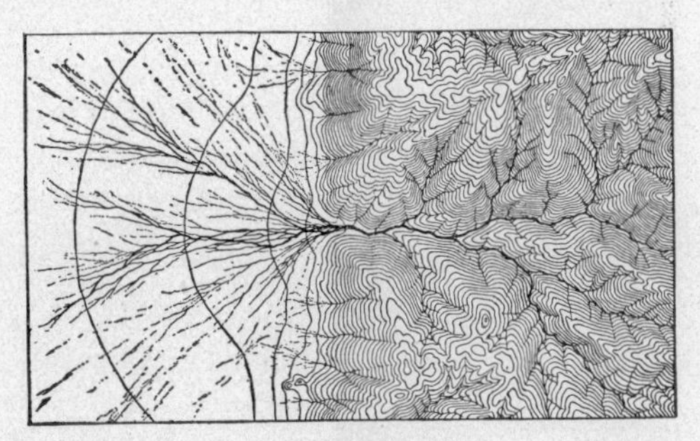

Fig. 68. — Contour map of alluvial fan. (U.S.G.S.)

Along the foot of the Wasatch Mountains, in Utah, and of the Sierra Nevada, in California, the alluvial fans are so large as to touch one another, forming a continuous *piedmont alluvial plain.* An alluvial fan sometimes affords extraordinary facilities for agriculture by irrigation. The water naturally spreads over the fan and can be easily guided to any part of it.

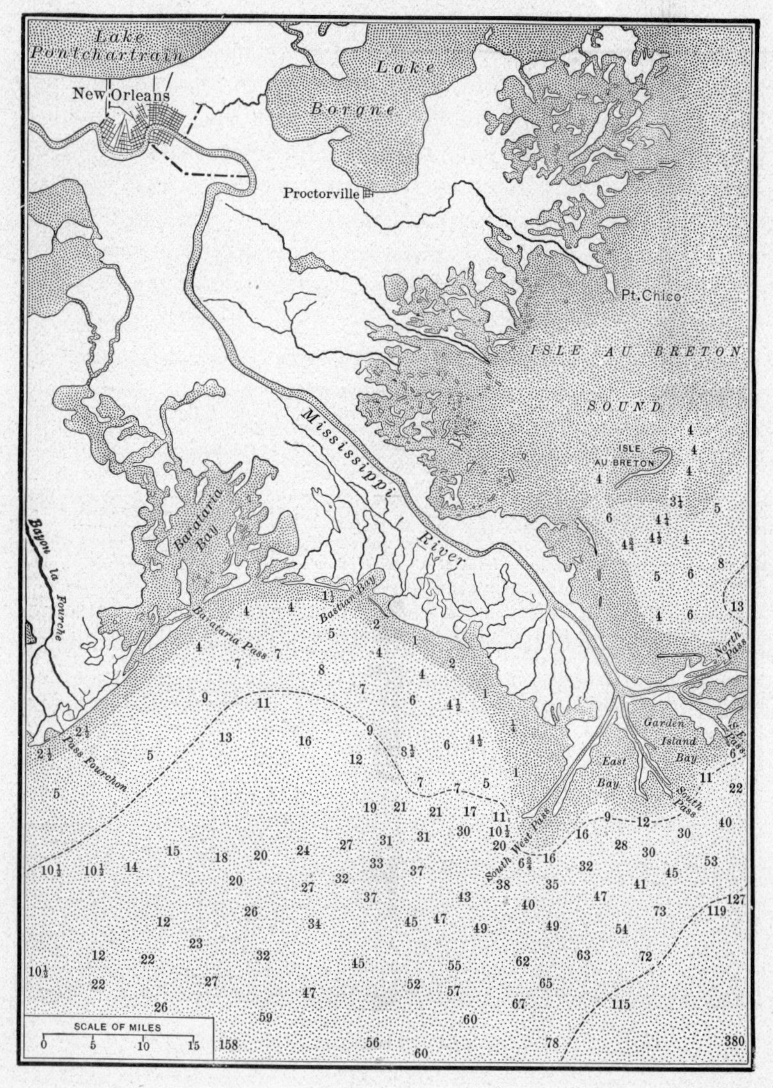

Fig. 69.—A part of the Mississippi delta. Numbers show depths in fathoms. **(U.S.G.S.)**

Whenever a stream overflows its banks it deposits sediment on the flooded ground and forms an alluvial plain, which in the lower course of a large river may become many miles in width. At the mouth of a river the alluvial plain may extend into a lake or the sea in the form of a *delta*, which is a flat alluvial fan built in the water. At the head of the delta the stream divides into *distributaries* and enters the sea by many mouths. The surface of a delta cannot be raised far above sea level, and is liable to be flooded by the river and by tides. The soil of delta lands is so fertile that it is often profitable to protect them by *dikes* or embankments, as has been done on a large scale at the mouth of the Rhine.

Sediment deposited by water is always more or less completely assorted, the finer from the coarser, and deposited in nearly horizontal strata. The stratified rocks which form a large part of the earth crust are nearly all made from sediment deposited by water.

Fig. 70. — Cut banks and bars.

The Crookedness of Streams. — The movement of water in a stream is retarded by friction against the bottom and banks, and against the air on the upper surface. Therefore the water moves fastest a little below the surface and along the line of the deepest channel. A flowing stream cannot be straight, because there is sure to be more resistance on one side than on the other, and a small obstruction is sufficient to turn the current toward the opposite bank. A strong stream on a steep slope is not easily turned aside and is comparatively straight, but the same stream on a gentle slope meanders from side to side and becomes very crooked. In a winding stream the current is swifter on the outside of the bend, and there it cuts away the bank and deepens its channel. On the inside of the bend the slower current is unable to carry its load and builds up a sloping bar of mud or sand. In this way the stream is constantly shifting its channel sidewise and widening its valley.

Fig. 71. — Gully in gravel.

Valley Forms. — A clear stream running over bed rock may dissolve it slowly, but a stream carrying a moderate load of sand and gravel uses them as tools with which it saws or files its way down through the hardest rocks. A swift stream erodes faster at the bottom than at the sides, and cuts a deep, narrow valley. A slow stream is usually unable to sweep its bed clear of sediment and therefore cannot cut it deeper. Its energy is expended in wearing away its banks, and in this way a small stream may

Fig. 72. — Meandering stream.

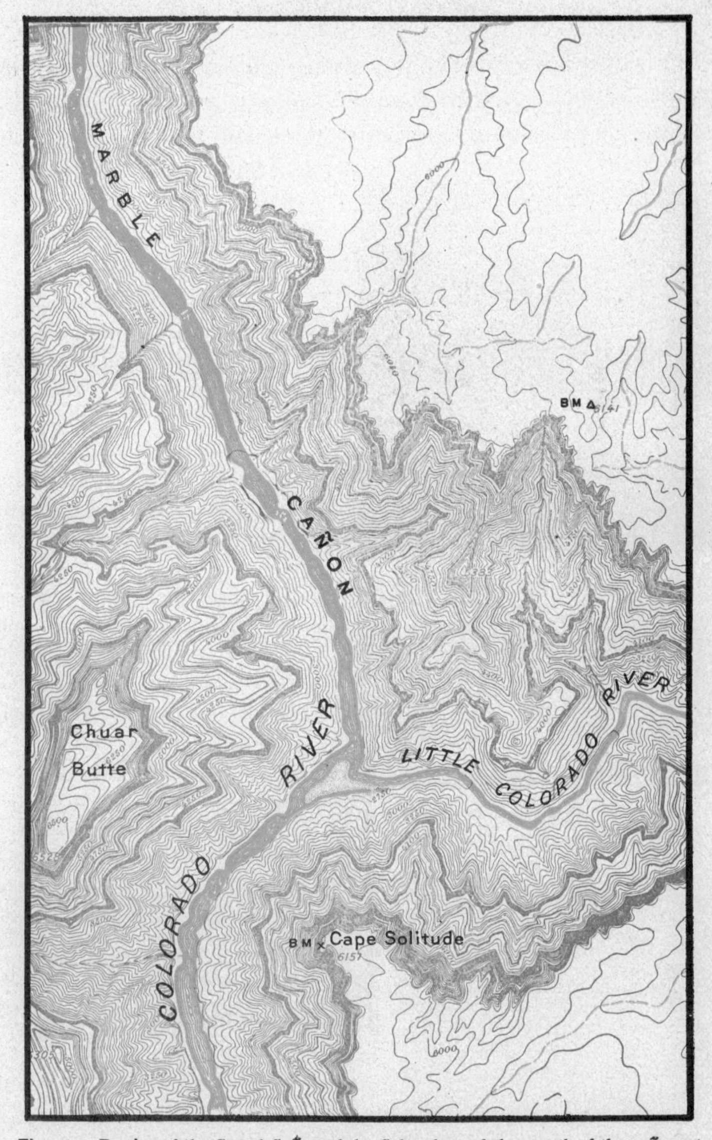

Fig. 73. — Portion of the Grand Cañon of the Colorado, and the mouth of the cañon of the Little Colorado River. Scale about 1 mile per inch. Contour interval 50 feet. (Vishnu, Arizona, Sheet, U.S.G.S.).

in the course of time make a wide valley. Its work may be done so slowly that scarcely any change is noticeable in a lifetime, but if it carries away only ten wagon loads of dirt from each mile of its course in a year, it can, in 50,000 years, make a valley 100 feet wide and 25 feet deep.

Fig. 74. — Royal Gorge, Colorado. 3000 feet deep.

A small but deep and narrow valley is called a *ravine* or *gorge*. In plateaus and mountains rivers are able to cut *cañons* of enormous dimensions. The Colorado River flows for about 1000 miles through a series of cañons, of which the Grand Cañon in Arizona is probably the most extensive cut anywhere in the face of the earth. It is 217 miles long, eight to fifteen miles wide, and about one mile deep. The river is not utilizable for navigation or irrigation, but the scenery of the cañon is unsurpassed for grandeur and beauty. The depth of the cut and the length of the main cañon and its tributaries present an exposure of rock strata so clear and extensive that geographers and geologists have probably learned more about the structure of the earth crust and the process of erosion from the Colorado cañons than from any other region in the world.

Upper, Middle, and Lower Parts of a Valley. — The headwaters of a large river are generally in highlands where the slopes are steep. The tributaries have a rapid fall and are often rushing torrents. Their erosive power is very great, but their volume is small. The valleys they cut are deep, narrow, strewn with large boulders, and interrupted by falls. In the middle part of its course the slope is more gentle, but the volume of water is larger, and it is here that the greatest amount of erosion takes place. The river carries away such quantities of sediment that its valley becomes both deep and wide. In the lower course the slope is very gentle, the current is feeble, and

Fig. 75. — Low water, Wabash River, Terre Haute, Ind.

the load too great to be carried. The land surface is not far above sea level, below which the river cannot deepen its valley. The current is continually obstructing itself by its deposits of

Fig. 76. — High water, Wabash River, Terre Haute, Ind.

sediment, which compel it to shift its channel. It cuts away its bank in one place and builds it up in another, developing a wide flood plain bounded by bluffs.

A stream which is actively deepening its valley is *young* (Figs.

Fig. 77. — Young valley. (Forty Mile Creek, Alaska.)

60, 73, 74, 77, 79, 83). A stream which has deepened its valley as far as possible, and has smoothed out rapids and falls, has reached *base level* and is *mature* (Figs. 63, 78, 79, 95). A stream which is widening its valley and aggrading its flood plain has reached a condition of *old age* (Figs. 31, 32, 64, 72, 79, 94, 97, 98).

Playfair's Law. — The relation of valleys and streams was stated by John Playfair in 1802:

> "Every river appears to consist of a main trunk fed from a variety of branches, each running in a valley proportioned to its size, and all of them together forming a system of valleys, communicating with one another, and having such a nice adjustment of their slopes that none of them join the principal valley either on too high or too low a level: a circumstance which would be infinitely improbable if each of these valleys were not the work of the stream which flows through it."

Streams and Relief. — The first effect of stream erosion upon the land surface is to cut it up into a system of valleys with broad ridges or divides between. As the valleys grow deeper and wider, the divides grow narrower and are gradually eaten away until their crests are sharp; the whole surface consists of slopes, and traveling across it is "all uphill and down." When the surface has been made as rough as possible and there is little or no level land left, it is said to be *maturely dissected*, or simply *mature* (Fig. 78). After the stage of maturity, continued stream work makes the divides lower and the valley bottoms wider. The country begins to grow smoother, and in the course of time is reduced to a plain of low relief, not far above sea level (Figs. 29, 30, 79, 111), called a *peneplain* (almost a plain).

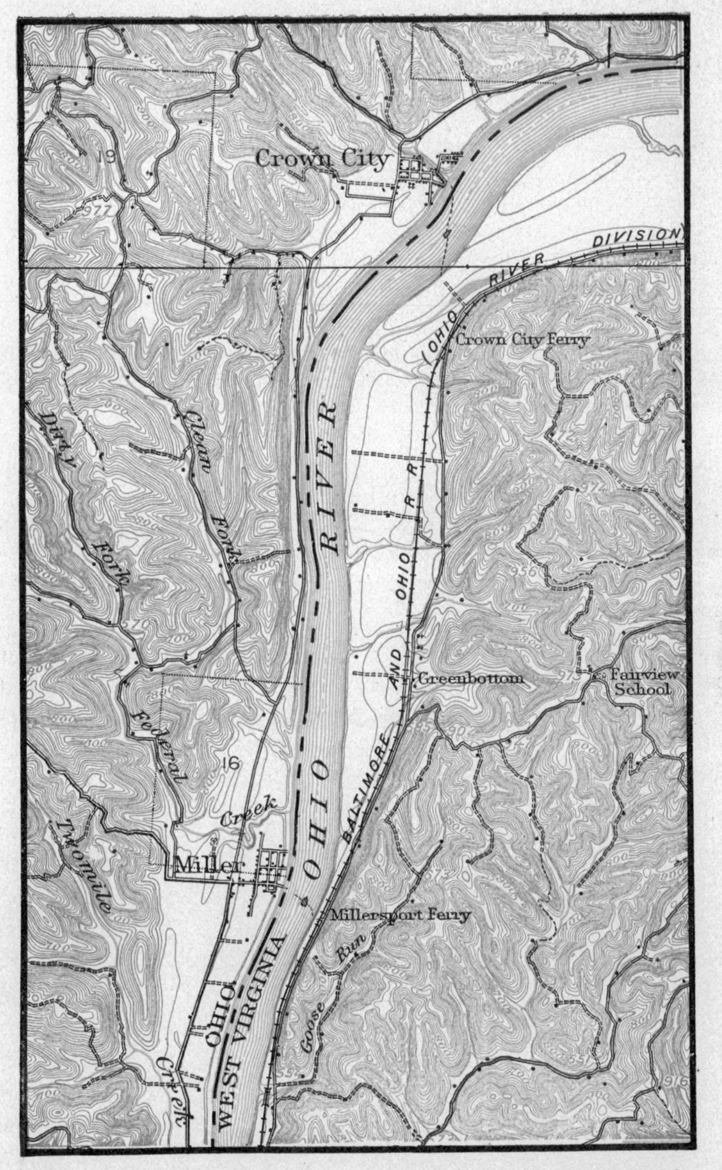

Fig. 78. — **Maturely dissected plateau, and graded valley, Ohio and West Virginia.** Scale about 1 mile per inch. Contour interval 20 feet. (Athalia Sheet, U.S.G.S.)

During the earlier stages of stream erosion the land surface is made rougher, during the later stages it is made smoother, and the final result is to degrade the land and aggrade the sea bottom, until they are both graded nearly to sea level.

Upon a completely graded peneplain the processes of stream erosion cease, because the streams have no longer a slope sufficient to enable them to carry sediment. But if a peneplain is uplifted by internal forces the revived streams will begin the process of gradation all over again. Gradation goes on most rapidly on mountains because weathering is more active there, and the slopes are so steep that gravity and running water can pull down and carry away great quantities of mantle rock. Consequently mountains do not last long, and all high mountains are comparatively young. For the same reasons, plateaus are degraded more rapidly than plains. Heavy rainfall favors rapid degradation because water helps to decompose and wash away rocks, and streams are larger and more numerous in wet regions. Some kinds of rocks are more resistant to weathering and erosion than others, and are left projecting as the general surface is lowered. A covering of forest or other vegetation generally retards erosion.

Economic Relations. — The value of a region for human occupation depends largely upon the stage of gradation it has reached. Young, low plains are smooth, gently sloping, easily accessible, and generally productive. The work of gradation progresses slowly and can never produce a surface of strong relief. All human occupations may be carried on with ease, and in all stages plains are fitted to support a large population with a minimum expenditure of energy.

Young plateaus of moderate height are second in value only to plains. Gradation begins as soon as the surface is exposed above the sea, goes on during the long, slow process of upheaval, and usually before any great height is reached has progressed so far as seriously to roughen the surface. As dissection of the plateau approaches maturity, it is cut up into an intricate system of deep valleys and narrow ridges, which is as inconvenient as possible for carrying on any kind of human business (Figs. 43, 78, 79). In the stages beyond maturity, as old age approaches, the relief of a plateau becomes smoother, and as a peneplain it finally reaches a condition not essentially different from that of a region originally a low plain.

Most young mountains are high and extremely rugged, like the Alps, and are of all regions the most difficult of utilization by man. In some young mountains, like the Jura (Fig. 39),

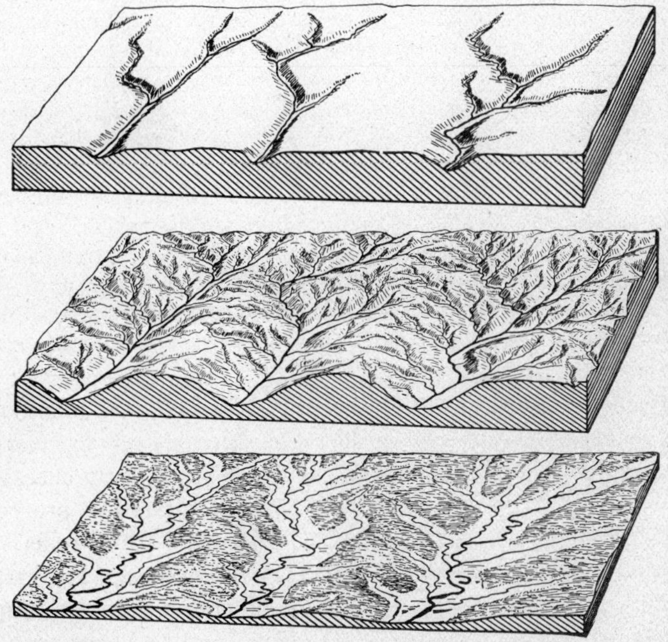

Fig. 79.—**Youth, maturity, and old age.** (Blackwelder and Barrows, *Elements of Geology.*)

the earth crust has been less violently disturbed, folded, and broken, and the region is correspondingly less forbidding. Such regions pass through changes somewhat like those of a plateau. As a rule, it is only in old age that mountain regions become so far worn down and smoothed off as to be fitted for occupation by any large number of people. The Appalachians furnish a notable example of an old mountain region. The general law is obvious that *lowlands are the homes of the most highly civilized peoples*.

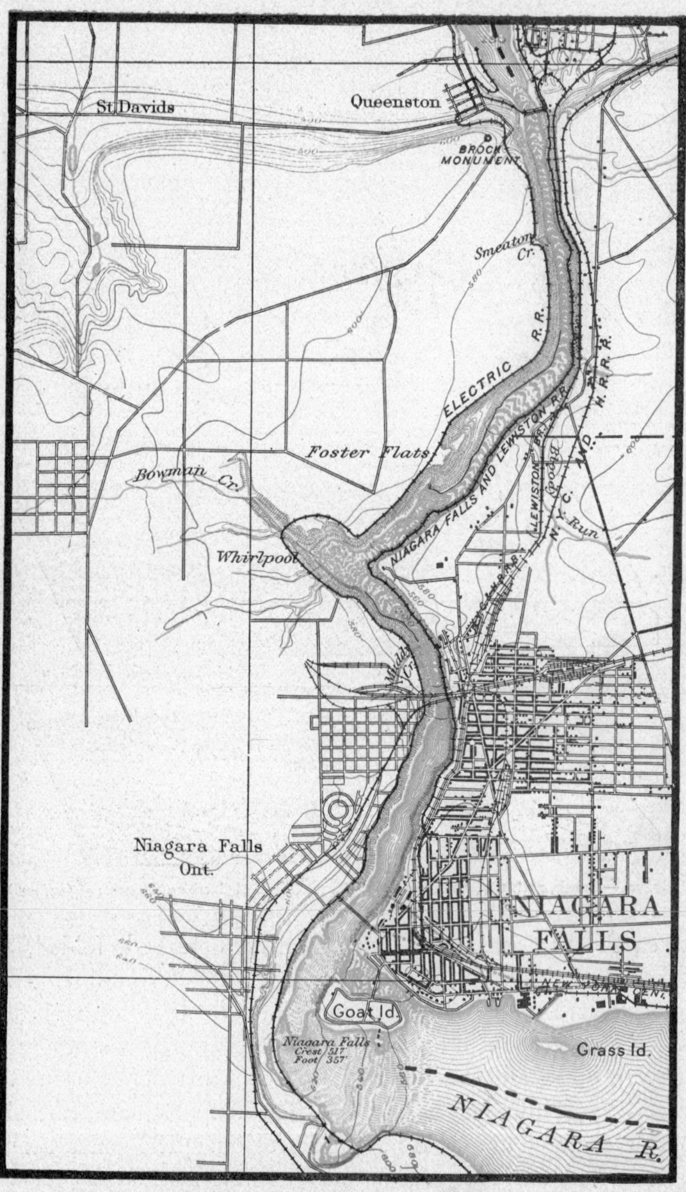

Fig. 80. — Niagara Falls and Gorge. Scale about 1.25 miles per inch. Contour interval 20 feet. (Niagara Falls Sheet, U.S.G.S.)

Waterfalls. — Wherever the slope of a stream bed is abrupt or steep, falls and rapids occur. They are usually due to an outcrop of resistant rock which the stream cannot wear down as rapidly as the softer material in other parts of its course. In a brook a tree root or a bed of clay on top of sand will make a fall. Glaciated valleys are often bordered by cliffs over which streams cascade. Such falls are sometimes of great height, like those of the Yosemite Valley in California (Figs. 84, 105), and many in Norway. Falls and rapids in large rivers generally occur where the stream crosses a bed of limestone, granite, or lava. The force of the falling water deepens the channel below the falls and undermines the cliff behind them, so that the falls retreat upstream, leaving a gorge below (Figs. 80, 81, 82, 86).

Fig. 81. — Gorge of Niagara River, made by retreat of the Falls.

The Niagara River falls over a limestone ledge into a gorge 400 feet deep and seven miles long, which the river has cut by the migration of the falls upstream. The gorge below the Victoria Falls on the Zambezi River in Africa, 500 feet deep and 40 miles long, has a peculiar zigzag course on account of cracks in the bed of lava. Rapids and falls are most numerous in mountains and plateaus, and in young streams everywhere. An old stream has had time enough to wear down and smooth out the irregularities of its bed.

Economic Relations. — Waterfalls are becoming more and more valuable as sources of power for running machinery. Most of them are not easily available because they occur in remote and inaccessible regions, but if the power cannot be brought to the present site of an industry, the industry may be moved to the place where the power is.

Fig. 82. — Gorge of the Zambezi.

Of all the water powers in the world that of Niagara Falls is the most valuable, because of the large and constant volume of water, and still more because it is situated in the midst of a densely populated district. A part of their power is now used to generate electricity which is transmitted over wires to run railroads and factories, and to furnish light to cities within 150 miles. There is power enough at Niagara to supply four or five of the largest cities in America.

Waterfalls are among the most attractive scenic features of the world and have a high value apart from any use that can be made of their power. On account of their beauty and grandeur and because they are so easily accessible, Niagara Falls are visited by about 600,000 people every year. The use of the water for power seriously impairs their beauty and might entirely destroy it. Whether it would be better for the human race to keep the falls in their natural state to give pleasure to future millions, or to destroy them by diverting the water for power purposes, is an important practical question which the present generation is called upon to decide.

CHAPTER VI

THE ECONOMIC RELATIONS OF STREAMS

Drainage. — The first important function of streams is to drain the land by carrying surplus rain water to the sea. When a land surface is first exposed to stream action by elevation above the sea, or by the melting of an ice cap, the drainage is imperfect. Depressions are occupied by lakes, ponds, and marshes, which, if numerous, are sure indications of youthful drainage.

The glaciated regions of northern North America and Europe and the recently elevated land of Florida are conspicuous examples. On low plains and gentle slopes drainage develops slowly and remains imperfect for a long time. The shallow lakes of the glacial drift are being filled with accumulations of mud and peat which promise to be of value in the future for cement and fuel. Wet, undrained land is comparatively worthless for human occupation. It produces at best only inferior timber or coarse herbage. Artificial drainage by open ditches and tile drains may convert such land into excellent farms and gardens. The area of marsh lands in the United States which might be drained is larger than the area of arid lands that can be irrigated.

In a mature drainage system every part of the land is drained, and any drop of rain falling upon its basin may find its way to the sea. On plateaus and in mountainous and hilly regions, slopes are steep and drainage is often too rapid. The soil is washed away, the surface is cut up by gullies, and the lowlands are buried in sand and gravel. In the old countries where soil is precious this waste is sometimes checked by a series of dams. Such areas ought to be used for the growth of forests, which retard the run-off and prevent waste by erosion.

Erosion. — Streams are not currents of running water only, but also of running rock. Through them the solid land is draining away to the sea. Everywhere except in desert regions the details of landscape are due to stream or glacial action. Valleys are cut in the earth crust, thus making its materials accessible, revealing its structure, and producing a great variety of scenery. Rocks and minerals originally buried far below the surface have been uncovered and exposed. There would be no coal mines in

Fig. 83. — Watkins Glen, New York: A very young gorge in shale rock.

Pennsylvania if streams had not removed from the surface of that region beds of rock several miles in thickness. The cuts made by streams into the earth crust are invaluable to the geologist, because he finds there exposed all kinds of rocks and is able to study their composition and arrangement, to determine their origin and history, and to learn how the earth has been made. He finds in the rocks the fossil remains of thousands of plants and animals which no human being ever saw

Fig. 84. — **Yosemite Valley, California.** A glaciated valley 3,000 feet deep in granite rock.

alive, and is able to read the history of life on the earth during past millions of years.

Fig. 85. — Red Butte, Nebraska. (U.S.G.S.)

If it were not for stream erosion the surface of the land would be as monotonous and uninteresting as the bottom of the sea. There would be no ravines, gorges, cañons, cliffs, buttes, mesas, spurs, passes, or peaks. Even mountain ranges would be tame and unimpressive. The most famous scenery in the world, the Grand Cañon, the Yosemite Valley, the Niagara Falls and Gorge, the valleys of the Hudson and the Rhine, the Scotch Highlands, the English and Italian lakes, the fiords of Alaska and Norway, would not be in existence. Few things in nature are more attractive to men than running water. Without it the world would be a much less pleasant place to live in.

Fig. 86. — Taghanic Falls and Gorge, New York.

Water Supply. — One of the prime requisites for plant or animal life is an adequate water supply. Many species of shellfish, fish, frogs, insects, waterfowl, and higher animals, from the muskrat to the hippopotamus, find in streams a home and a storehouse of food. All the higher animals visit them frequently to drink. The hunter in pursuit of game, whether it be duck, deer, giraffe, lion, or elephant, lies in wait by the water's edge, where he knows thirst will bring his victim in due time. A man consumes nearly a gallon of water a day, and if it happens to contain the germs of disease it may be a fatal poison as well as a food. Travel and settlement have been strongly influenced by water supply. Springs have determined the location of trails, camps, homesteads, and villages.

Scattered and rural populations depend generally upon ground water obtained from wells, but in cities, where thousands or millions of people are crowded together upon a few square miles, wells are inadequate and dangerous. Large cities must almost always depend upon streams for water supply. A lake forms a natural reservoir of generally clear, pure water, and if necessary an artificial lake can be made by means of a dam.

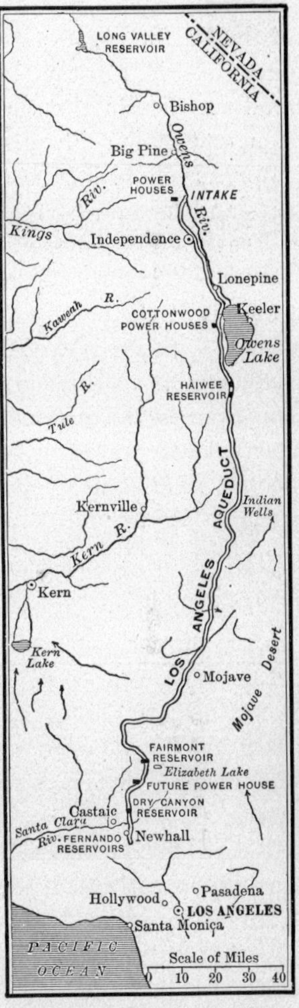

Fig. 87. — Los Angeles aqueduct.

Few cities are so fortunate as Chicago in having a fresh-water sea at its doors. Yet Chicago has had to reach out under the lake with a tunnel six miles long to obtain water free from pollution, and to spend thirty million dollars on a canal to carry away its drainage. St. Louis and New Orleans have the mighty flood of the Mississippi to draw upon. The water is muddy, but the mud is harmless and can be filtered out. New York has taken possession of the Croton River basin, and brings a larger supply 85 miles from the Catskills. Glasgow brings water from Loch Katrine, 42 miles, Manchester from Thirlmere, 96 miles, and Liverpool from artificial Lake Vyrnwy, 67 miles. Los Angeles is constructing an aqueduct 250 miles long, and tunneling through a mountain range, to get water from Owens River. London has sanitary control of the whole Thames basin, which is hardly adequate to supply water to seven millions of people. No city can afford to spare pains or expense to obtain a sufficient and safe water supply.

Food Supply. — Nearly all streams contain fish of some kind, and in large rivers and lakes, such as the St. Lawrence system, fisheries form an important source of food supply. The rivers of the Pacific coast of America, from the Sacramento northward, once furnished in the form of salmon one of the most abundant food supplies in the world. The United States Fish Commission, and similar bureaus in other countries, have been organized to preserve and increase the supply of fish food by distributing eggs and fry and by regulating seasons and methods of fishing.

Travel and Transportation. — Streams furnish easy routes ot travel and transportation. In new and undeveloped countries they are often the only practicable routes. They are extensions of sea facilities into the land, and of lowlands into highlands. Explorers, from Hudson, Champlain, and La Salle to Livingstone and Stanley, have penetrated the continents by way of great rivers. After a country has been long occupied by civilized people, rivers still remain cheap and ready-made freight routes, without expense for construction and maintenance.

The Amazon admits large vessels 2,000 miles into the interior of Brazil, and, with its many large tributaries, constitutes the only means of travel through an area nearly as large as the United States. The Belgian Kongo is being opened to trade and civilization by means of its rivers. In China one fourth of the human race depend upon their great waterways for circulation of people and goods. In Europe the Seine, Rhine, Elbe, Danube, and Volga are to-day great highways of commerce. North America has been settled largely through its great rivers, and while water transportation is now to a great extent superseded by railroads, the St. Lawrence and the Great Lakes transport as many tons of freight as the Mediterranean Sea.

Fig. 88. — Railroad following grade of Allegheny River. (U.S.G.S.)

Rivers have been at work for ages grading their valleys, and when man undertakes artificial highways he avails himself of their work. Canals and railways follow stream valleys wherever possible. Their construction would be everywhere more costly, and in rough and mountainous countries impossible, if the streams had not first cleared the way. Nearly every important city in the world is located upon a river and stands where it does because of the river.

Water Power. — Wherever water runs downhill, the force of gravity or the weight of the water can be used to drive machinery.

Fig. 89. — Water power on Genesee River, Rochester, N. Y.

The most valuable water powers are found at natural cataracts or rapids where the fall, usually distributed over many miles, is concentrated in a small space. In the absence of natural rapids or falls, an artificial fall must be made by means of a dam. For this purpose swift streams with deep, narrow valleys, like those of New England, are most advantageous. Abundant water power, with few exceptions, is found in highlands and along the upper courses of streams. For this reason mountainous countries such as Switzerland, Italy, and Norway are becoming important manufacturing centers.

Irrigation. — To have water to use whenever needed is an ideal condition for raising any crop, and is far better than dependence upon irregular and uncertain rainfall. Irrigation is as

Fig. 90. — Irrigating ditches in orange grove, Arizona.

old as civilization. It is a remarkable fact that the localities where civilization first appeared were deserts which, in their natural state, were almost uninhabitable.

Six or seven thousand years ago men learned to make use of the overflow upon flood plains and to improve and extend the natural process by means of reservoirs, canals, and ditches. In the valleys of the Tigris, Euphrates, and Nile, populous and powerful communities depended for existence upon irrigation. In the present century the British in Egypt have constructed immense dams which retain enough water to make thousands of acres of desert productive. Similar works have been undertaken by the British to restore the ancient prosperity of Mesopotamia. Irrigation has been practiced from time immemorial in Turkestan, India, Spain, Italy, and Mexico. The United States government is now engaged in the construction of an extensive system of irrigation works which will result in the reclamation of millions of acres of arid land. Irrigation on a large scale is possible only in the lower courses of rivers where the valley is wide, or on plains and plateaus bordered by mountains from which the water may be distributed over the land.

The Utilization of Rivers. — A river is most usable for navigation when it has a large and comparatively constant volume of water, a small or moderate load of sediment, a graded slope, a gentle current, and a wide, shallow valley. Such rivers occur in plains and low plateaus of medium or heavy rainfall. A lake in the course of a river adds greatly to its advantages. The lake is wide, its water is deep and still, and its surface is level. The river below the lake is clear and not subject to floods or low stages of water. Drowning of the lower part of a river valley produces conditions similar to those of a lake.

Fig. 91. — Lake steamer.

In the possession of these characteristics the St. Lawrence is preëminent among the rivers of the world. Its valley is drowned to a point 900 miles from the sea, and the five Great Lakes have an aggregate length of nearly 1,500 miles, leaving only 300 miles of the system with any perceptible current. In sailing from Buffalo to Chicago, a distance of 800 miles, a vessel ascends only nine feet, or to Duluth, a still greater distance, only thirty feet.

In most streams there is some variation of volume dependent upon seasonal rainfall, snow melting, and evaporation. In the middle latitudes of Europe and eastern North America, high water is due to winter rains, or melting snow on frozen ground, and occurs in the late winter or spring. The Ohio, Seine, Rhine, Elbe, and Danube belong to this group. The rivers of northern North America and Eurasia derive their main water supply from melting snow and have high water in the spring. The floods are made much more extensive and prolonged by great ice dams in their lower courses, which persist and hold the water back long after the upper courses are clear of ice. On account of such conditions these rivers are of little use. They include the Yukon, Mackenzie, Saskatchewan-Nelson, Dwina, Petchora, Ob, Yenisei, and Lena.

In the tropical regions of South America and Africa and the monsoon regions of Asia high water occurs with the heavy rains of summer. The rivers of this class include the Orinoco, Amazon, Parana, Kongo, Zambezi, Nile, Ganges, Brahmaputra, Yangtse, Hoang, and Amur.

Rivers in mountains and high plateaus are utilizable chiefly for power in their upper courses and for irrigation in their lower. Their main water supply is from melting snow, and they are subject to great changes of volume. The most important flow from the interior highlands of North America and Asia, and in crossing arid lowlands in their way to the sea lose a large part of their volume by evaporation. Among these are the Missouri, Arkansas, Red, Colorado, Columbia, Euphrates, Tigris, Amu, Syr, and Indus. The rivers of southern Europe and California belong to this class, and being small, almost run dry in summer.

In desert and semi-arid regions the streams are generally intermittent or occasional, drying up a part of every year, or flowing only at irregular intervals. They are useful only for irrigation.

The Savannah River. — Some rivers are utilizable for all purposes. The Savannah River, between Georgia and South Carolina, is an example. Although the total length of its basin is only 250 miles, it traverses three distinct belts, — the mountain, the plateau, and the plain.

Its headwaters are in the Blue Ridge, where the rainfall is heavy, the slopes are steep, and there are many falls and rapids. One tributary, the Tallulah, presents a succession of good water-power sites for thirty miles, ending in a fall of 400 feet in five miles. This region should be wholly devoted to the growing of hardwood forests, and the power should be used to run saw-mills and other machinery.

The second or piedmont belt is a farming region, and raises cotton. A group of reservoirs located at the foot of the mountains would prevent floods, store water for use during the low-water periods, and help in furnishing power for cotton mills and wood-working factories. At the lower edge of the piedmont plateau is the "fall line," where the river descends an escarpment to the coastal plain. The power here has made the city of Augusta, with twenty-one cotton mills.

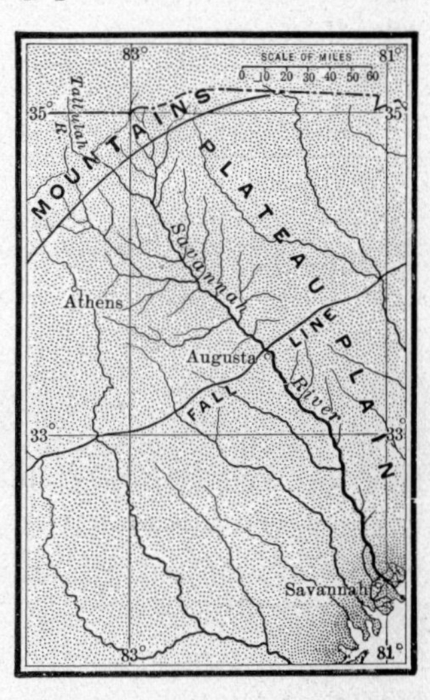

Fig. 92. — The Savannah River.

From Augusta to its mouth, about 150 miles, the Savannah is a navigable tidal stream flowing in an alluvial valley. With its flow properly regulated, there would be a good depth of water all the year, and the harbor of Savannah at its mouth would be one of the best in the southern states. If the possibilities of the river were fully utilized, it would furnish power, cheap transportation, and a seaport for a rich agricultural and manufacturing community.

The Mississippi System. — Any one looking at a map of the United States would be impressed with the importance and advantages of the Mississippi River system which drains nearly half the country. The extreme headwaters on the west rise in the Rocky Mountains, and, flowing through narrow valleys and cañons, with numerous rapids and falls, furnish water power and opportunities to irrigate the dry plains below (Figs. 60, 74, 94). The eastern tributaries from the Appalachian Mountains and plateau have reached a later stage of development, and their valleys are generally mature and well graded, but rather narrow (Figs. 78, 95). The northern sources are in a region of numerous lakes which act as reservoirs and help to equalize the flow at all seasons. The branches of the system penetrate nearly every square mile of the interior plain, and furnished to the canoe of the Indian, and the white explorer and trader, easy routes of travel. The early settlement of the "Middle West" was largely accomplished by means of flatboats and steamers, and homesteads, towns, and cities were located along the streams, which continued to be the chief arteries of travel and trade until the advent of railroads about 1850. The lower Mississippi was closed to commerce during the Civil War (1861-65) and since that time its use for transportation has rapidly declined. The Mississippi system on the map appears to furnish thousands of miles of navigable waterway, but it has proved inadequate to the needs of to-day. The river towns which are still prosperous and growing owe more to the railroads than to the river. This condition is due chiefly to natural causes.

Western Tributaries. — The Missouri and other western tributaries north of the Red River receive most of their water from the mountains, and in crossing the plains traverse a region of scant rainfall. As a result the volume of water decreases toward their mouths by evaporation, and they are overloaded with sediment. Their channels are shallow, crooked, and constantly shifting by the cutting away of banks and the formation of bars. In some cases the river becomes *braided*, or divided into a network of small streams which spread out over an area a mile wide, but are not more than a foot deep. In the dry season the water may disappear from the surface, and the stream become apparently a river of sand. The volume of the Missouri varies greatly with the seasons. The water from the melting snows in the mountains reaches the lower river in June, when the volume may be thirty times as great as at low water in November. At high water it floods a wide area of bottom lands and scours

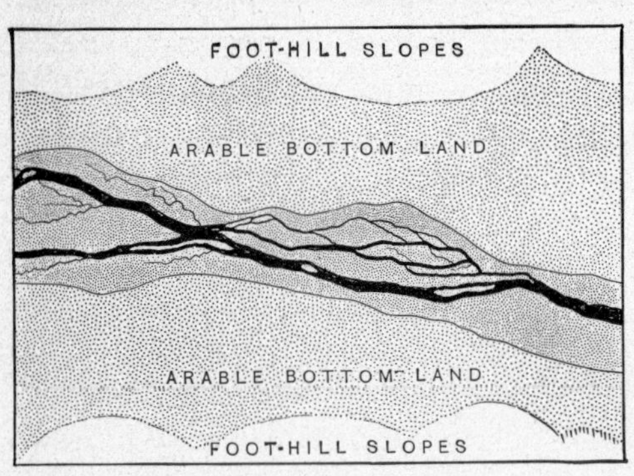

Fig. 93. — Braided stream. (U.S.G.S.)

out its channel to great depths, only to refill it as the current slackens. The Missouri is nominally navigable to Fort Benton, but navigation has been generally abandoned. Small steamers do a local business as feeders to the various railroads which cross the river.

Fig. 94. — Bighorn River in the plains, Wyoming. Irrigation canal on right bank. (U.S.G.S.)

The upper Mississippi drains a country of moderate rainfall and is not subject to extreme fluctuations in volume. It discharges nearly as much water as the Missouri, and is navigated without much difficulty as far as St. Paul.

The Ohio. — The Ohio basin receives a heavier rainfall than any other part of the Mississippi system, and the river discharges three fourths as much water as the Missouri and upper Mississippi combined. The large tributaries are not overloaded and contain no cataracts and few rapids. The valleys are generally narrow and bordered by high bluffs (Figs. 78, 95). The streams are subject to excessive fluctuations of volume. The rains and melting snows of spring sometimes raise the level of the Ohio at Cincinnati seventy feet above low-water mark, and the droughts of summer and autumn may reduce its depth to three feet. On a river whose level varies so much it is impossible to maintain permanent docks and landing places, the water front of towns is liable to be flooded or left out of reach by boats, and navigation is inconvenient and dangerous. In spite of these difficulties considerable business is done on the Ohio, chiefly in transport-

Fig. 95. — Ohio River, near Madison, Ind.

ing coal from Pennsylvania in barges, which are lashed together and pushed in front of a steamer. The United States government is now building a series of dams in the Ohio which will maintain a depth of nine feet at all seasons.

Fig. 96. — Ohio River barges and steamer. Landing place, Evansville, Ind.

The Lower Mississippi. — The lower Mississippi, from the mouth of the Ohio to the Gulf, flows through an alluvial valley

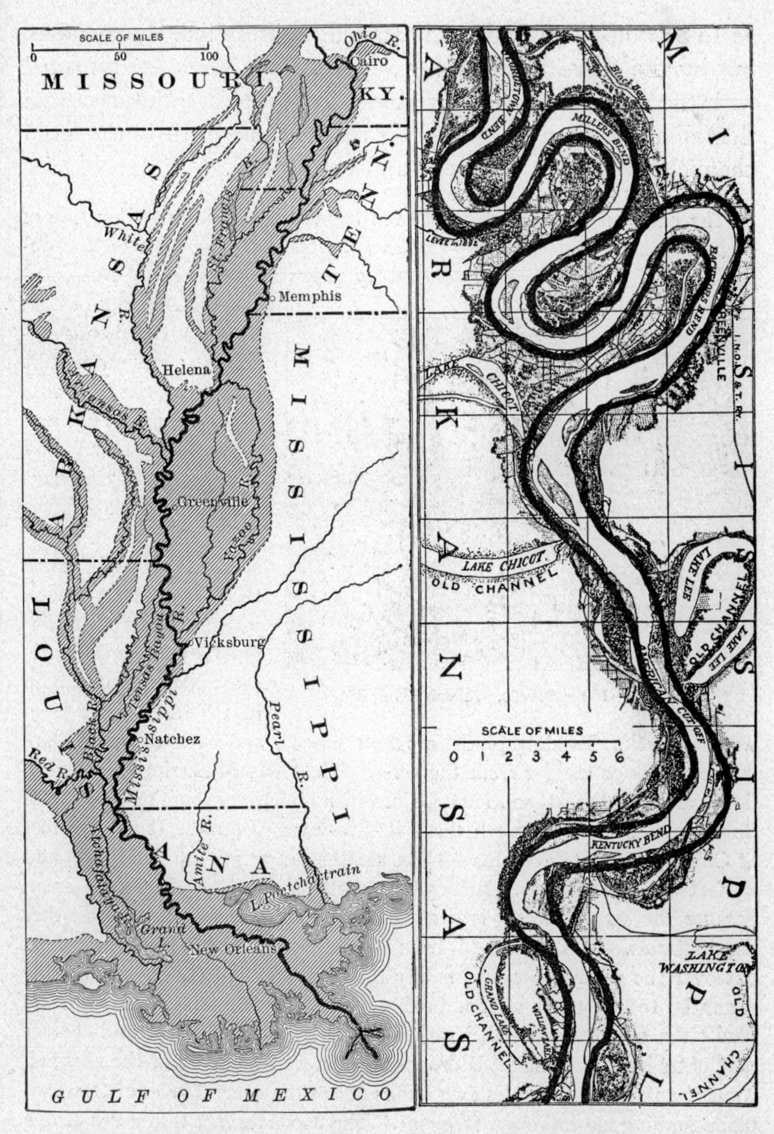

Fig. 97. — Lower Mississippi flood plain.

Fig. 98. — The Mississippi, near Greenville, Miss. The heavy lines show changes in channel in 12 years.

25 to 80 miles wide. The distance in a direct line is 600 miles, but by the course of the river 1,075 miles. The river is loaded with the mud of the Missouri and other western tributaries, and the fall is less than six inches per mile. Consequently the main channel is extremely tortuous and changeable.

The bank on the outer side of each bend and on the up-valley side of each tongue of land is rapidly cut away, while bars are built on the opposite sides. Thus the river continually grows more crooked. But occasionally the neck of land between two bends becomes so narrow that at high water the river cuts through and straightens itself. The new *cut-off* becomes the main channel, and the old bend is left at one side as a horseshoe lake (Fig. 98). Thus the deep-water channel, which steamers can follow, is constantly shifting, and does not remain in the same place from week to week. Landing places must be moved, and even town sites are washed away or left far from the river. The lower Mississippi carries the flood waters of the Missouri and Ohio, which sometimes combine to increase its volume to more than ten times its low-water volume. It rises 53 feet at Cairo, 36 feet at Memphis, 48 feet at Helena, 53 feet at Vicksburg, and 15 feet at New Orleans. Below the mouth of the Red the rise is small because the surplus water is carried away by the Atchafalaya and other distributaries. In the natural state of the river the flood waters spread out over the valley floor, and finally drain off through the *bayous*, or side channels, to the main stream farther down. As the river overflows its banks the current is checked rather suddenly, and the larger and coarser part of its load of sediment is dropped within a mile or two of the channel. Thus the river builds up its own banks above the general level of the flood plain, forming natural *levees* (Fig. 99). The floods leave a thin layer of fine and fertile mud over the submerged lands, which thus acquire a soil of great and frequently renewed fertility. But the floods are destructive to prop-

Fig. 99. — Natural levee, Wabash River, Ind.

erty, and render the utilization of such lands for agriculture difficult and precarious.

The governments of the United States and of the various states concerned have spent many millions of dollars in works designed to prevent floods and to improve the navigable channel. These works include the

Fig. 100. — A Mississippi levee, Greenville. High water above the level of the town.

construction of reservoirs at the sources of the upper Mississippi to store water for use during low stages, the dredging of channels across bars, and the protection of banks which are liable to be cut away. But the most important and expensive work done consists in the building of artificial levees or embankments of earth, which are now completed on both sides of the river nearly up to the mouth of the Ohio. Confining the flood water to the narrow space between the levees causes it to rise higher than before, and it sometimes runs over or breaks through, but about three fourths of the alluvial valley seems to be effectually protected from floods. Whether the confinement of flood waters will cause the river to scour out and deepen its channel, to the advantage of navigation, remains to be seen. A deep water way (fourteen feet) from the Great Lakes to the Gulf is greatly needed, but the expense of construction and maintenance would perhaps be too great for even so rich a country as the United States.

Fig. 101. — Mississippi steamer.

Fig. 102. — Bernina and Roseg glaciers, Switzerland. Note jagged peaks, smooth lower slopes, snow fields, and medial and lateral moraines.

CHAPTER VII

GRADATION BY ICE

WHILE running water is the most effective agent in modifying the relief of the land surface, many important features are due to moving ice. On high mountains and in polar regions at low levels, more snow falls than can be melted, and it therefore accumulates from year to year. A bank of permanent snow slowly changes by thawing, freezing, and pressure into solid ice which drains away down the slopes, somewhat as water does.

Valley or Alpine Glaciers. — A valley or alpine glacier is a stream of ice, fed by a snow field above and following a valley

Fig. 103. — Confluence of three glaciers, Switzerland. (Robin.)

line down to the sea, or to warmer levels where it is melted and changed into a stream of water. In comparison with a river, an ice stream is slow, stiff, and awkward, progressing only a few feet a year, yet it accomplishes great results. At its very head

Fig. 104. — A cirque in the Sierra Nevada, California. (U. S. Bureau of Fisheries.)

Fig. 105. — Glaciated valley, Lauterbrunnen, Switzerland.

Fig. 106. — Nunatak Glacier, Alaska, discharging bergs into a fiord.
Ice divide in the distance. (U.S.G.S.)

it freezes to loose rock fragments and drags them away from the valley walls and bottom. Thus a semicircular hollow is gradually eaten into the mountain side, which comes to resemble a gigantic armchair and is called a *cirque* (Figs. 104, 40). Several glaciers working on different sides may reduce the mountain summit to a thin, sharp, and jagged ridge. Great quantities of dirt and stones slide and fall from the steep sides of the valley upon the surface of the ice and are carried downstream. The ice is often a thousand feet or more in thickness, and its pressure on the valley bottom over which it slides amounts to many tons per square foot. The sand, gravel, and boulders frozen into the under surface convert the glacier into a powerful rasp which scratches, rubs down, and planes off the bed rock. The valley is deepened and widened into a rounded shape, like the letter U, easily distinguished from the sharp V-shaped valley of a river (Fig. 105).

If the glacier reaches the sea, the ice breaks off in large chunks, or *icebergs*, which drift about and are finally melted. In most cases a glacier is brought to an end far from the sea by melting, and the whole load of

Fig. 107. — Glacial drift, Ontario County, N. Y. Boulders in stream have been washed out of clay banks.

loose rock which it carries is left in a heap called a *terminal moraine*. A glacier can carry an almost unlimited load of sediment, fine or coarse. It carries a boulder as large as a house as easily and rapidly as a grain of sand. Therefore it has no power of assorting materials, as running water has, and does not deposit them in layers. *Glacial drift* is recognizable as a mixture of mantle rock of different kinds and sizes, from clay as fine as flour to boulders weighing many tons, all mixed together in a heap or spread out in a sheet.

Fig. 108. — Glacial boulder, Indiana.

A valley glacier often consists of a trunk stream with many tributaries like a river system. The main ice stream deepens its valley faster than the weaker tributaries can, so that a glaciated valley from which the ice has disappeared is characterized by numerous waterfalls, where the streams from the "hanging" tributary valleys cascade down to the floor of the main valley (Figs. 84, 86, 105). In an old glaciated mountain system, such as that of Alaska, all the valleys are deeply filled with ice which streams from the divides and snow fields in various directions, so that it is possible to pass easily

Fig. 109. — Peaks worn down to snow level, Alaska.

from one side of the range to the other over ice divides (Fig. 106). The peaks left projecting like islands above the snow surface, and exposed to severe and continuous frost action, become extremely jagged and disintegrate down to snow level, which thus acts as a base level of erosion (Fig. 109). Below the upper limit of snow the rocks are protected from frost, but exposed to the abrasive and smoothing action of moving ice. Thus a valley which has been formerly occupied by a glacier may present a striking contrast between the smooth and polished surface of its lower slopes and the rough and splintered surface above (Figs. 102, 103).

Valley glaciers and glaciated mountain valleys furnish some of the most impressive and fascinating scenery in the world. They have a peculiar charm for the physiographer, the artist, and the adventurous pedestrian who uses the ice surface as a path by which to climb the peaks or cross the range.

Ice Caps.—An ice cap is a mass of snow and ice which accumulates upon a plateau and moves outward in all directions, as molasses candy spreads out on a plate. Existing ice caps vary in dimensions from twenty miles in diameter in Iceland to those of Greenland and Antarctica, where an area larger than the United States is completely buried. Fifty thousand or a hundred thousand years ago North America north of 40° N. Lat. and Europe north of 50° were nearly covered by a succession of ice sheets which profoundly modified the relief, drainage, and soil. The glaciated area may be roughly divided into two contrasted parts: (1) the area of ice accumulation and erosion, corresponding to the upper and middle course of a river; (2) the area of ice destruction and drift deposition, corresponding to the flood plain and delta portion of a river.

American Ice Sheets. — In America the snow and ice accumulated on the Cordilleras of Canada and around Hudson Bay, and extended southward to the Columbia, Missouri, and Ohio rivers. Near the centers of accumulation the ice was perhaps two miles thick, and in moving outward it swept away the mantle rock, wore down the less resistant bed rock, and left a surface of peculiar relief, characterized by shallow basins and low, rounded hills, with no regularity in shape or arrangement.

The basins, filled with water, constitute the innumerable lakes which cover southern Canada with tangled chains of waterway. The great lakes around the border of the severely glaciated area, from Ontario to Great Bear, owe their form, size, and ex-

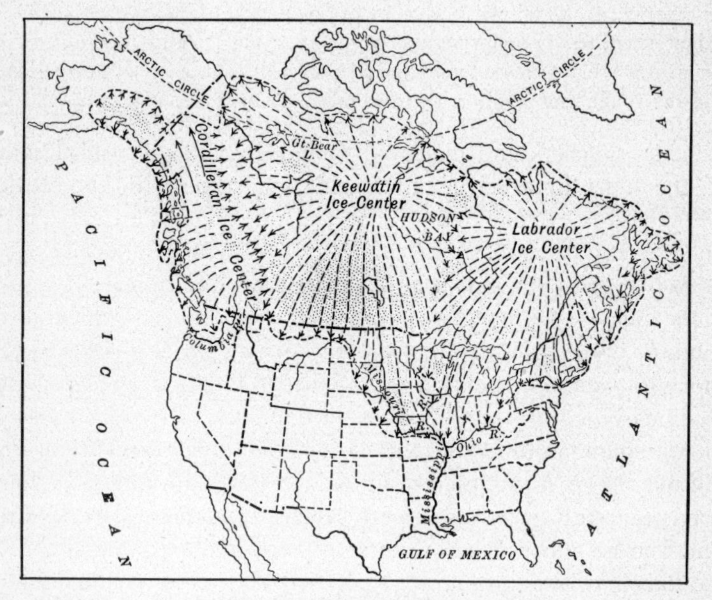

Fig. 110. — Ice sheets of North America. (N.J.G.S.)

istence largely to the work of the ice sheets. The general elevation of the country was reduced some hundreds or perhaps thousands of feet, and the bed rock was left bare or covered with thin, coarse mantle rock. This of itself renders agriculture generally impossible. The vegetation growing on such a soil consists of coniferous forest, dense and of great value for timber in favorable localities, thin and worthless in unfavorable. On account of poor drainage, "muskegs," or marshes covered with mosses and shrubs, are numerous and extensive. The economic products of the country consist almost entirely of furs, of which it furnishes a large part of the world's supply. Lumbering is carried on in those parts accessible to markets, and in recent years the great mineral wealth of the region is being utilized.

Fig. 111.—Laurentian peneplain. (U. S. Biol. Surv.)

The Area of Glacial Drift. — The area of ice destruction and drift deposition lies chiefly south and west of the chain of great lakes in northeastern United States and southern Canada. Here the ice was relatively thin and its erosive power was generally

Fig. 112.—Terminal moraine, Sheboygan County, Wis. (U.S.G.S.)

feeble. In melting it deposited its whole load of mantle rock in a continuous sheet, from a few feet to several hundred feet

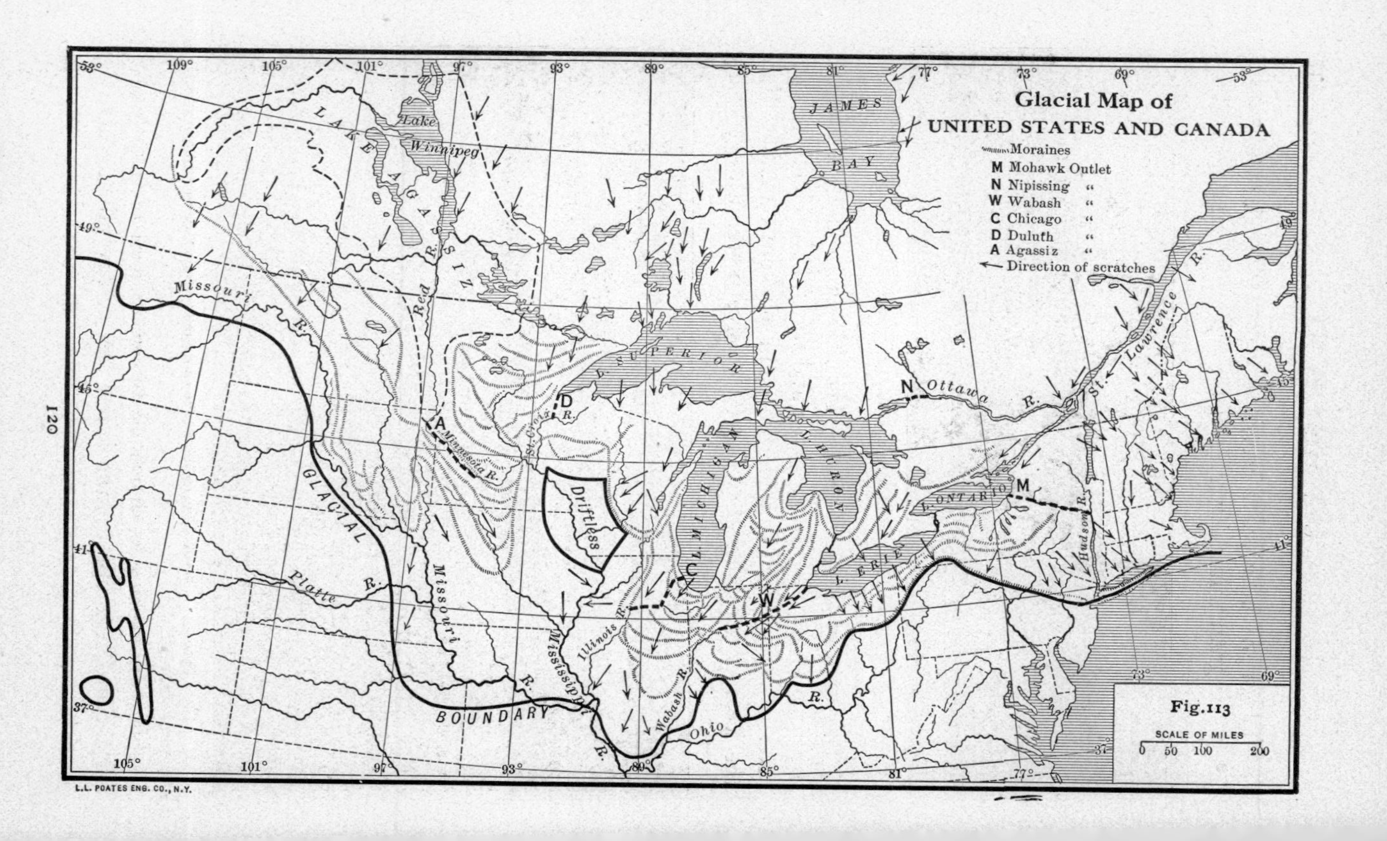
Glacial Map of
UNITED STATES AND CANADA
Moraines
M Mohawk Outlet
N Nipissing "
W Wabash "
C Chicago "
D Duluth "
A Agassiz "
Direction of scratches
Fig. 113
SCALE OF MILES
0 50 100 200
JAMES BAY
LAKE AGASSIZ
Lake Winnipeg
L. SUPERIOR
L. MICHIGAN
L. HURON
L. ERIE
L. ONTARIO
St. Lawrence R.
Ottawa R.
Hudson R.
Driftless
Mississippi R.
Missouri R.
Missouri
Ohio R.
Wabash R.
Illinois R.
Platte R.
Red R.
Minnesota R.
St. Croix R.
GLACIAL BOUNDARY
L.L. POATES ENG. CO., N.Y.

in thickness. The bulk of the drift is composed of *boulder clay*, a stiff clay containing many pebbles and boulders of various

Fig. 114.—Drumlin, Macedon, N. Y. (Partly plowed.)

sizes. Generally west of Pennsylvania the old valleys were filled and the general level of the country slightly raised. The surface was converted into a smooth plain of accumulation

Fig. 115.—Esker, Freeville, N. Y.

(Figs. 34, 35), varied by many ridges and belts of hills which mark the temporary position of the ice edge.[1] East of Ohio the

[1] Glacial drift ridges are:

(1) *Marginal moraines*, formed by an accumulation of drift along the edge of the melting ice sheet (Figs. 45, 112).

(2) *Kames*, irregular heaps of sediment deposited at the point where a stream of water escaped from the ice margin (Fig. 47).

(3) *Eskers*, sharp winding ridges of sand and gravel deposited in stream channels on or under the ice.

(4) *Drumlins*, lenticular or prismatic hills of clay, formed under the ice at some distance back from its edge.

glacial drift was too thin to do more than slightly modify the previous rough relief of the country. All the drainage systems, from the Columbia to the Ohio, were greatly changed by valley filling, damming, and ponding, displacement of channels, and transference of tributaries from one system to another.

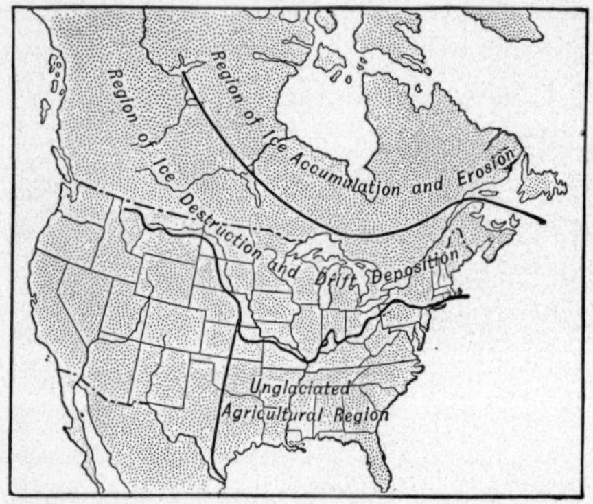

Fig. 116. — Relation of the drift sheet to agriculture.

Economic Relations. — Of more importance than these changes is the fact that the glacial drift, brought from the north and east and liberally spread out over the country to the south and west, constitutes a rich, deep, and enduring soil, which makes the northern states

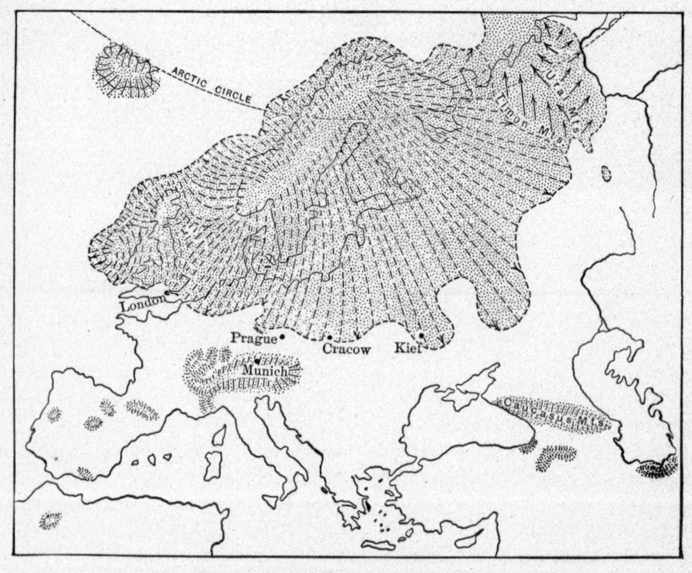

Fig. 117. — The continental glacier of Europe. (James Geikie.)

and southern Canada east of the Rocky Mountains the greatest food-producing region of the world, and one of the most densely populated parts of North America. This region also owes to the ice sheets the most important inland waterway in the world, the Laurentian Great Lakes. The states heavily coated with glacial drift have a population of about thirty millions, or forty-five to the square mile. The states south of the glacial boundary have a population of about twenty-seven millions, or thirty-two to the square mile.

European Ice Sheets. — In Europe the main region of ice accumulation was in Scandinavia and Finland, and the region of ice destruction and drift deposit in central Russia and north Germany. The same contrasts between the two in relief, drainage, and soil are found as in North America. Scandinavia and Finland form a country of lakes and forests with a very small area of arable land, while Germany and central Russia are rich agricultural states. The European glacial drift is not generally so heavy or so productive as the American, and lying in higher latitudes has not influenced products and population to any such extent.

CHAPTER VIII

STANDING WATER

Lakes, Ponds, and Marshes. — Lakes, ponds, and marshes are bodies of standing water which occupy depressions in the land surface. Lake basins are due to a variety of causes. The largest basins have been produced by the warping or breaking of the earth crust by internal forces. In some cases these basins are so large that the excess of rainfall over evaporation is insufficient to fill them, and the lake has no outlet. Salts brought by streams in solution accumulate, and the water becomes a brine. Of such lakes the Caspian Sea is the largest and the Dead Sea the lowest, 1,300 feet below sea level. The Great Basin in western United States contains many lakes, of which Great Salt Lake in Utah is the largest. They are all subject to fluctuations of level and area, according to the seasons, or the periodic variations of rainfall. Many of the smaller ones are temporary, containing water for a few days or months, or lasting for a year or two before they dry up. Most of the lakes of central Africa lie in the course of the great rift valley (p. 64). Some of them have no outlet, but the great lakes Nyassa, Tanganyika, and Victoria are sources of the Zambezi, Kongo, and Nile. The great lakes of North America lie along the southwestern border of the Laurentian peneplain (p. 45), from New York nearly to the Arctic Ocean.

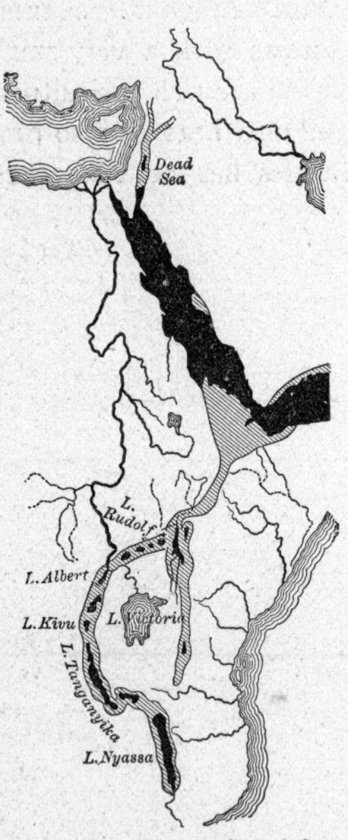

Fig. 118.—East African lakes and rift valley.

Their basins are due primarily to warping and stream erosion, but have been considerably modified by glacial action. On account of their size and location, the Laurentian lakes are of special importance. Lakes Superior, Michigan, Huron, Erie, and Ontario form the largest connected body of fresh water on the globe. Their form and relative positions suggest that their basins are parts of an old river valley which has been divided by a series of dams. Their great depth, extending in all except Lake Erie below sea level, may be due to glacial erosion.

During the retreat of the North American ice sheet and subsequently the Laurentian lakes were subjected to many changes of form, area, and outlet. Their waters at different periods overflowed through the upper Mississippi, the Illinois, the Wabash, the Ottawa, and the Mohawk (Fig. 113). Their former outlets at Chicago, Fort Wayne, Ind., Rome, N. Y., and Nipissing, Canada, furnish easy routes for canals and railroads. Lake Winnipeg is a shrunken remnant of Lake Agassiz, which, held in by an ice dam on the north, once covered 110,000 square miles in Canada, Minnesota, and North Dakota, and emptied through the Minnesota River. The sediment deposited upon its bottom now forms the soil of the famous wheat fields of the Red River region.

Glacial Lakes.—Lakes are nowhere else so numerous as in the regions formerly covered by the North American and European ice sheets, as large-scale maps of Canada, northeastern United States, Sweden, and Finland will show. Glacial lake basins are hollows in bed rock eroded by moving ice, or hollows made by irregular deposition of drift. Many are partly or wholly due to drift dams in the course of a stream. Some are kettleholes left by the melting of detached blocks of ice (Fig. 48).

Fig. 119. — Glacial lake, Derwentwater, England.

The courses of terminal moraines are generally marked by thousands of small lakes, as may be seen in Indiana, Michigan, Wisconsin, Minnesota, and northern Russia and Germany.

Alpine Lakes. — Long, narrow, and very deep lake basins which occur in mountain regions, and are hence called alpine lakes, are characteristic

Fig. 120. — Glacial lake, Lima, N. Y.
Esker in left margin.

Fig. 121. — Alpine lake, Lugano.

results of ice work. The Italian, Swiss, and Scotch lakes and Lake Chelan in Washington belong to this class and are unrivaled for scientific interest and for grand and picturesque scenery. The Finger Lakes of New York, on the northern slope of the Appalachian plateau, are of similar but less extreme character, and are probably due to similar causes.

Fig. 122. — Finger lake: Hemlock Lake, N. Y.
Valley is 13 miles long, half a mile wide and 1,000 feet deep.

Volcanic Lakes. — Lakes are in some cases due to the damming of a stream valley by a flow of lava from a volcano. Old volcanic craters sometimes fill with water, forming lakes of which Crater Lake, in southern Oregon, is a famous example. It is five miles in diameter and bounded by precipitous cliffs from 500 to 2,200 feet high. The water is 2,000 feet deep.

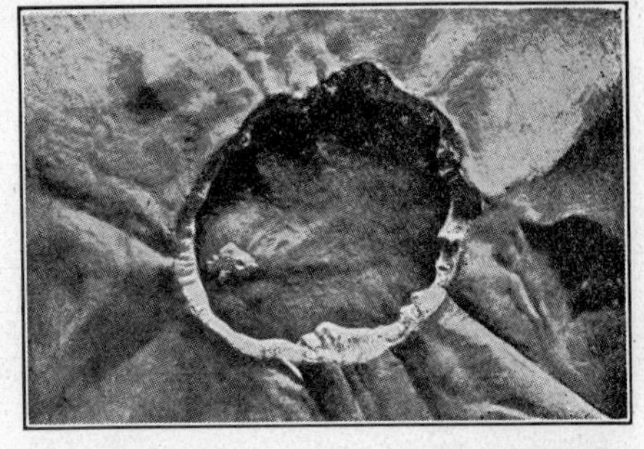

Fig. 123. — Model of the basin of Crater Lake, Oregon. (U.S.G.S.)

Life History of Lakes. — In arid regions, where the rainfall is insufficient to equal the water lost by evaporation, the lakes have no outlet and are salt. They often dry up, leaving beds of salt, soda, borax, and other valu-

Fig. 124. — Lake filling with vegetation. (Fletcher's *Soils.*)

able minerals. In regions of abundant rainfall lakes overflow at the lowest point of the basin rim. As the outlet stream cuts its channel deeper, the water is drained away and the lake level is lowered. This process is often hastened by cutting an artificial ditch which may drain the lake completely, leaving rich agricultural land. At the same time inlet streams are filling up the basin with sediment and will in time convert it into a lacustrine plain. Therefore lakes are among the most short-lived of natural features and are always relatively young.

In the case of small, shallow lakes, their destruction is hastened by the growth of vegetation. Aquatic plants, which absorb the greater bulk of their food from the air, grow and decay year after year, until the basin is filled with vegetable matter and the lake is converted into a marsh, peat bog, or wet meadow. Some lake basins fill with marl, which is valuable as a fertilizer and for making cement.

Economic Relations. — Lakes act as reservoirs which regulate the flow of outlet streams and prevent both floods and extreme stages of low water. They are also settling basins for sediment, so that a stream flowing out of a lake is usually clear. The Niagara and St. Lawrence rivers are striking examples of streams which are clear and subject to slight changes of volume. Large lakes furnish the best of inland waterways (p. 100). The smaller ones are sources of food supply and add greatly to the variety and beauty of landscape. Lakes are everywhere favorite summer resorts, which attract thousands of people who find pleasure and recreation in camping, boating, fishing, and bathing. The "Chautauqua," or summer assembly for religious, educational, social, and sanitary purposes, takes its name from Lake Chautauqua in New York.

Gradation by Standing Water. — Seas and lakes are bodies of standing water but not of still water. Their waters have no general and continuous movement in one direction, as a stream has, but under the influence of the wind and the moon are agitated by waves, currents, and tides. These movements accomplish their most important work along the margin where land and water meet, and produce a characteristic series of coast forms. These may be found in miniature along the shore of almost any small lake or pond.

Beaches and Bars. — Where the coast land is low and the coast waters are shallow the waves build up a ridge of sand or gravel which is as high as the highest storm waves can lift the material. Behind this *beach* there is generally a strip of shallow water called a *lagoon*. A *barrier beach* is a long, continuous ridge some distance off shore (Fig. 28). Where the shore line is indented by a bay the beach is often extended across its mouth, forming a *bay bar*.

Fig. 125. — Beaches and lagoons, Cayuga Lake.

A bar built out from shore into deeper water is called a *spit*, and if bent back at the end, a *hook*. Barrier beaches and bars,

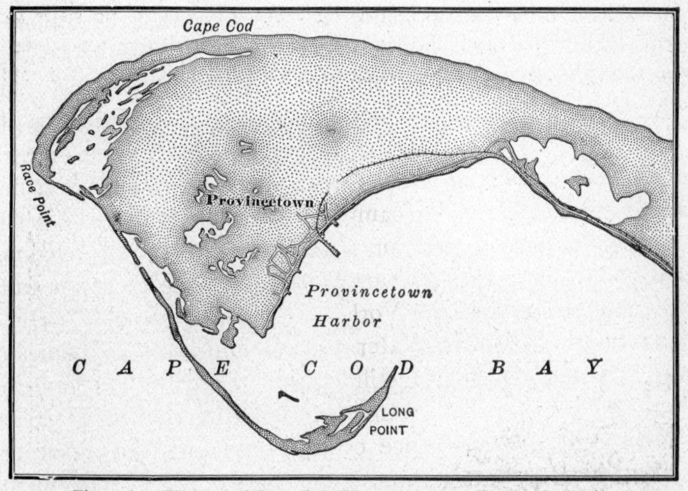

Fig. 126. — The end of Cape Cod, Massachusetts. Two hooked spits.

as the names imply, render a coast difficult of access from the water and form serious obstructions to commerce. The lagoons, inlets, and bay mouths are usually too shallow to admit vessels of considerable size. Where the tides are high and strong enough to keep the inlets scoured out, good harbors are found. On a low, sandy coast wind and waves work together and dunes are combined with beaches.

The Gulf and Atlantic coasts of the United States south of Cape Cod present perhaps the longest stretch of barrier beach coast in the world. On the coast of Texas the beach extends 100 miles without a break. Galveston and other bays are rendered inaccessible except by artificial channels. The keys and reefs of Florida are peculiar in being partly the work of coral animals. Along the coast of Georgia and South Carolina the tides are strong enough to break up the beach into the so-called "sea islands," and the numerous deep inlets lead to good harbors. From Charleston to New York the coast is bordered by a nearly continuous beach, which sweeps in long, gentle curves from point to point. Behind it is a belt of lagoons and tidal marshes, expanding in North Carolina into shallow sounds. This coast belt is interrupted by the drowned valleys of the Chesapeake, Delaware, and Hudson, which let deep tide water and the largest vessels far into the interior. The beaches of New Jersey and Long Island are popular summer resorts. Railroads have been built to and along them, and towns and cities have sprung up, with hotels and places of entertainment for visitors, who come by the hundred thousand to enjoy the sea breezes and the bathing (Fig. 28).

Fig. 127.—Sea cliff, Lake Erie. (N.Y.G.S.)

Sea Cliffs.—Where the coast land is high and the coast waters are deep, the waves pound against the shore with tremendous force and undercut it into a vertical cliff. The fragments are rolled over, ground up, and carried away by the *undertow*, or backrush of water along the bottom. The result of this is a platform or terrace a little below sea level, partly cut into solid rock, partly built of mantle rock, and bordered by a constantly retreating cliff. The character of a cliff coast varies with the kind of rock. If the rock is of uniform hardness and without joints or seams, the cliff is smooth and unbroken, like the chalk cliffs of England and France and the clay cliffs of Lake Michigan (Fig. 35). Such a coast may be entirely without indentations or harbors. If the rock is complex in material and structure, the waves soon eat away the weak places and leave the more resistant masses standing out as promontories and islands (Fig. 43). Small isolated masses of rock along the shore are called *skerries* in Norway and *stacks* in Scotland. Such a coast may be extremely jagged and dangerous to shipping, while at the same time it offers numerous coves where small boats may find shelter and concealment.

Fig. 128. — Chalk cliffs, France. Arch and stack.

Economic Relations. — On the whole, the general result of the work of standing water is to cut the bordering lands down to its own level and to surround itself with barriers which make access to the land more difficult. If it were not for the power of running water and ice to break through the barriers, ocean and lake commerce would be much more restricted than it is.

CHAPTER IX

GRADATION BY GROUND WATER AND WIND

The Ground Sea. — A large part of the rainfall sinks into the ground and penetrates the earth crust to great but unknown depths. The ground water may be thought of as forming a sea many miles in depth and extending through the rock sphere beneath the land surface from ocean to ocean. Thus the water sphere is really continuous around the globe. The upper surface of the ground sea, called the *water table*, is not level, but is roughly parallel with the surface of the land. In lakes, marshes, and streams the water table stands at the surface of the ground. In regions of small rainfall it may lie a thousand feet or more below the surface. The level of the water table is not constant at the same locality, rising during a wet season and sinking during a dry season. The water of the ground sea is seldom at rest. In compact rocks the movement is very slow, in porous rocks more rapid, and in rocks traversed by open joints and cracks there is a circulation in streams comparable to that on the land surface.

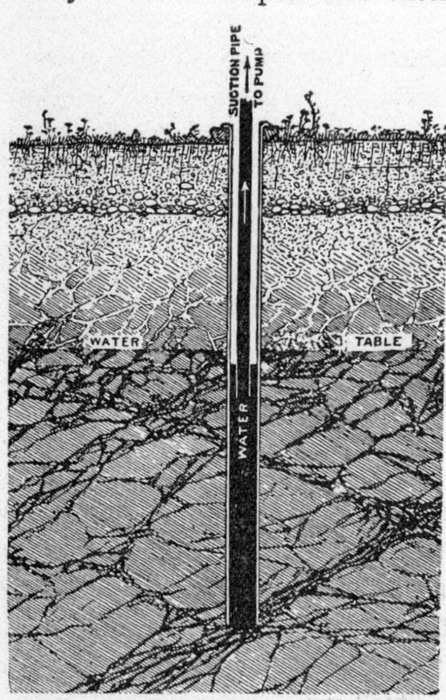

Fig. 129. — Section of fissured rock and well. (U.S.G.S.)

Work of Ground Water. — Most of the minerals of the earth crust are more or less soluble, and as the ground water penetrates more deeply it becomes more highly charged with them. Its temperature also increases with the depth, and the lower parts of the ground sea are probably composed of hot water saltier than the ocean.

Fig. 130. — Hot spring deposits, Algeria. (Robin.)

In many places the deep ground water rises to the surface, forming mineral springs. These waters contain gases, sulphur, iron, and various salts in solution, which render them of value in the treatment of disease.

Fig. 131. — Old Faithful geyser, Yellowstone Park.

Hot Springs, Ark., and Saratoga Springs, N. Y., are famous health resorts, and there are hundreds of similar character in all parts of the world. In old volcanic regions the earth crust is hot near the surface, and steam generated in subterranean conduits throws out columns of hot water, forming *geysers*, or spouting springs. The geysers of the Yellowstone Park are unsurpassed in number, variety, and size. As hot ground water rises toward the surface the pressure upon it diminishes, it cools and deposits the minerals held in solution, eventually filling the passage. In this way ores of gold, silver, and other metals are concentrated and placed within reach of the miner.

Limestone is a very soluble rock, and in some limestone regions the earth crust is honeycombed with underground drainage channels, leaving few streams on the surface. Some of the channels have been enlarged by solution and the falling in of the roof to a diameter of hundreds of feet and a length of many miles. Most of the great caves of the world are in limestone rock, among them Mammoth Cave in Kentucky, and Wyandotte Cave in Indiana.

Fig. 132. — Mouth of cave, Indiana.

Economic Relations. — Ground water is everywhere a common source of water supply for domestic use. The outflow of natural springs is sometimes large and of good quality, but the main dependence is upon wells. If a hole is sunk into the ground to a point below the water table, it will fill up to that level with water. In shallow wells the largest supply is obtained from strata of sand and gravel. Such wells, especially in towns, are unsafe for domestic use, on account of pollution by drainage from cesspools, sewers, barnyards, and other sources of filth. The clearest and most agreeable well water may be the most dangerous. Deep wells are less liable to contamination.

In some cases water flows from a well without pumping, or even spouts into the air like a fountain. Very deep flowing wells are called *artesian*. The water of a flowing well comes from a porous stratum which outcrops on the surface somewhere at a higher level than the mouth of the well. The outcrop and source of supply may be hundreds of miles from the well.

Over a large area of the plains east of the Rocky Mountains artesian wells are common, some of which furnish water enough to irrigate a hundred-acre farm. The water comes from thick strata of porous sandstone which

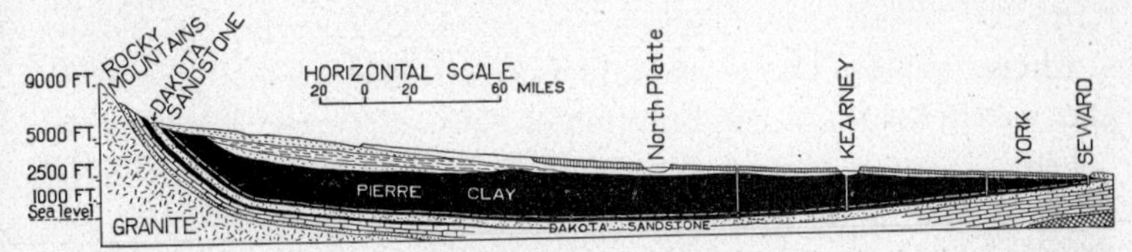

Fig. 133. — Cross section from Rocky Mountains across Nebraska. Dakota sandstone under Pierre clay carries water from Rocky Mountains and supplies artesian wells on the plains. Note nearly horizontal strata of plains turned up against granite core of the mountains (U.S.G.S.)

underlie the plains at considerable depths. The sandstone outcrops along the foothills of the mountains, where it absorbs the rainfall and transmits the water eastward. Wherever a well penetrates the overlying strata and reaches the sandstone, water rises to the surface.

Ground water plays an important part in the work of gradation by extending the processes of weathering and rock decay to great depths, and by promoting chemical changes and transporting material in the earth crust.

Fig. 134. — **Artesian well, North Dakota.** (U.S.G.S.)

Work of Wind. — Wherever fine, dry mantle rock is exposed without a cover of vegetation the wind is able to transport it in almost unlimited quantities. As in the case of running water, both the quantity and the coarseness of sediment which running air is able to carry increase in a high ratio to the velocity, but air is so much less dense than water that its sediment is generally limited to dust and sand. Only tornadoes are capable of lifting pebbles and boulders. The wind is therefore a delicate assorting agent, and its deposits may usually be recognized by the fact that they have been thoroughly winnowed. Unlike running water, air moves in broad sheets and carries material as freely up a slope as down. There is a strongly marked rhythm in its motion, and its effects are a combination of those of currents and waves.

One fourth of the land surface of the globe has less than ten inches of annual rainfall, and in such areas outside the polar regions wind action is generally more important than other processes. Rocks, subjected to great daily changes of temperature, crumble rapidly. The lighter mineral particles, like mica, are carried away by the wind, and quartz grains are left as sand. The sand itself is blown about and acts as a powerful erosive agent, undercutting cliffs and enlarging valleys. In general, mantle rock accumulates, and hollows at all elevations are filled. Some of it is transported entirely outside the desert region. A wind-worn surface is much less varied than a water-worn surface. While running water cannot erode below the level of the sea or of the lake into which it flows, there is no definite downward limit to wind erosion. Its tendency is to produce a stony peneplain with projecting knobs of hard rock and belts of drifting sand dunes (Fig. 37). When the surface is reduced below sea level, the sea is liable to overflow it and stop the process. The margin of the desert is indefinite and fluctuating. Its sands often encroach upon neighboring cultivated areas unless stopped by human agency.

Dunes. — A tornado in the desert may raise a sand column or spout many hundred feet and sustain it as long as the whirl of air continues, finally dropping it over the surrounding country, but the ordinary winds seldom lift sand more than a few feet. A slight lull causes most of it to be dropped, and it accumulates in the lee of any obstruction, as snow is drifted behind a fence. The pile of sand itself forms an obstruction beyond which more sand accumulates, and the drift or dune grows to be a hill with a long, gentle slope on the windward side and a steep slope on the leeward side. The wind blows the sand up the long slope and drops it in the eddy beyond. Thus the pile becomes a

Fig. 135.—Dunes, Algeria. (Robin.)

"marching dune" which slowly advances, burying forests, buildings, or whatever lies in its way. In the course of years the dune may move on far enough to uncover what it previously buried.

Coast Dunes. — The margins of seas, lakes, and retreating ice sheets are generally bare of vegetation, and present conditions favorable for wind action. Low windward coasts are often bordered by belts of drifting dunes, as in Holland, Germany, France, the Atlantic coast of the United States, and the east and south shores of Lake Michigan. The dunes form a barrier which protects the land from storm waves and high tides, but also makes commerce difficult (Fig. 28). In France the progress of the dunes inland has been stayed by the planting of pine trees. Moving sand is very unfavorable for the growth of vegetation, and forms the ground of nearly

Fig. 136. — **Dunes near coast of North Carolina.**

absolute desert. Sand dunes are among the most destructive agents in nature, and can be controlled only where some kind of vegetation can be made to grow upon them and hold them down.

Dust. — Very fine dust ejected from volcanoes to a height of many miles has remained in the air for months, and even years, before settling, and has been carried around the world. The snow fields in the interior of Greenland, far from any exposed ground, are covered with fine dust, which may settle upon it from extraterrestrial space. Dust from the Sahara is sometimes carried by the wind to northern Germany.

CHAPTER X

SOILS

THE loose rock material in which plants take root and find food is called *soil.* Practically the whole vegetative covering of the land, and consequently all animal and human as well as plant life, depend upon the soil for existence. Soils are portions of mantle rock and have been formed by the physical and chemical disintegration of bed rock by the agents and processes of weathering (p. 72). They may be thought of as "rock meal," or "rock flour."

Sedentary Soils. — Soils are at first *sedentary* or *residual*, that is, formed by the decay of the bed rock which lies under them, and vary according to the kind of rock from which they are formed. Sedentary soils are usually thin, but may accumulate to the depth of some hundreds of feet. They contain undecomposed fragments of bed rock, which increase in number and size downward.

Fig. 137. — Residual gravel, Texas.

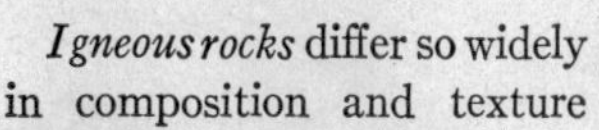

Igneous rocks differ so widely in composition and texture that they weather into a great variety of soils, from very poor to very rich. Granite and gneiss often crumble at first into a barren gravel like that of the English moors. Chemical changes finally reduce the quartz to sand, and the feldspar and mica to clay, the latter being decomposed very slowly. The fertility of granitic soils is roughly proportional to the amount

Fig. 138. — Residual clay on shale, Indiana.

of feldspar present, quartz and mica being distinctly unfavorable. *Lava* soils vary in their rate of weathering and fertility with their chemical composition.

Limestone soils are famous for fertility, as in the bluegrass region of Kentucky and the prairies of Texas. The lime is dissolved and washed away, and the soil consists largely of the residue of insoluble impurities. *Sandstones* weather into sandy soils which are generally poor, but may be productive from the presence in the rock of other ingredients acting as a cement. *Shale* weathers into clay, which, if not too fine and compact, makes a good soil. *Conglomerate* weathers into gravel, which is apt to be very barren.

Colluvial Soils. — On moderate or steep slopes the native soil creeps slowly downward by the action of gravity, frost, and rain wash, and in arid regions sometimes accumulates in valleys between the mountains to a depth of several thousand feet. Such slowly moving soil masses are called *colluvial*.

Fig. 139. — Colluvial soil near Crawfordsville, Ind. The surface material creeps faster than that at a slight depth, tipping the trees. (*Forestry and Irrigation.*)

Transported Soils. — The surface of plains, valleys, and lowlands is generally covered with soil which has been brought down from higher

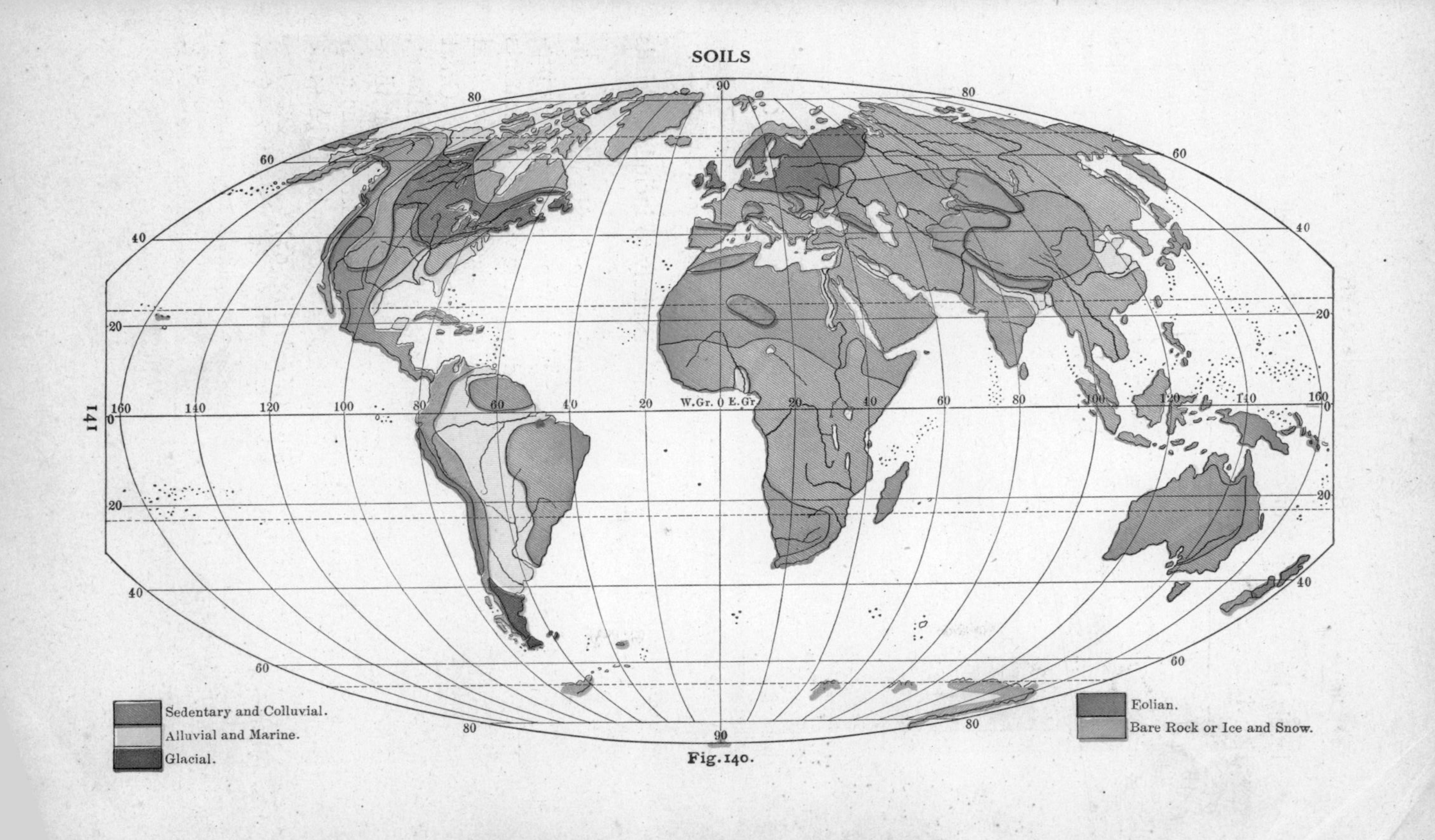
SOILS
W.Gr. 0 E.Gr.
Sedentary and Colluvial.
Alluvial and Marine.
Glacial.
Eolian.
Bare Rock or Ice and Snow.

Fig. 140.

levels by water, ice, or wind. Transported soils are generally rich because they are derived from many kinds of rocks and

Copyright by Doubleday, Page & Co.

Fig. 141.—Eolian soil, "Palouse Country" of Oregon and Washington. (Fletcher's *Soils.*)

contain a mixture of minerals which is likely to include all kinds of plant food.

Alluvial soils are deposited by streams on flood plains, "bottom lands," and deltas, and are well known as exceedingly productive. Their productiveness is due to the variety of elements of which they are composed, to the fineness of division, and to their frequent renewal by deposits from flood waters. Great flood plains and deltas, such as those of the Nile, Hoang, Ganges, Rhine, and Po, have produced great crops for thousands of years and will continue to do so in future. The alluvial valley of the Mississippi and its tributaries is of the same character, but is not yet fully utilized (Fig. 97).

Glacial soils are the deposits from melting ice sheets (p. 122) and are more variable than alluvial soils, but generally not far behind them in productiveness. Glacial or boulder clay contains a great variety of minerals, finely ground and intimately mixed, and when it includes enough of sand and gravel to make it pervious and workable it is extremely rich and enduring. The glacial drift of the United States is one of the most valuable food-producing areas in the world (Figs. 113, 116, 117).

Eolian soils are deposited by the wind and are fine and sandy. Since they occur mostly in arid regions, where plant food is not washed out by rains, they retain the elements of fertility much better than the sands of humid regions. On desert sands, when wetted by slight rainfall, vegetation springs up at once, and if kept moist by irrigation becomes remarkably luxuriant.

Physical Composition of Soils. — Physically soils consist of clay, silt, sand, gravel, and humus.

Clay is an extremely fine, soft powder produced by the chemical decomposition of various minerals, of which feldspar is the most important. It consists of thin, rounded scales from $\frac{1}{250000}$ to $\frac{1}{5000}$ of an inch in diameter. When wet, clay swells up into a sticky, plastic substance which shrinks in drying to a tough, coherent mass. It is very retentive of water, gases, and minerals in solution and presents such a large surface for the plant rootlets to work upon that clay soils are "strong." At the same time clay acts as a cement which holds other ingredients together and renders soil difficult to till.

Silt and *sand* are rock powders produced by the mechanical pulverization of various minerals, of which quartz is by far the most abundant. Common sand consists almost entirely of quartz crystals more or less rounded. If the crystals are unworn and angular, the sand is "sharp." The diameter of silt grains is from $\frac{1}{5000}$ to $\frac{1}{500}$ of an inch, that of sand grains from $\frac{1}{500}$ to $\frac{1}{25}$ of an inch, but even the finest silt can be recognized by its harsh, gritty feel between the fingers or teeth. Pure silt or sand is incoherent and easily worked, but does not retain moisture well, and is less fertile than clay.

Gravel is composed of generally hard, rounded grains or pebbles from $\frac{1}{25}$ of an inch up to 2 or 3 inches in diameter, and is looser and more permeable than sand.

Humus is a loose, black mold produced by the partial decay of vegetable and animal matter, and is an essential ingredient of all good soils.

Types of Soils. — The common types of agricultural soils are classified as follows:

Sandy soils contain	80 % sand,	10 % clay.
Sandy loams "	60–70 % "	10–25 % "
Loam soils "	40–60 % "	15–30 % "
Clay loams "	10–35 % "	30–50 % "
Clay soils "	10 % "	60–90 % "

Gravelly and stony loams contain gravel and pebbles and are common in regions covered with glacial drift.

Peat and *muck* soils are formed by the decay of vegetation in shallow lakes, ponds, and swamps. Some clay and silt are blown in by the wind and carried in by streams. They contain from 30 to nearly 100 per cent of humus. If the vegetable matter is sufficiently decayed and is mixed with considerable mineral matter, good drainage renders such soils productive.

Loess soils are peculiar deposits consisting of a mixture of silt and clay laid down partly by wind and partly by water, and are generally very productive. They cover extensive areas along the borders of the glacial drift in the United States and Europe. The loess of China is an eolian deposit blown from the central plateaus and is in some places 1,000 feet thick (Fig. 142).

Adobe soils are peculiar to semi-arid regions and common in southwestern United States. They are very sticky when wet, and hard when dry, but are unusually rich in plant food.

Alkali soils are common in arid regions. They contain large quantities of common salt, carbonate and sulphate of soda, and other compounds which are brought to the surface in solution and left by evaporation of the water as a whitish or black crust. Few plants will grow in such soils, but they can be improved by irrigation and drainage, which wash out the salts.

Tropical Soils. — The high temperature of tropical regions favors rapid decomposition of soil ingredients and hastens all chemical changes. The luxuriance of tropical vegetation is not wholly due to the heat and moisture of the air, but also to the fertility of the soil, which is therefore in part responsible for

Fig. 142.—Loess deposits, eroded, China. (Carnegie Institution, *Research in China.*)

the easy-going and indolent ways of tropical people. Tropical soils are exceptionally rich in humus, but plant food is rapidly leached out by the heavy rains. They are often of a deep-red color due to the diffusion of iron oxide. The red clay soils produced by the weathering of volcanic rocks are called *laterite* (brick earth). The name is often applied to any red soil.

Chemical Constituents of Good Soil.—For plant growth at least seven chemical elements must be present in the soil in soluble form,—nitrogen, potash, phosphorus, lime, iron, magnesium, and sulphur. The last three are usually present in such abundance as to require no attention, but the first four are sure to be exhausted by continuous cropping and must be supplied artificially. Therefore, nitrogen, potash, phosphorus, and lime are the essential ingredients of all fertilizers. The total quantity needed is relatively small because plants obtain about 90 per cent of their substance from the carbon and oxygen of the air.

Soils contain air and other gases which are necessary to plant life. The roots of most plants need air to breathe, and for farm crops the soil should be well ventilated by tillage and underdraining. The presence of air hastens the chemical processes which render plant food available, and thus increases fertility.

Plants as Soil Makers. — Plants perform a very important work in soil-making. Two years after an eruption of Krakatao, a volcano in Sunda Strait, which destroyed all vegetation, the surface of the lava was found to be slimy with microscopic plant life, active in breaking down silicates into clay, combining elements, and preparing soil for higher plants. Most soils swarm with bacteria, fungi, molds, and algæ which literally eat the rocks, and by living upon mineral matter produce humus. They flourish best in warm, moist, well-ventilated soils, where they hasten the decay of vegetable matter. Some are injurious, but most of them are harmless and many are beneficial. It has been said that the soil is not primarily a medium on which to grow herbs and trees, but a domain created by the activities of low forms of life for their own benefit, and that the higher plants exist by virtue of these, just as animals live by virtue of the herbage.

Temperature of the Soil. — The temperature of the soil is as important for plant growth as that of the air above it. Few seeds will germinate if the soil temperature is below 45 degrees, and 65 to 100 degrees is most favorable. Gravelly and sandy soils are warmer than clay. Wet soils are cold because much of the heat received from the sun is used up in evaporating water; consequently soils are warmed by drainage. Lands which slope toward the sun are warmer than those sloping away from it, and dark-colored soils absorb more heat than light-colored. The temperature of the soil is raised by the fermentation and decay of vegetable and animal matter.

Soil Water. — All fertile soils contain large quantities of water. The *free* or *ground* water fills the spaces between the particles up to the level of the water table (p. 132). The depth of the water table may generally be determined by the height at which water stands in surface wells. If the water table stands too near the surface, the plant roots may be drowned and the soil is of little value until it is drained.

Above the water table the surface of each soil grain is covered by a thin film of water which sticks to it and supplies the plant roots with food. The driest road dust contains some *film water*, and a good soil may hold more than half its weight. Film water is mostly derived from the free water below, but a little may be absorbed from the air. Film water is constantly rising from the water table and evaporating from the surface of the ground. Thus plants are kept alive through a dry season.

The water contains salts in solution which are left by evaporation, forming a surface crust. It is often important to conserve the film water by checking evaporation. This may be done by tillage, which pulverizes the crust, or by covering the surface with a mulch of vegetable matter or even of fine dust. The finer the soil the more surface the particles present for film water and the plant food it contains. Therefore "fineness is richness." A good soil may contain from 250 to 450 billion particles per ounce, and the aggregate surface of all the particles in one cubic foot may measure from one to four acres.

The life and growth of plants require a very large quantity of water, which they obtain entirely from the soil. Average farm crops use from 300 to 400 tons of water per acre. Plant roots absorb food only when it is dissolved in soil water, and the solution is so weak that to get food enough they must use great quantities of water, most of which escapes by evaporation through the leaves. Under ordinary conditions, production is almost directly proportional to the water supply during the growing season. Including losses by run-off and evaporation from the soil, a rainfall of from 5 to 25 inches just before and during the growing season is necessary to produce farm crops. In middle latitudes the rainfall of autumn and winter is of little benefit to the farmer, who must depend upon the rains of spring and early summer.

Irrigation does not add anything to the actual quantity of water on the land, but utilizes for crop growing water which would naturally evaporate or run off to the sea. Water is obtained from lakes, streams, and wells, and is distributed over the fields at times and in quantities which can be regulated according to the needs of the crop (Figs. 36, 60, 90, 94). The product per acre of irrigated lands far exceeds that of lands naturally supplied with water, but the area of lands which can be irrigated is relatively very small. Irrigated lands in India aggregate 25 million acres, in Egypt 6 million, in Italy 3.7 million, and in the United States 10.5 million. The area in the United States which may possibly be irrigated is estimated at 75 million acres, which is less than one tenth of the total arid region.

Fig. 143.—Soil wash and gullying, North Carolina. (U.S.G.S.)

The Conservation of Soils. — Soil is especially subject to erosion, and is carried away by every stream, to be finally deposited in the sea. In some places the soil is liable to removal by the wind. A covering of vegetation, especially a forest, largely prevents the washing away of soil. On forested slopes the cutting of the trees is often followed by rapid gullying and destruction of the land for any useful purpose, while the valleys below suffer almost as much from excess of mantle rock brought down and deposited. In old countries a series of "breaks" or dams is sometimes built across the valley to stop the waste of soil. All such regions are more valuable if kept in forest, which can be thinned out at intervals and renewed by planting. Many species of grass, sedge, rush, willows, and other plants which form a dense network of roots are useful as soil binders.

Soil and Population. — The population which any given region, or the world as a whole, can support is strictly limited by the amount of water available for crops. This is as true in humid as in arid regions. Notwithstanding the large proportion of the face of the earth occupied by water, less than half the land surface has sufficient rainfall to support a moderately dense population, and one third of it is either frozen or too dry for agriculture. As long as men depended chiefly upon agriculture for a living, population was necessarily most dense on fertile and easily cultivated soils, and these were generally alluvial. To-day the density of population is greatest in manufacturing regions, where the character of the soil is of no importance. Facilities for transportation are so great that food and clothing may be supplied from distant lands, and the best agricultural regions have a relatively sparse or medium population. In the most advanced industrial countries, like the United States, the population of purely agricultural counties and states has remained stationary, or has grown actually smaller for several decades. This is due to improvements in farm machinery, which enable one man now to do the work done by four or five men fifty years ago.

CHAPTER XI

THE SEA

THE sea is a continuous body of salt water which covers about 72 per cent of the surface of the earth crust. The average depth of the sea is a little over two miles, and its greatest about six miles. Its depth in proportion to its area would be like that of a lake three miles wide and one to six feet deep, and would be represented on a seven-foot globe by a film of water from one twentieth to one third of an inch thick. The relative shallowness of the ocean basins is of importance from the fact that they are not deep enough to hold all the water, which consequently spreads over the low margins of the continental platform and covers more than one sixth of it (p. 24). The sea surrounds four great land masses and thousands of islands, and is divided into five great oceans (Figs. 16, 17, 18, 150).

The Oceans. — *The Southern Ocean* forms a continuous belt around the earth south of 40° S. Lat., and is a means of communication between the other oceans which open into it. It is about 1,600 miles wide, comprises about one fifth of the sea area, and is more than two miles deep.

The Pacific Ocean comprises about 40 per cent of the sea area, or nearly 30 per cent of the face of the earth. It is roughly circular in outline, with a diameter of about 10,000 miles, and is nearly surrounded by land except on the south. Its bed is broken by numerous ridges which bear upon their crests thousands of small islands. It also contains many holes where the water is five or six miles deep.

The Atlantic Ocean is 9,000 miles long, and between Africa and South America only 1,700 miles wide. Its greatest depths are from four to five miles. It forms a broad channel of communication between the north and south polar waters. It comprises about one fourth of the sea area.

The Indian Ocean has been called "half an ocean" because it extends northward only to the tropic of Cancer. Its area is about one eighth of the whole sea, and its average depth is over two miles.

The Arctic Ocean is small and nearly inclosed by land at about 70° N. Lat. An opening 1,200 miles wide between Norway and Greenland connects it with the north Atlantic. A large part of it is covered with drifting ice, and its depths are little known. Soundings by Nansen north of Eurasia and by Peary at the pole show that it is more than 9,000 feet deep.

Sea Water. — The sea water contains about $3\frac{1}{2}$ per cent of mineral matter in solution, more than three fourths of which is common salt. Most of this mineral matter has probably been brought by rivers from the land. While sea water contains minute quantities of almost every known element, more than 97 per cent of the dissolved matter consists of salts of soda, magnesia, and lime. The gases of the atmosphere penetrate the sea in varying proportions to the bottom. The quantity of oxygen diminishes and that of carbon dioxide increases with increasing depth.

Temperature. — The temperature of the surface water of the sea is between 30° and 40° F. near the poles and between 70° and 90° near the equator (Fig. 150). The temperature of the deep bottom water varies from 29° in the polar regions to 35° under the equator.

The layer of water warmer than 40° is nowhere more than 4,800 feet deep, and generally much less. Eighty per cent of all the water in the sea has a temperature below 40°. This is due to the fact that the heat of the sun does not penetrate the water more than about 600 feet, and to the creep of the cold bottom water of the Southern Ocean into the Pacific, Atlantic, and Indian, crowding the warmer equatorial waters upward. Owing to many physical causes the temperature of the sea is more constant than that of the land, the seasonal change being seldom more than 10 or 20 degrees. Lands swept by winds from the sea have an oceanic climate marked by relatively small differences of temperature between summer and winter.

Pressure and Density. — The pressure of sea water is equal in all directions and increases at the rate of more than one ton per square inch for every mile of depth. The density varies with the temperature, pressure, and quantity of salts in solution. The density of the surface water is greatest in tropical regions of small rainfall and rapid evaporation, and least in the equatorial regions of heavy rainfall and the polar regions of freezing and melting ice.

Waves. — Waves are usually produced by the friction of the wind. They present a series of parallel or irregular ridges and hollows which follow one another across the surface of the water. They are very superficial, seldom disturbing the water to a depth greater than 100 feet. Each wave appears to consist of a ridge or mound of water moving forward with the wind, but

Fig. 144. — Breakers.

in the open sea the water really moves up and down in a circular or elliptical path. A field of standing grain in the wind or a cloth shaken up and down may be thrown into similar waves. Waves 10 or 15 feet high lift and drop a vessel about ten times a minute. Storm waves sometimes reach a height of 50 feet and travel 60 miles an hour, passing a given point at the rate of about four a minute. In shallow water the front slope of the wave becomes steeper and the crest higher, until finally it falls forward and breaks, rolling over and over like a barrel. On a shelving shore such *breakers* may reach a height of 100 feet or more, and hurl forward many tons of water, striking blows like a hammer and pounding cliffs, breakwaters, and lighthouses to pieces. The undertow, or backward rush of the water along the sea bottom, is efficient in grinding up and removing rock fragments.

Waves are the principal agents in breaking down the seaward margin of the land and in building beaches, bars, and spits (p. 129). Their effects are on the whole unfavorable to man by rendering navigation more difficult and dangerous and the coasts of the land less accessible. Shipwrecks are generally caused by waves. Mariners sometimes succeed in calming the sea and making a space of relatively smooth water around a ship by pouring overboard a quantity of oil. The floating oil so reduces the friction of the wind upon the surface of the water that wave motion nearly ceases.

Tides. — The level of the sea is subject to a regular, periodic rise and fall which is called the *tide*. It varies in amount at different places. On the deep, open ocean it is probably less than one foot. On the coasts of oceanic islands it is not more than six or seven feet, while at the heads of funnel-shaped inlets, such as the Bay of Fundy, it amounts to as much as fifty feet. If we should watch the tide from any point along the coast at low water, we should see the rocks, bars, and portions of the beach and sea bottom laid bare; then the water would slowly *flow* or creep up for several hours and cover them. High water would be followed by an *ebb* or fall, lasting six hours or more. The interval between two periods of high water or low water is twelve hours and twenty-six minutes, but it is not always equally divided between ebb and flow, the rise being generally more rapid than the fall.

The difference of level between high and low water varies not only at different places but at different times at the same place. These phenomena must have been observed by all peoples who have lived along the shore of the sea, and it must have been noticed at a very early period that the times of high and low water have some relation to the position and phases of the moon. The connection between the moon and the tides was not understood, however, until Newton's discovery of the law of gravitation.

If the earth were a globe of water, it is easy to understand how the attraction of the moon would draw it out of shape and

Fig. 145.—High tide, North Haven, Maine. (Blackwelder and Barrows, *Elements of Geology.*)

produce a slight elongation in the direction of a line connecting the earth and moon. The effect upon the spheroidal shell of sea water is the same as though it were a complete sphere.

Fig. 146.—Low tide, North Haven, Maine. (Blackwelder and Barrows, *Elements of Geology.*)

If the moon were always above the same point on the earth, there would always be high water at that point, the moon would cause no change in the level of the sea anywhere, and consequently there would be no lunar tides; but as the earth rotates on its axis from west to east, the point directly under the moon and the other points of high and low water travel around the earth from east to west at the same rate as the apparent motion of the moon.

Thus every part of the sea has two stages of high water and two of low water within the time between two transits of the moon over any given place (24 hours and 52 minutes). The period is more than twenty-four hours, because the moon is actually moving in its orbit eastward in the

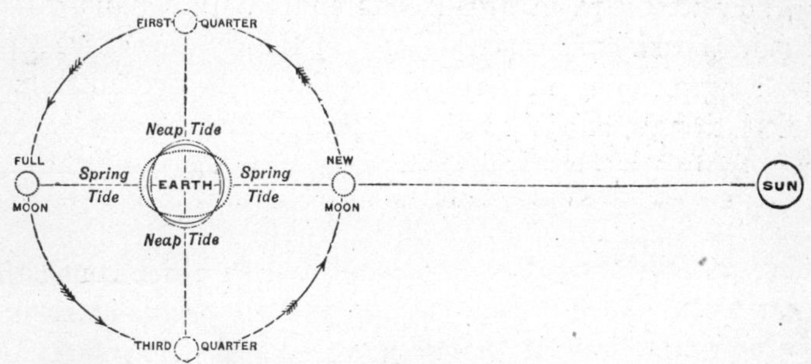

Fig. 147.

same direction as the rotation of the earth, and after one rotation of the earth on its axis, it takes fifty-two minutes for any given point on the earth to overtake the moon.

The sun also produces tides in the sea in the same manner as the moon, but on account of its greater distance the solar tides are much smaller than the lunar. At new moon and full moon the sun, earth, and moon are all in the same straight line, as shown in Fig. 147, and the lunar and solar tides combine to produce a greater rise and fall than usual, called *spring* tide. At intermediate periods the sun and moon act at right angles to each other and produce a smaller rise and fall than usual, called *neap* tide.

The increased rise of the tide in shallow water near shore, in river mouths, and in wide-mouthed indentations of the coast enables large vessels to penetrate the land. The inward movement of water during a rising tide gives sufficient depth and a favorable current for ingoing vessels, and the outward flow during a falling tide is favorable for outgoing vessels. These conditions are especially important on coasts where the continental shelf is wide, and in estuaries and drowned valleys like those of eastern United States, the British Isles, France, the Netherlands, and Germany.

Currents. — Under the influence of the prevailing winds the surface waters of the sea are driven in wide, shallow streams, or currents, from shore to shore. Deflected by the land masses, they perform great circuits in the ocean basins on each side of the equator. The map on pages 160–161 shows the location and direction of the principal ocean currents. What may be called the trunk streams are the north and south equatorial currents, which, under the influence of the trade winds (Figs. 170, 171, 172), flow westward in broad belts and are turned northward and southward by the eastern shores of the continents. Helped on by the prevailing westerly winds, they recross the oceans in middle latitudes, and, returning toward the equator on western shores, complete the circuits. The eddy in the north Atlantic is joined by a large branch from the south equatorial current and attains exceptional speed, depth, and temperature off the coast of Florida, where it is called the Gulf Stream. This current loses velocity and depth, and, north of 40° N. Lat., spreads out into a sheet of warm surface water which drifts at the rate of a mile or so a day far into the Arctic Ocean.

This large body of warm water in the north Atlantic raises the temperature of the winds which blow over it and contributes to the mildness and humidity of climate in western Europe. The water returns from the Arctic Ocean southward along the east coast of Greenland and Labrador, forming a reversed eddy of cold water.

In the north Pacific the Japan Current, or Kurosiwo, behaves in a similar manner.

In middle southern latitudes the circuit in each ocean is partly merged into the west wind drift, which circulates eastward around the earth in the Southern Ocean. In the northern part of the Indian Ocean the direction of circulation is reversed in winter by the northeast monsoons (Fig. 150).

As a general rule between 40° N. Lat. and 40° S. Lat. the currents bring relatively warm water to the eastern coasts of the continents and relatively cool water to the western coasts. In higher latitudes this rule is reversed. By this circulation of waters the temperatures of the oceans are partly equalized, and, through the influence of the water upon the temperature of the winds blowing over it, the climate of the continents is greatly modified. The most notable effects, due in part to the ocean currents, are the mild winter temperatures and heavy rainfall of western Europe and northwestern North America, and the cool summers of northeastern North America and Asia and southwestern South America.

Ocean currents bring food supply to fixed marine animals such as the coral polyps, which flourish best in the strong, warm equatorial currents, and also to fish which swarm in the cool waters off Newfoundland, Alaska, Norway, and Japan. Most of the numerous small islands in the Pacific,

Fig. 148. — Coral reef, Australia.

and some in other tropical waters, have been built by coral animals, which flourish in such numbers that their skeletons, converted into limestone rock, are piled up by the waves into low ring-shaped reefs and islands.

Economic Relations. — The sea never affords a home or fixed habitation for man. It is essentially a wide, empty space which he cannot occupy or permanently control, but which he can cross whenever he chooses. It therefore plays two contrasted parts in human affairs. It is at the same time a barrier which separates one people from another, and a broad, free, uncrowded highway of communication between them. It keeps nations apart and forms the most easily defended boundary of states, and it brings all the nations of the world together, enabling them to exchange goods and ideas. It is generally barren and unproductive in itself, but the people who use it most become rich, powerful, and enlightened.

With the introduction of steam vessels in the early part of the nineteenth century, the transformation of the sea from a barrier of separation to a highway of communication was begun. The change may now be said to be complete, and constitutes the most important adaptation yet made by man to his environment. More than by any other means, the mobility and circulation of men and goods has been promoted by the use of the sea. Since man is essentially a land animal, adaptation to the sea is for him more difficult than to the land. Consequently the use of the sea has required and developed the highest types of intellect. It requires more skill and courage to command an ocean vessel than to run a railroad train. A modern first-class passenger and freight steamship or a battleship is the most complex and costly piece of mechanism on a large scale man has yet achieved. To construct and run it requires all the material and mental resources of engineering. The profits and rewards of ocean traffic are so large that the great nations of the world rival one another in the invention and construction of merchant vessels to carry their goods, and of warships to protect them.

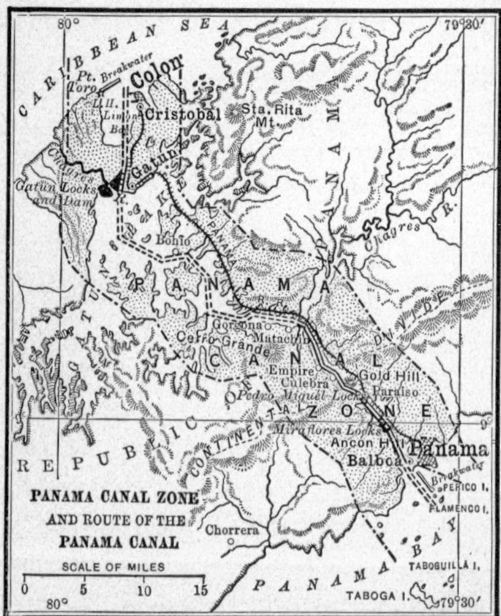

Fig. 149. — Map of Panama Canal and Canal Zone.

The sea promotes civilization also by bringing people into many-sided relationships. Along its land boundaries a nation is in contact with one or a few foreign neighbors, but if it has even one seaport it is brought in contact with people from nearly every part of the world. Sea trade has been greatly modified and facilitated by cutting through the narrow isthmuses at Suez and Panama. To go around the world by sea, it is no longer necessary to sail around the Cape of Good Hope and Cape Horn, but by the short-cut canals the whole voyage may be made between 35° N. Lat. and the equator.

The great maritime nations have coöperated in making a careful survey of all the coasts of the world, and have published charts showing the depth of water, the trend of coast lines, and the position of islands and light-houses, and giving sailing directions for the use of mariners. The great commercial peoples live around the north Atlantic, which thus becomes the oceanic center of the world. The north Pacific bids fair to become in the near future a secondary center of scarcely less importance.

Classification of Coasts (Fig. 150).

(1) *Folded mountain coasts, elevated.* — Slopes steep above and below water. Coastal plains and shelves absent or narrow. Large rivers, deltas, and estuaries rare. Fiords in high latitudes. Sea cliffs almost continuous. Few harbors available for seaports.

(2) *Folded mountain coasts, depressed.* — Coast line double. Outer line of partly submerged mountain chains, forming festoons of islands. Slopes very steep. Inner line of deep border seas with numerous gulfs, bays, and peninsulas. Very complex. Harbors numerous.

(3) *Fault scarp coasts.* — High, smooth, and unindented. Coastal plains and shelves absent or narrow. Estuaries and drowned valleys absent. Deltas at the mouths of large rivers only. Fiords in high latitudes. Harbors rare.

(4) *Plain coasts.* — Bordered by wide coastal plains and shelves. Slopes gentle. Barrier beaches, lagoons, and dunes extensive. Estuaries and drowned valleys numerous.

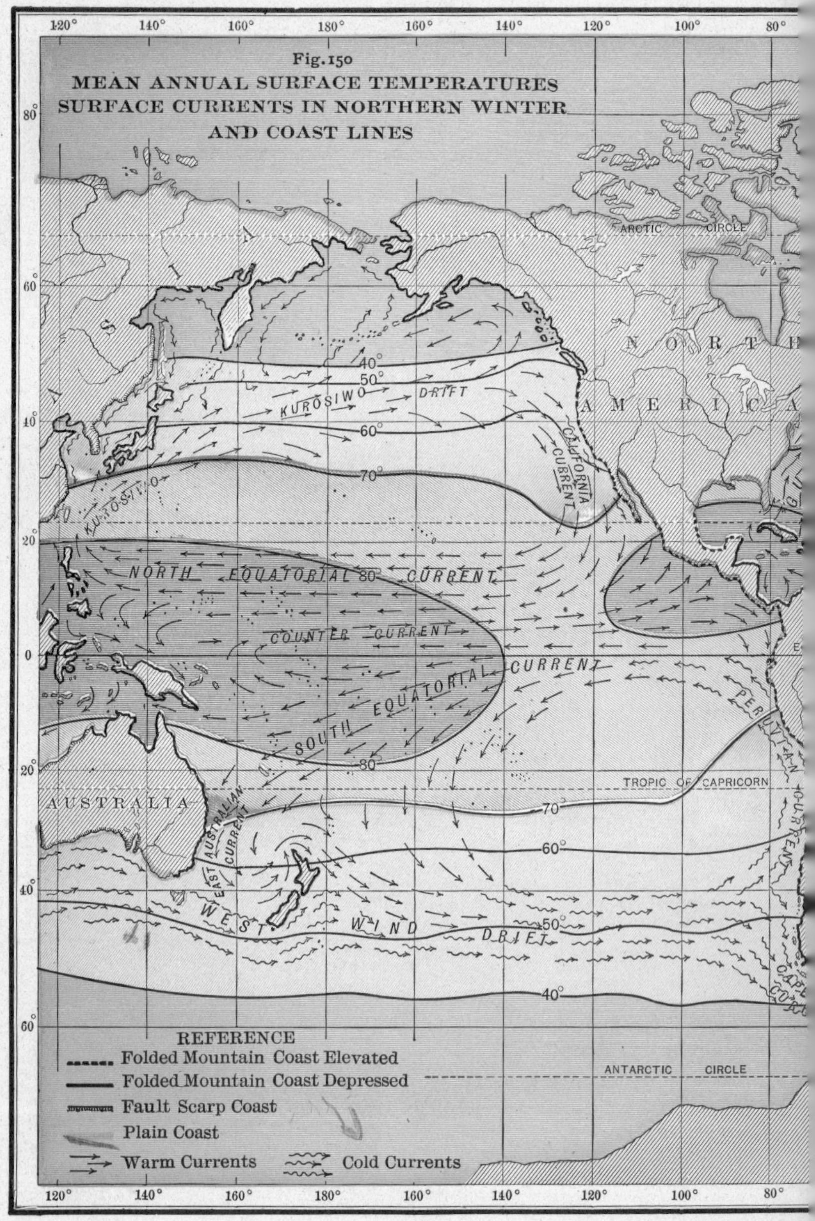

Fig. 150
MEAN ANNUAL SURFACE TEMPERATURES
SURFACE CURRENTS IN NORTHERN WINTER
AND COAST LINES
120° 140° 160° 180° 160° 140° 120° 100° 80°
80° 60° 40° 20° 0 20° 40° 60°
ARCTIC CIRCLE
NORTH
AMERICA
AUSTRALIA
KUROSIWO DRIFT
KUROSIWO
CALIFORNIA CURRENT
NORTH EQUATORIAL CURRENT
COUNTER CURRENT
SOUTH EQUATORIAL CURRENT
PERUVIAN CURRENT
EAST AUSTRALIAN CURRENT
WEST WIND DRIFT
TROPIC OF CAPRICORN
ANTARCTIC CIRCLE
40° 50° 60° 70° 80°
REFERENCE
Folded Mountain Coast Elevated
Folded Mountain Coast Depressed
Fault Scarp Coast
Plain Coast
Warm Currents
Cold Currents

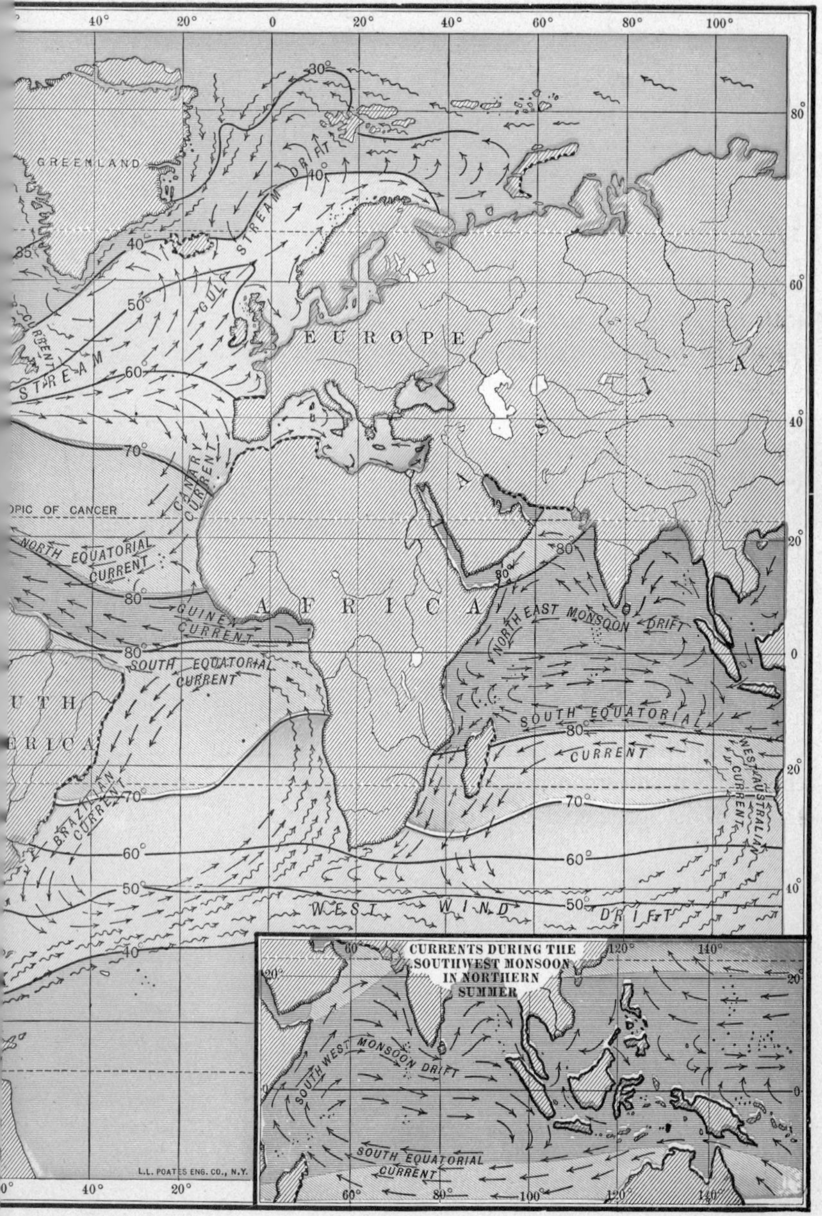
GREENLAND
GULF STREAM DRIFT
GULF STREAM
EUROPE
A S I A
CANARY CURRENT
TROPIC OF CANCER
NORTH EQUATORIAL CURRENT
GUINEA CURRENT
SOUTH EQUATORIAL CURRENT
AFRICA
NORTH EAST MONSOON DRIFT
SOUTH EQUATORIAL CURRENT
WEST AUSTRALIAN CURRENT
BRAZILIAN CURRENT
WEST WIND DRIFT
CURRENTS DURING THE SOUTHWEST MONSOON IN NORTHERN SUMMER
SOUTH WEST MONSOON DRIFT
SOUTH EQUATORIAL CURRENT
L.L. POATES ENG. CO., N.Y.

CHAPTER XII

COASTS AND PORTS

INDEPENDENTLY of the work of standing water, the large features and general character of coast lines depend primarily upon the present and past relief of the land. If in the past the land has stood higher than at present and the streams have graded their valleys down to base level, then sinking of the land drowns all the bars, lets tide water far up the valleys, and converts them into long, deep arms of the sea. Many of the best harbors in the world are such *drowned valleys*, or *estuaries* (Figs. 153, 154, 155). A coast line which is rising, or has been recently elevated, is established upon what was formerly sea bottom, and is therefore smooth and only slightly indented by stream valleys. It is apt to be bordered by cliffs and to present few inlets to the land. The gulfs and bays are generally curved in outline and wide open to the sea (Fig. 43).

The Southern Continents. — Of all the continents Africa has the simplest and smoothest coast line (Figs. 16, 150). More than half of it is bordered by plateaus and mountains, and between Guinea and Good Hope and on the Red Sea it is bounded by a fault scarp. Much of the Sahara coast is low, but there are no rivers or inlets except the mouth of the Nile. The coast of Australia resembles that of Africa. But one large river enters the sea. The south coast is smooth and cliffed, with but one large break,—Spencer Gulf,—which is a rift valley (p. 64). The east coast is bordered on the land side by mountains and on the sea side by the Great Barrier coral reef. On the Atlantic side of South America a coastal plain extends from the northern end of the Andes Mountains to Cape St. Roque, and from the mouth of the Plata to the Strait of Magellan, including the deltas of the three great rivers of the continent. Between Cape St. Roque and the Plata low plateaus and mountains rise from a shore which is little indented.

The Pacific Coast of America. — The Pacific coast of America extends about 12,000 miles along the foot of a lofty mountain system. The slopes above and below sea level are steep, and the streams are generally insignificant. Only the Colorado and the Columbia cut through the mountain barrier and bring large volumes of water from the interior. One flows into the Gulf of California, the only long sea arm on the coast and probably a rift valley. The other has a wide estuary. South of 40° S. Lat. and north of 50° N. Lat. this coast is cut into a ragged fringe of long, narrow, steep-walled inlets and high peninsulas, bordered by outlying islands. These arms of the sea are of great depth and often extend as far below sea level as their walls rise above it. They are called *canals* and *fiords*. These coasts are swept by west winds from the ocean, which bring a heavy rainfall. On account of large volume and steep slope the streams have great erosive power, and are able to cut valleys far back into the mountains. On account of high latitude and altitude the snowfall is heavy enough to fill the valleys with ice and to bring about glaciation, which has been more extensive in the past than it is at present. The ice has widened and deepened the valleys, converting them into fiords (Figs. 106, 152, 153, 154). The great depth of water, amounting in some cases to

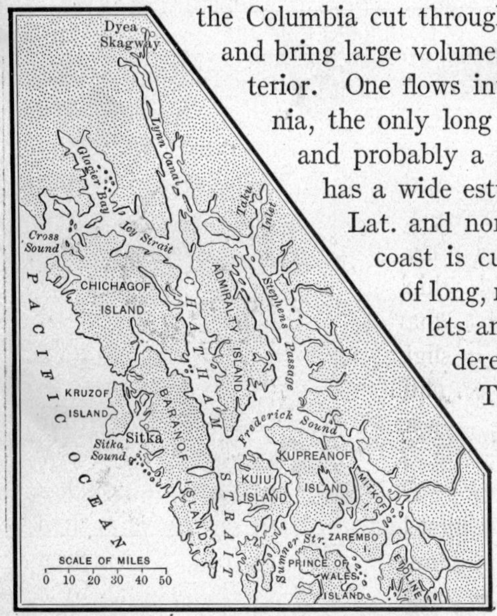

Fig. 151. — Canal coast, Alaska.

4,000 feet, is partly due to sinking of the land. Glaciation has been more severe on some coasts than on others, but all fiord coasts owe their distinctive characters to ice action. Fiord coasts occur also in Norway, Iceland, Scotland, New Zealand, Greenland, and Spitzbergen.

Even after the ice has disappeared fiord coasts are generally unfavorable for human occupation. Deep harbors are superabundant, but the shores are so high and precipitous that landing is difficult, and there is little room for

Fig. 152.—Fiord, Norway. Glacier in the distance.

settlement. Land resources are small and population sparse. The people are compelled to take to the sea for a living and become fishermen and sailors. In the past, when the sea was not so well policed as at present, the Norwegian fiords were the nesting places of pirates, who raided and plundered their richer neighbors. The scenery of the Norwegian fiords has long been famous as among the grandest, but is inferior to that of Alaska, where the combination of sea, mountain, forest, and glacier is unrivaled in the world. Fiord coasts of a mild type, such as those of Scotland and Maine, attract thousands of visitors by their agreeable summer climate and picturesque scenery.

Asia. — The Pacific coast of Asia is characterized by a series of island chains arranged in festoons which inclose deep border

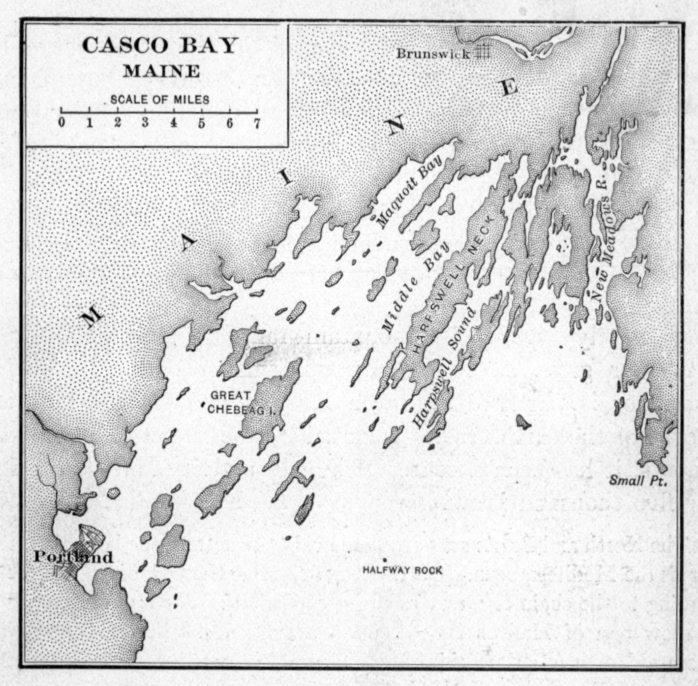

Fig. 153.—Part of the Maine coast. Fiords and islands.

seas between them and the mainland. The islands are mountainous and volcanic, and their slopes plunge seaward into very deep water (Fig. 16). It looks as if the earth crust of Asia had slid toward the sea and wrinkled up around the edge. The mainland coast abounds in peninsulas, bays, and gulfs of varied size and character, and many large, navigable rivers flow into the border seas. This coast in complexity and accessibility is unequaled elsewhere in the world.

Between the South China Sea and the Bay of Bengal the ends of parallel mountain ranges project into the sea, but the rivers have smoothed the coast line by filling in the spaces between the ranges. The head of the Bay of Bengal is occupied by the enormous delta of the Ganges-Brahmaputra. The coasts of India, Persia, and Arabia are defined by lines of fracture, and are generally high and without indentations. The lowlands about the mouth of the Indus and the nearly inclosed Persian Gulf lead to valleys which are desert except for irrigation.

North Atlantic Coasts. — The north Atlantic exceeds all other oceans in the number, variety, and area of its coast waters. The basins of the Caribbean Sea and Gulf of Mexico are very deep and bordered by submerged mountain ranges forming a festoon of islands similar to those of Pacific Asia. The Mediterranean Sea with its branches, on account of its area, depth, and complexity, might be considered a distinct ocean basin. It is nearly divided by mountain ranges, partly submerged, into four great basins and several smaller ones. Its varied character is partly due to the faulting and sinking of great blocks of the earth crust. Inclosed by the shores of three continents, it has been a center of human activity and civilization for five thousand years.

The North and Baltic seas are shallow, but penetrate the land almost as far as the Mediterranean. On the American side the Gulf of St. Lawrence, leading to the chain of Great Lakes, occupies an analogous position. The shallow pan of Hudson Bay occupies a sunken portion of the interior plain of North America behind the highland of Labrador, as the White Sea lies on the European plain behind Scandinavia.

The American and European coasts of the north Atlantic are low and not bordered by highlands except in the north. Many of the river mouths are drowned, forming estuaries. The American and European Mediterraneans are so nearly tideless that the rivers have been able to build great deltas such as those of the Orinoco, Mississippi, Ebro, Rhone, Po, and Nile.

Arctic Coasts. — The coasts of the Arctic Ocean are almost everywhere low and bordered by a wide coastal plain and shelf. The White Sea and the Gulf of Ob are the only important arms. Large rivers, such as the Mackenzie, Petchora, Yenisei, and Lena, have built deltas. On account of the severe climate, and the persistence of snow and ice on land and sea, the Arctic coasts are comparatively inaccessible and unfavorable for human occupation.

Coast Factors. — The degree of indentation of a coast may be expressed mathematically in different ways. If the length of the actual mainland coast line of each continent is divided by the circumference of a circle having an area equal to that of the continent, the following ratios, or *coast factors*, are obtained:

North America	4.9	Australia	2.0
Europe	3.5	South America	2.0
Asia	3.2	Africa	1.8

That is, North America has a coast line nearly five times as long as the shortest possible, while the coast line of Africa is less than twice as long as necessary.

If the mainland area of each continent is divided by the length of its coast line, the following ratios are obtained:

Europe has 1 mile of	coast line to		151 square	miles of	area.
North America	"	"	164	"	"
Australia	"	"	242	"	"
Asia	"	"	368	"	"
South America	"	"	386	"	"
Africa	"	"	593	"	"

That is, Europe has nearly four times as much coast line in proportion to its area as Africa, and North America has more than twice as much as South America. These facts help to explain why Africa is shut in, isolated, and backward, while Europe has been the center of the highest civilization for 3,000 years, and why North America has become the chief center of civilization outside of Europe.

Ports. — A harbor is primarily a place of shelter from storms. A port is a gateway or place of entrance. In a commercial sense a port is a place where vessels are loaded and unloaded. The existence of a good port depends upon many conditions:

(1) *Accessibility from the water;* that is, a channel deep enough for large vessels, not too crooked, free from rocks and shoals, and not subject to fogs.

(2) *A harbor* well protected from winds and waves, free from ice and strong currents, large enough to furnish anchorage for many vessels, and deep enough to permit them to float near shore.

(3) *A long, low coast line*, where wharves may be built to bring vessels and vehicles alongside of each other.

(4) *Accessibility from the land* by river, canal, or railroads.

River Ports. — The great ports of the world are, with few exceptions, situated at or near the mouths of rivers, usually as far inland as large vessels can go. The distance of the port from the river mouth is greatly increased by the drowning of the lower valley and the occurrence of tides. These conditions may convert a coastal plain with small, shallow rivers, a line of barrier beaches, and a wide coastal shelf, into a first-class commercial seaboard. The Atlantic coasts of North America and Europe furnish striking examples (Fig. 16).

Delta Ports. — In the delta of a large river there is usually one distributary channel which is deep enough for ocean vessels, and on this, at some point where the land is safe from tidal overflow, a seaport is apt to be located. New Orleans, the Rhine ports, and Calcutta are examples. The growth of a sand bar off the mouth of the channel and the shifting of the discharge to some other channel are difficulties liable to occur.

New Orleans, eighty miles from the sea, is above the point where the Mississippi divides into the "passes" of the "goosefoot." A sufficient depth of water was maintained through the South Pass for about thirty years by Captain Eads's jetties, which are embankments designed to narrow the channel, quicken the current, and compel it to remove the bar. A jetty is now being built at the mouth of the Southwest Pass (Fig. 69).

Lagoon Harbors lie behind beaches, bars, spits, or reefs. They are well protected, but are usually too shallow to admit the largest vessels without artificial deepening (Fig. 28). Galveston, Tex., Venice in the Adriatic, and Danzig on the Baltic, are situated on or behind barrier beaches.

Fiord Harbors. — Fiords afford excellent harbors as far as depth of water, clear entrance, and complete protection are concerned, but are seldom favorable for ports on account of high, steep shores and inaccessibility from the land. It is only where these features exist in moderate degree that considerable seaports occur, as Christiania, Norway, and Glasgow, Scotland. In the latter case the fiord cuts entirely through the marginal highland and penetrates the lowland, where the little river Clyde has been enlarged to a canal which admits vessels of all sizes.

Where the sinking of the land has drowned a series of valleys parallel with the coast, a chain of islands is separated from the mainland by straits, sounds, and canals (p. 163), which form an "inside passage," protected from the open sea and traversable by large vessels. The northwest coast of North America and the east shore of the Adriatic furnish striking examples (Fig. 151).

Round Inlets. — A coast inlet with a rounded or semicircular outline is called a *cuvette*, meaning a bowl or basin. Cuvettes are sometimes due to faulting along a succession of curves, as on the west coast of Italy and south coast of France. The greatest seaports of the Mediterranean — Marseilles, Genoa, and Naples — are situated upon such bays.

Deep Straits connecting large bodies of water are highways of commerce, and are apt to develop important seaports, of which Constantinople and Singapore are examples.

Artificial Harbors. — All harbors have to be improved more or less by artificial works to accommodate large shipping. Wharves must be built, alongside of which vessels may be tied, and facilities for transferring cargoes must be furnished. Often channels must be deepened by dredging, and in some cases canals are dug to admit ocean vessels to inland cities.

Ships reach Amsterdam only by the North Sea Canal, recently constructed. A canal 35 miles long has converted Manchester from an inland manufacturing city to a seaport and financial center. At Hamburg $44,000,000 has been spent in providing wharves and basins, and London is facing the necessity of spending $100,000,000 to improve the port and hold supremacy in trade. Large sums have recently been spent in making artificial harbors at Puerto Mexico, and Salina Cruz, the termini of the railroad across the Isthmus of Tehuantepec, in Mexico, and at Colon and Panama where the Panama Canal reaches the sea.

In cases where it is impossible to extend the sea into the land, the land is built out into the sea in the form of a breakwater, which creates an artificial lagoon harbor behind it. At San Pedro Bay, now the harbor of Los Angeles, California, the breakwater is nearly two miles long.

Lake Ports are generally situated on river harbors and are improved by dredging the river mouth and building a breakwater outside. The harbors of Chicago, Cleveland, and Buffalo are of this character.

Fig. 154.—Drowned valley of the Hudson: a fiord.

The Port of New York. — New York is situated upon a harbor of a mild fiord type, combined with a lagoon. The lower Hudson is a fiord which has been partly filled with sediment. The East River and Long Island Sound constitute an "inside passage" between the mainland and Long Island. The fiord and passage expand at their junction into the deep upper bay. The tidal currents are strong enough to scour out the channels. The shores furnish fifty miles of wharf line with deep water, and there is room enough to build piers at right angles to the shore, so as to accommodate a large number of ships. The lower bay is an antechamber of an entirely different character. It is a shallow indentation partly fenced from the open sea by the barrier beach of Coney Island and the spit of Sandy Hook, both of which are growing farther into the bay and threatening to close it. Much difficulty and expense are incurred in maintaining a channel deep enough for the largest vessels.

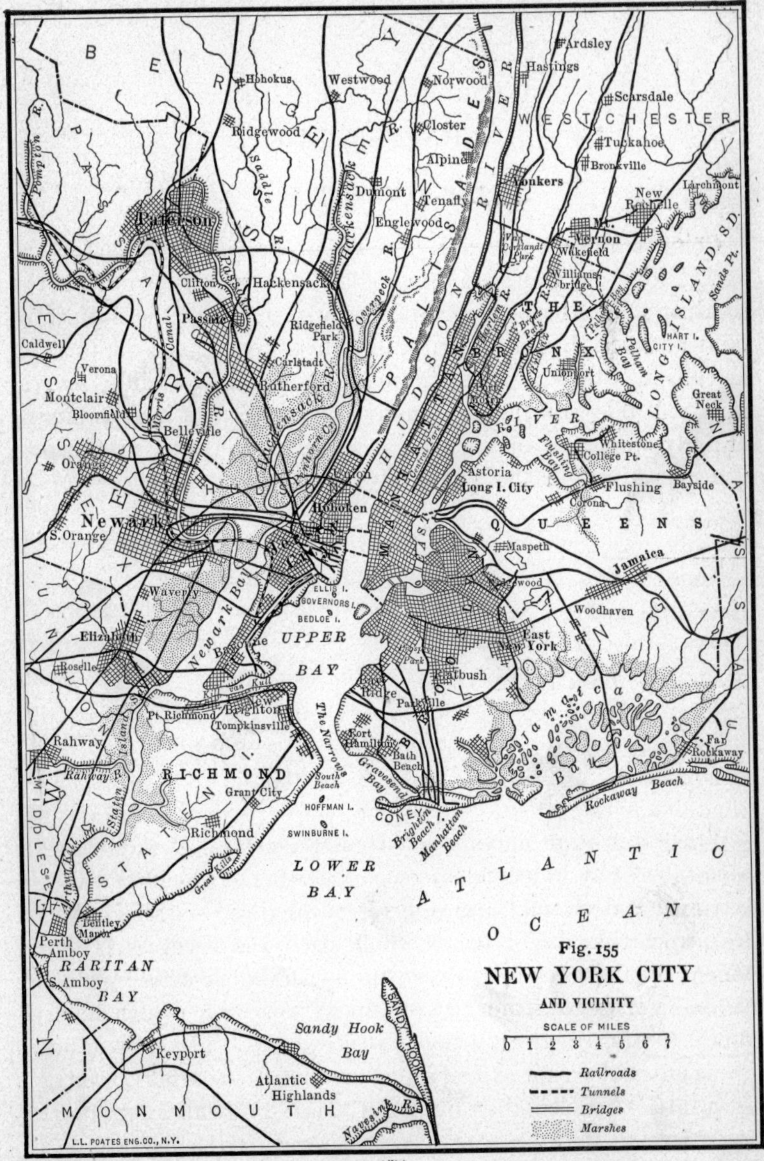

Fig. 155
NEW YORK CITY
AND VICINITY

CHAPTER XIII

THE ATMOSPHERE

Composition. — The atmosphere, or gaseous portion of the earth, forms a complete spheroidal shell which surrounds the solid and liquid globe, and not only rests upon the surface of land and sea, but also penetrates them to a great depth. Its thickness, which is not definitely known, is certainly several hundred miles and may be many thousand. Its bulk is almost entirely made up of five gases, which are present in the proportions given in the following table:

COMPOSITION OF THE AIR

Gas	Per cent of Volume	Density
Nitrogen	76.95	.971
Oxygen	20.61	1.105
Water vapor (average)	1.40	.624
Argon	1.00	1.380
Carbon dioxide (average)	0.03	1.529
Air	99.99	1.000

These gases are not united or combined in any way, but are almost entirely independent of one another. They act like five separate and distinct atmospheres occupying the same space at the same time. The space which each gas occupies is determined by the balance between its own expansive force, tending to make it expand indefinitely, and gravitation, which holds it down to the earth. Carbon dioxide, being the heaviest of all these gases, does not extend so far upward as the others. Oxygen is a little heavier than nitrogen, and its relative proportion decreases in the upper air. Water vapor is the lightest of all, but its existence as vapor is so far dependent upon a warm temperature that it is absent at great heights.

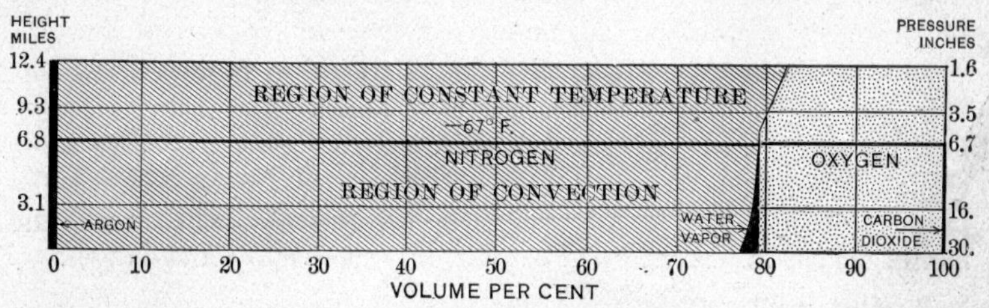

Fig. 156. — Composition of lower atmosphere.

Properties and Functions. — *Oxygen* combines freely with nearly all the elements, and in its numerous compounds forms about half of the whole weight of the globe. By the process of respiration it supports the life of all plants and animals, and it is the universal agent of combustion. By respiration, combustion, decay, and other processes of oxidation the quantity of oxygen in the air is being continually diminished. This loss is partly compensated by the oxygen set free from plants in the process of food manufacture.

Nitrogen is extremely inert and enters into combination with other elements with difficulty. To it is due three fourths of the pressure and density of the air. Without it birds could not fly, clouds and smoke would settle to the ground, and the force of the wind and the loudness of sound would be proportionately diminished.

Argon resembles nitrogen, with which it was confounded until near the end of the nineteenth century.

Carbon dioxide (CO_2), or carbonic acid gas, is a compound of carbon and oxygen formed in the active, growing parts of plants and in the tissues of all animals and given off by them in the process of respiration. It is also produced by the combustion of all the ordinary forms of fuel, and sometimes escapes in large quantities from active volcanoes, old volcanic regions, and from many mineral springs. It forms the chief food supply of plants. The green parts of plants in the sunlight absorb carbon dioxide, separate it into its elements, retain the carbon, and give off the oxygen. Carbon dioxide plays an active part in rock formation, entering into combination with lime and other bases to form limestones. It also enters largely into the composition of the bones and shells of animals. While the absolute quantity of carbon dioxide is the least of all the principal constituents of the air, the part it plays in the economy of nature is second to none.

Water vapor is supplied by evaporation from all damp surfaces, but chiefly from the sea. When cooled it condenses again into water and forms clouds, rain, and snow. The quantity present in the air at different times and places is very variable, amounting sometimes to five per cent.

Dust. — The lower air generally contains more or less matter in the form of dust, analogous to the sediment suspended in running water. Dust consists of finely pulverized rock lifted by the wind or blown to great heights by volcanic eruptions, carbon particles from the smoke of fires, particles of plant and animal tissue, vegetable spores, bacteria, and other minute organisms. A cubic inch of air in dry regions may contain thousands of these particles.

Dust in the air diffuses and scatters the rays of sunlight. In a dustless atmosphere all shadows would be a deep black, and the sky itself would appear black. Dust scatters the blue rays more than the red, and is the chief cause of the blue color of the sky and of the red and yellow colors at sunrise and sunset. Dust plays an important part in the formation of fog and clouds by supplying nuclei upon which the water vapor begins to condense. The dense fogs of London and other cities occur when the air is full of smoke particles. Minute organisms in the air furnish the germs of disease and the agents of decomposition, as when fermentation is set up in cider or grape juice exposed in open vessels.

Temperature. — The temperature of the air is determined by the amount of heat received and absorbed from the sun and earth. As the sun heat passes through the air on its way to the earth, about one third of it is absorbed by the air and goes to raise its temperature, while the remaining two thirds reaches the surface of the land and water. A part of this is reflected back without warming the earth, and another part, being absorbed, goes to raise or maintain the temperature of the land and water. The warm earth in turn warms the air next to it slightly by conduction and still more by radiating its heat upward.

The lower air absorbs much more heat than the upper air, and consequently is maintained at a higher temperature. This is due largely to the presence of cloud, fog, dust, and smoke. The larger proportions of carbon dioxide and water vapor in the lower air also increase its absorptive power for heat. Currents of warm air are constantly rising from land and water and cooling by expansion. In consequence of these conditions, the temperature of the atmosphere falls at the rate of about one degree for every 300 feet of ascent, from sea level up to a height of six or seven miles (Fig. 156).

Distribution of Light and Heat. — If the earth were a flat disk and one side were always turned toward the sun, the sun's rays would strike everywhere at the same angle and every part of that side would be constantly and equally lighted and heated (Fig. 157, *A*). If a spheroidal earth stood still, the same half of it would be always lighted and warmed, but not uniformly. The spot where the direct rays strike would be strongly lighted and would become very hot, but the more slanting rays would cause the light and heat to decrease in every direction to the margin of the hemisphere. The dark side of the earth would be uniformly cold. Thus the light and heat belts would be arranged concentrically around the center of the lighted side (Fig. 157, *B*). If such an earth should

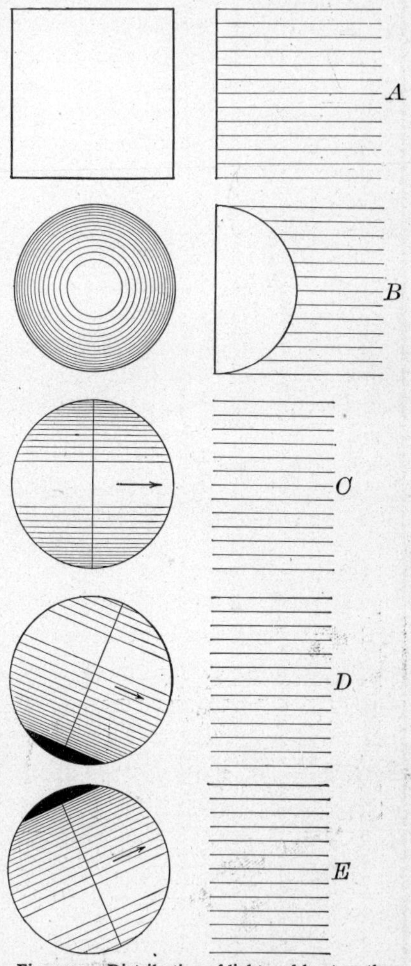

Fig. 157. — Distribution of light and heat on the earth under various conditions.

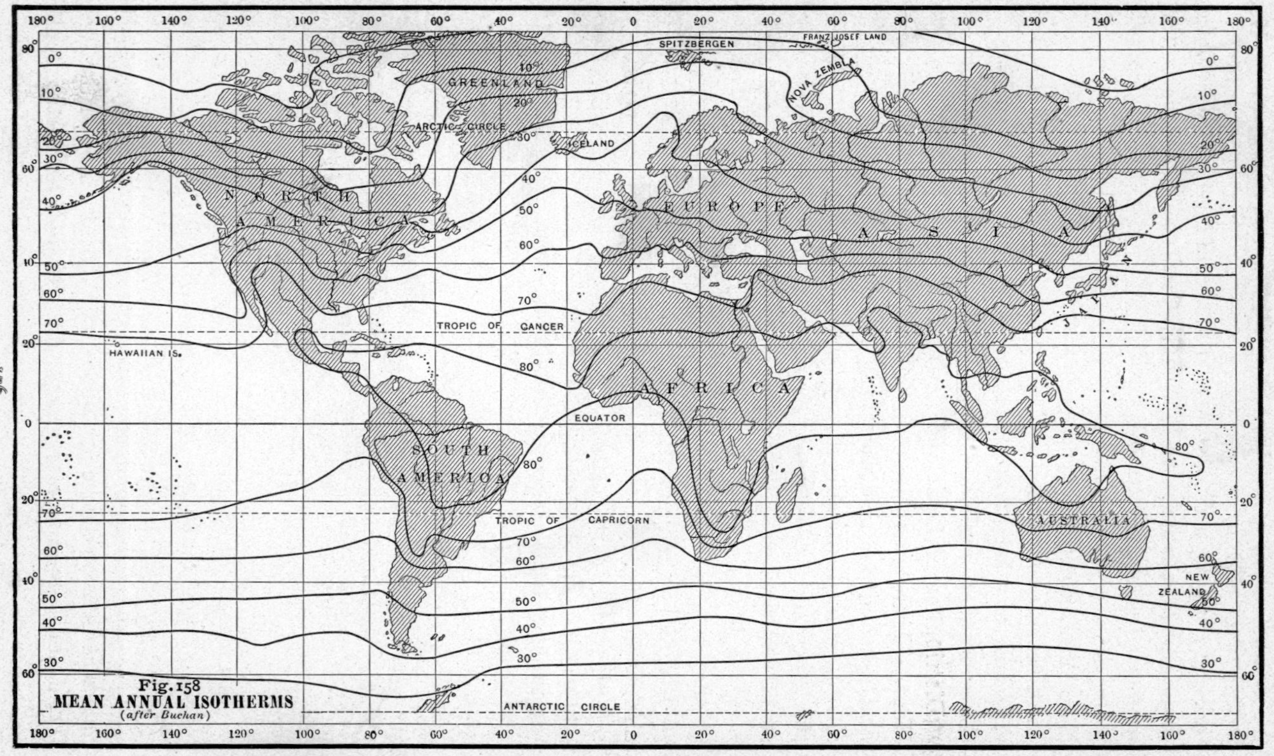

Fig. 158
MEAN ANNUAL ISOTHERMS
(after Buchan)

begin to rotate with the sun directly over the equator, the light and heat belts would be strung out into zones extending around it parallel with the equator, the light and heat would decrease everywhere uniformly from the equator to the poles, and all places would have days and nights of equal length. Our earth is in about that condition in March and September (Fig. 157, *C*). If a spheroidal, rotating earth should begin to revolve around the sun with its axis inclined so that the sun is not always over the equator, the light and heat belts would follow the sun, swinging back and forth, north and south, once in every revolution. The days and nights would not be of the same length at different places or at the same place at different times. Thus a change of seasons would occur such as we have upon our earth (Fig. 157, *D* and *E*).

Heat Belts. — A state of things exactly as described above exists on our earth so far as the light belts are concerned, which always extend around the earth parallel with the equator; but the heat belts are bent out of shape by land and water, by winds, and by ocean currents. The land is heated and cooled more rapidly than water, consequently continents are warmer in summer and colder in winter than oceans which receive the same amount of heat from the sun. In summer the heat belts are bent away from the equator over the land and toward the equator over the water; in winter, the reverse. Heat belts cannot be bounded by parallels of latitude, like the tropics and polar circles, but by *isotherms*, or lines of equal temperature (Figs. 158, 159, 160), which are quite crooked.

Winds and ocean currents carry their temperatures, whether warm or cold, to the regions toward which they move, and sweep the isotherms along with them. In general, currents of air or water moving from the equator carry warmth with them and bend the isotherms poleward, and currents moving toward the equator carry coolness and bend the isotherms equatorward.

The isotherms as a whole shift north and south with the seasons according to the varying angle of the sun's rays. They are not in exactly the same positions on any two successive days. Their

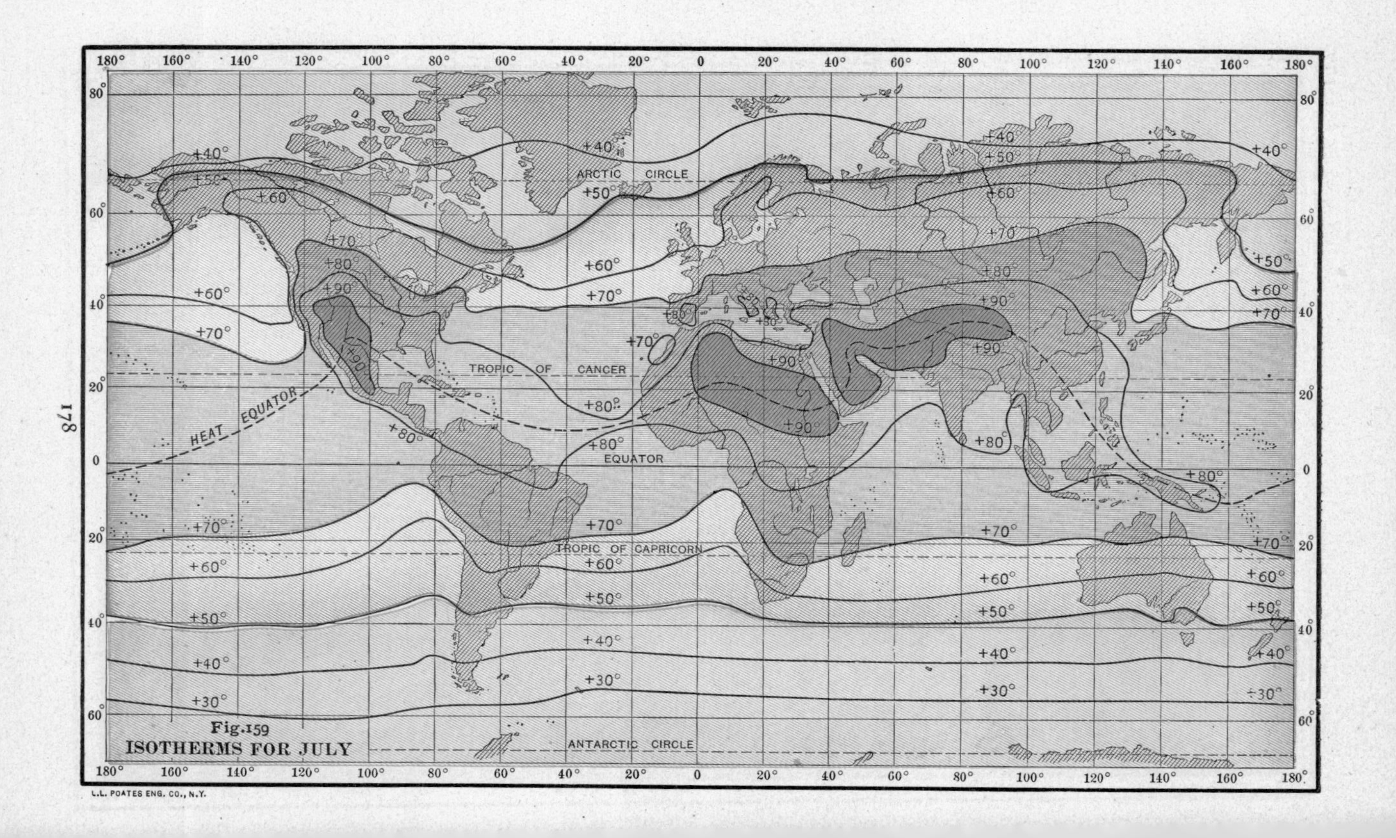

Fig. 159
ISOTHERMS FOR JULY

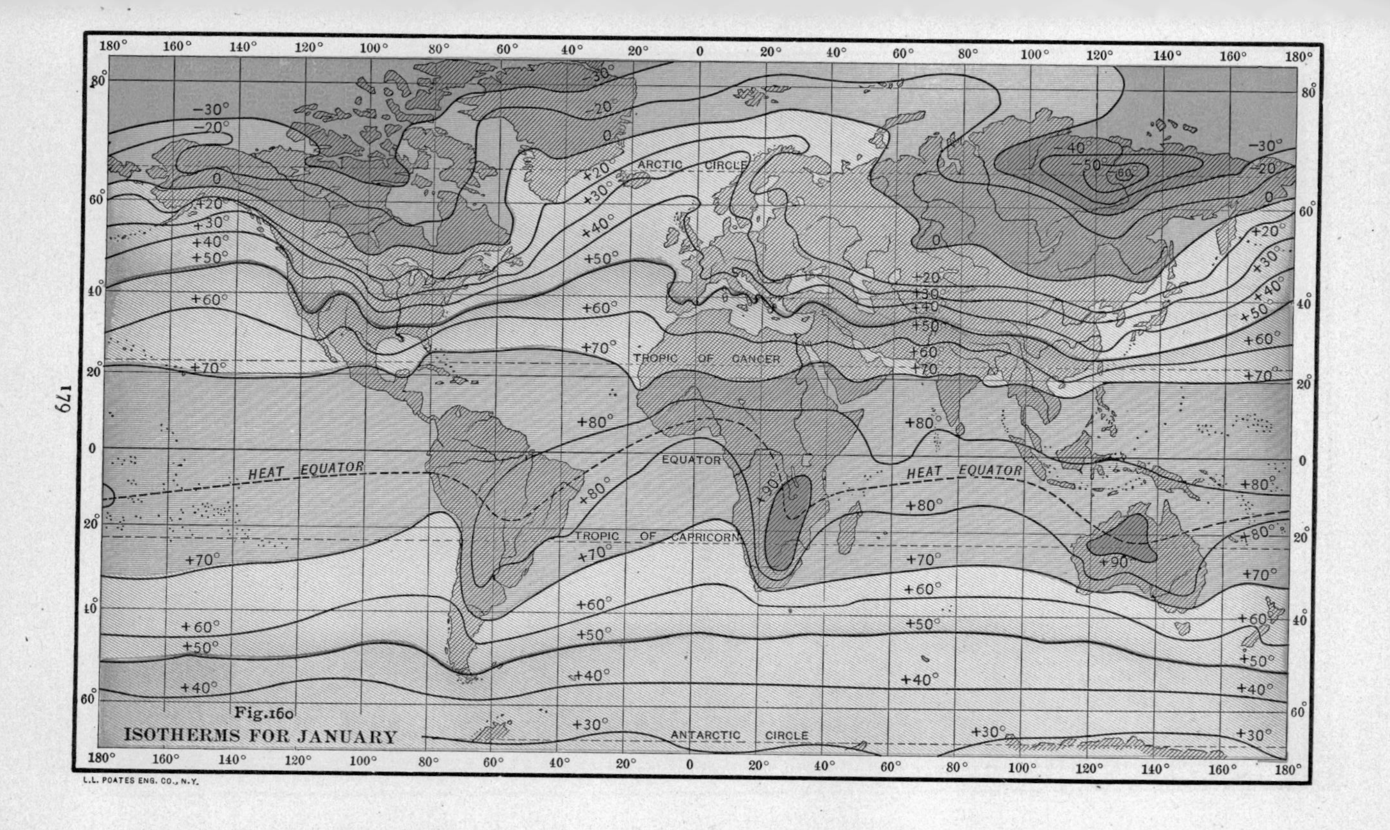

Fig. 160
ISOTHERMS FOR JANUARY

positions in July and January, the months of extreme position, show the character and extent of the shifting (Figs. 159, 160). Instead of calculating the temperature by months, it may be calculated for a series of years, and the resulting isotherms show the mean annual temperatures (Fig. 158).

Range of Temperature. — The mean annual temperature of any place is important, but the temperature of the warmest month and day, and that of the coldest month and day, are more important. The difference between the temperature of the warmest month and that of the coldest month at any place is called the *annual range*. The difference between the temperature of the warmest day and that of the coldest day is called the *absolute* annual range. The range of temperature is greater on land than on water in the same latitude.

Bodies of water are warmed more slowly than land in the day and the summer, and cooled more slowly at night and in the winter. The relatively uniform temperature of the ocean throughout the year and the extreme variations of temperature on land cause a marked contrast between oceanic and continental climates. The range of temperature increases with latitude, because in the course of a year both the angle of the sun's rays and the length of day and night vary more toward the poles than near the equator. The range of temperature is greater in the northern hemisphere than in the southern on account of the large land areas in one and the expanse of water in the other (Fig. 161).

The mean annual temperatures at London, New York, Seattle, and Yokohama are about the same, but the annual range at London and Seattle is about 20 degrees, and at New York and Yokohama about 40 degrees. This is due to the prevailing westerly winds, which blow from the ocean in one case and from the land in the other.

Zones of Temperature. — Along any meridian the temperature changes gradually, but it is convenient to divide the face of the earth into zones bounded by certain definite isotherms. In middle and high latitudes the summer temperatures are far more important than the winter temperatures, because they determine what plants can grow, what crops can be raised, and the number of people any region can support. The annual isotherm of 70° in each hemisphere is not far from the tropics, and is practically the limit of tropical plants such as palms, bananas, and dates. The isotherm of 50° for the warmest month in each hemisphere is about the polar limit of cereal grains and forest trees. Beyond that men maintain themselves only with great difficulty. These lines surround two caps of polar climate, between which lies the whole habitable world. This again is divided into a zone of tropical climate and two zones of temperate climate, of which the northern is much wider than the southern and covers the most favorable regions for human life (Fig. 162).

There are many schemes for dividing the earth into zones of temperature, among which this is one of the simplest and most useful. For some purposes a more exact and detailed subdivision is necessary.

Temperature Belts. — Temperatures above 70° may be called hot, between 70° and 50° temperate, and below 50° cold. If the isotherms of 70° and 50° for July and January are drawn on the same map, the result is a system of nine zones which show the annual and seasonal conditions of temperature with sufficient exactness (Fig. 164).

In the equatorial zone, which lies approximately between the tropics, the average monthly temperature is above 70° at all seasons. The subtropical zones are hot with a temperate season, or temperate with a hot season. In the temperate zones the monthly temperature would be between 70° and 50° at all seasons, if it were not for the influence of the land masses. In the northern hemisphere these truly temperate conditions are reversed over nearly all the land surface of the zone. In North America and Eurasia wide areas have hot summers and cold winters, and the climate deserves the name of *intemperate*. These regions have a temperate climate in spring and fall, a hot summer and a cold winter. In the southern hemisphere these intemperate conditions prevail only in small portions of South America and Australia. The rest of the zone is truly temperate. The cold temperate zones have a temperate climate with a cold season, or a cold climate with a temperate season. In the polar caps the monthly temperature is below 50° at all seasons.

Pressure. — At sea level a cubic foot of air weighs about one ounce and a quarter, and the weight of all the air above sea level produces an average pressure of 14.74 pounds upon every

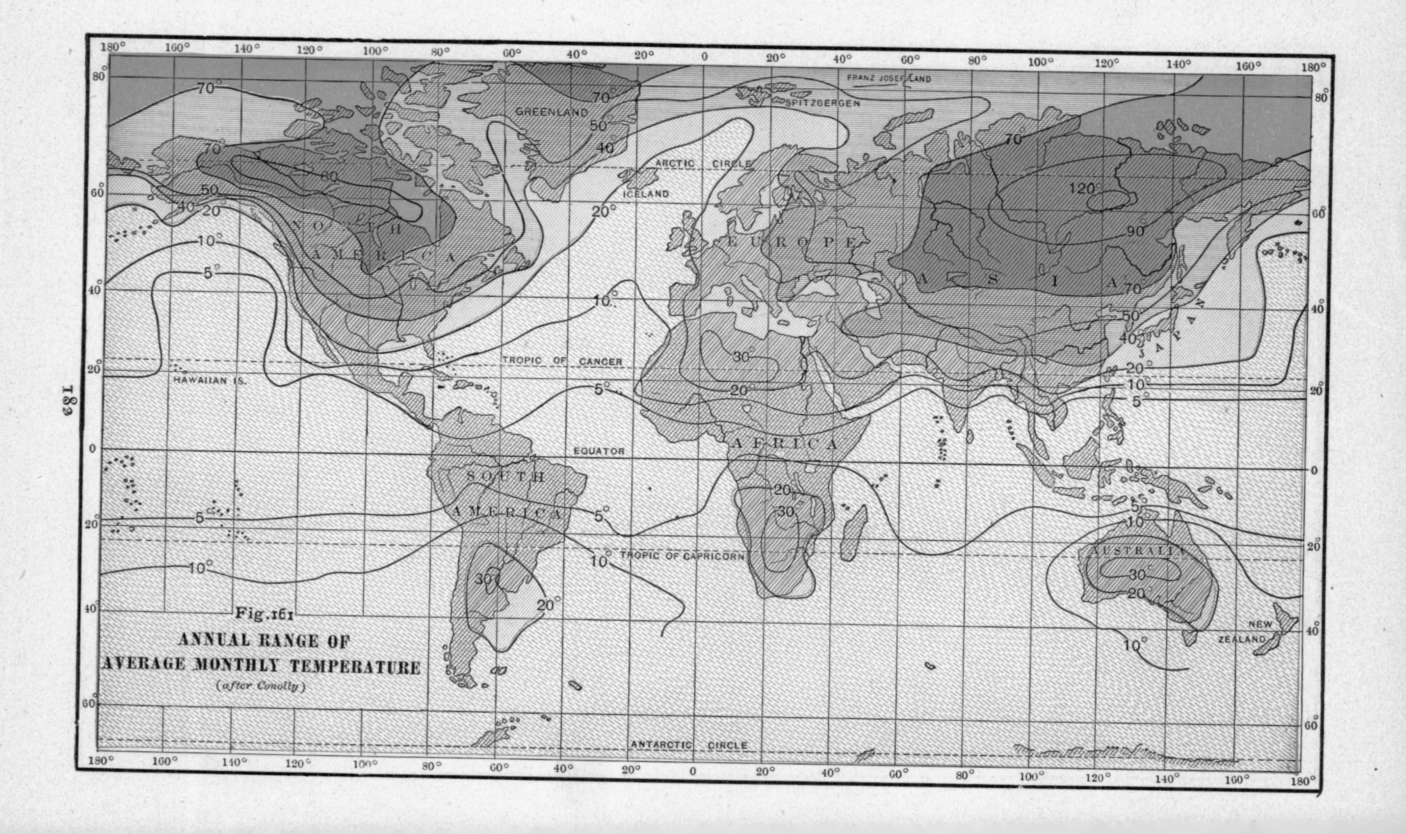

Fig. 161
ANNUAL RANGE OF AVERAGE MONTHLY TEMPERATURE
(after Conolly)

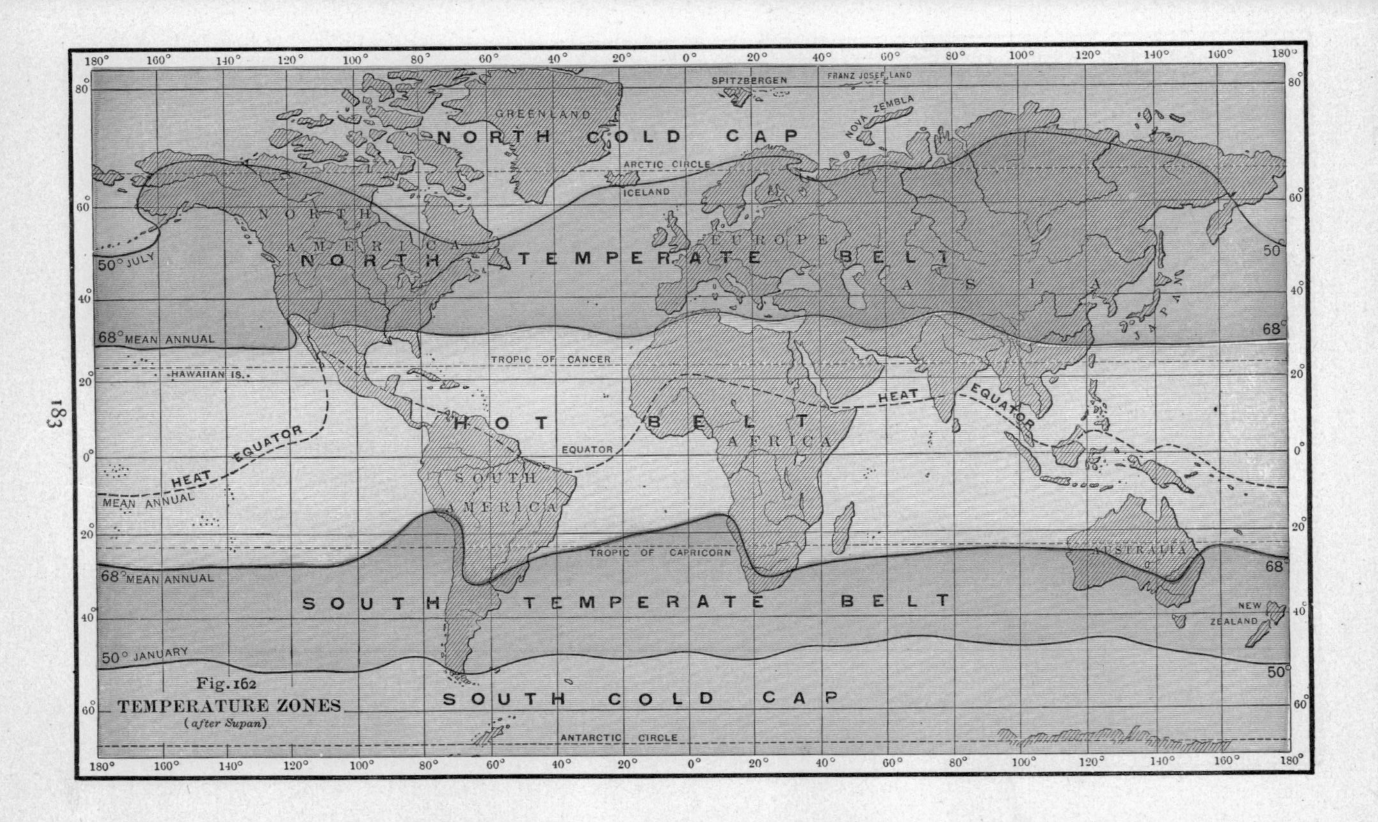

Fig. 162
TEMPERATURE ZONES
(*after Supan*)

square inch of surface. This pressure is equal in all directions, — downwards, upwards, or sidewise at any angle. The pressure of the air is measured by the *barometer*.

Density. — The air being easily compressed, its density is proportional to the pressure to which it is subjected, and consequently diminishes as the height above the sea increases. Density and pressure are also influenced by other conditions, of which temperature and humidity, or quantity of water vapor it contains, are the most important. When air is heated it expands and becomes less dense. The same effect is produced by the addition of water vapor. On warm, damp days the pressure and density are less, and the barometer stands lower than on cold, dry days.

Fig. 163. — Two forms of the barometer.

The distribution of pressure is shown on a map by *isobars*, or lines drawn through places where the pressure is the same (Figs. 165, 166).

Laws of Winds. — Of all the materials of the earth, the air is the most mobile and sensitive to change. When air is heated or made more damp by the addition of water vapor, it expands and becomes less dense than the surrounding air, which crowds in from all sides and buoys the lighter air upward. The updraft in a chimney or over an open fire, and the slower movement of the air toward the fire, furnish familiar examples of convection currents on a small scale. Every wind that blows is a part of a similar movement, in which gravitation pulls heavy air downward and compels light air to move upward. In the regions of ascending and descending air the movement is usually imperceptible and a calm prevails, but between these regions, which may

TEMPERATURE BELTS

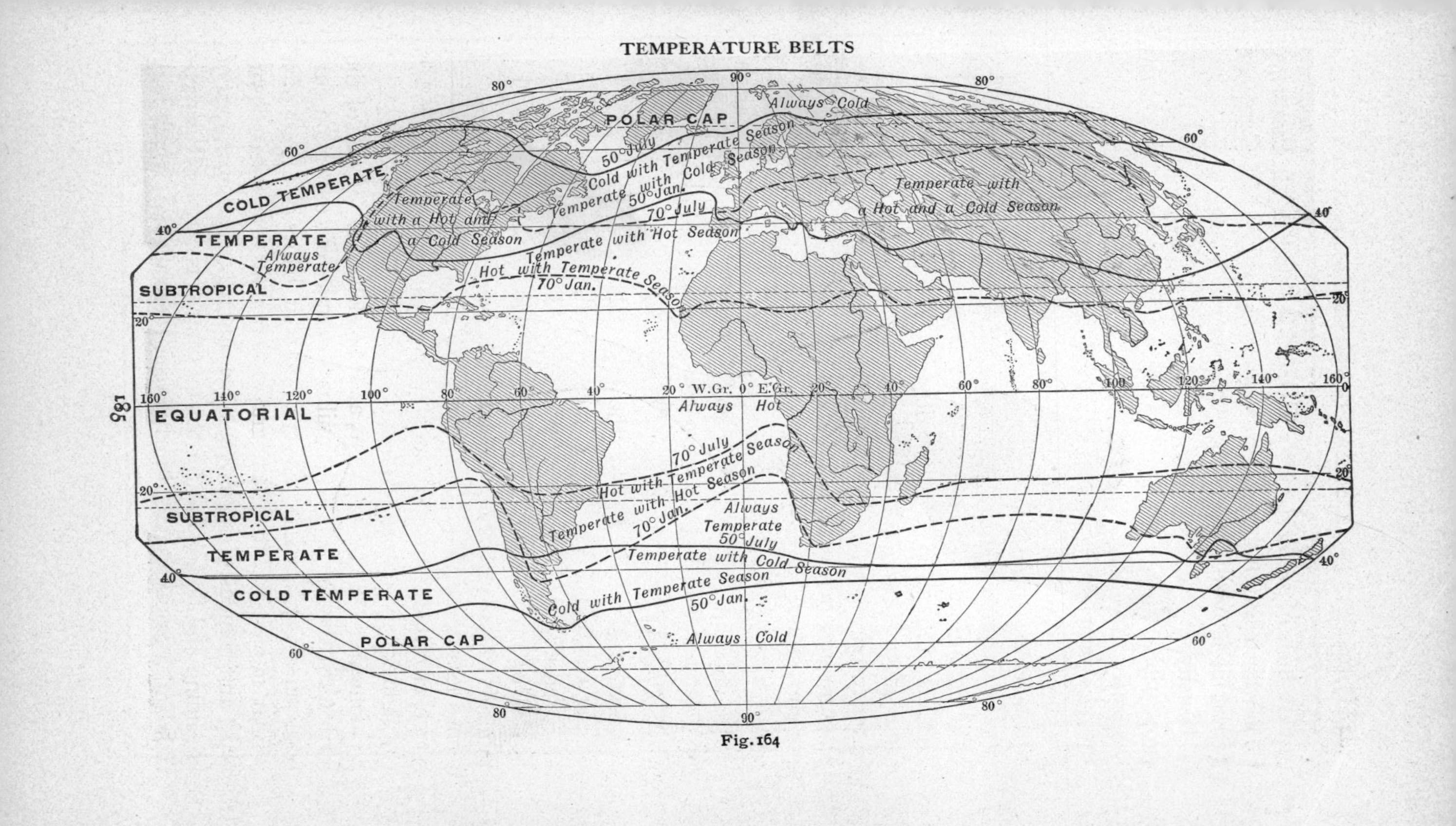

Fig. 164

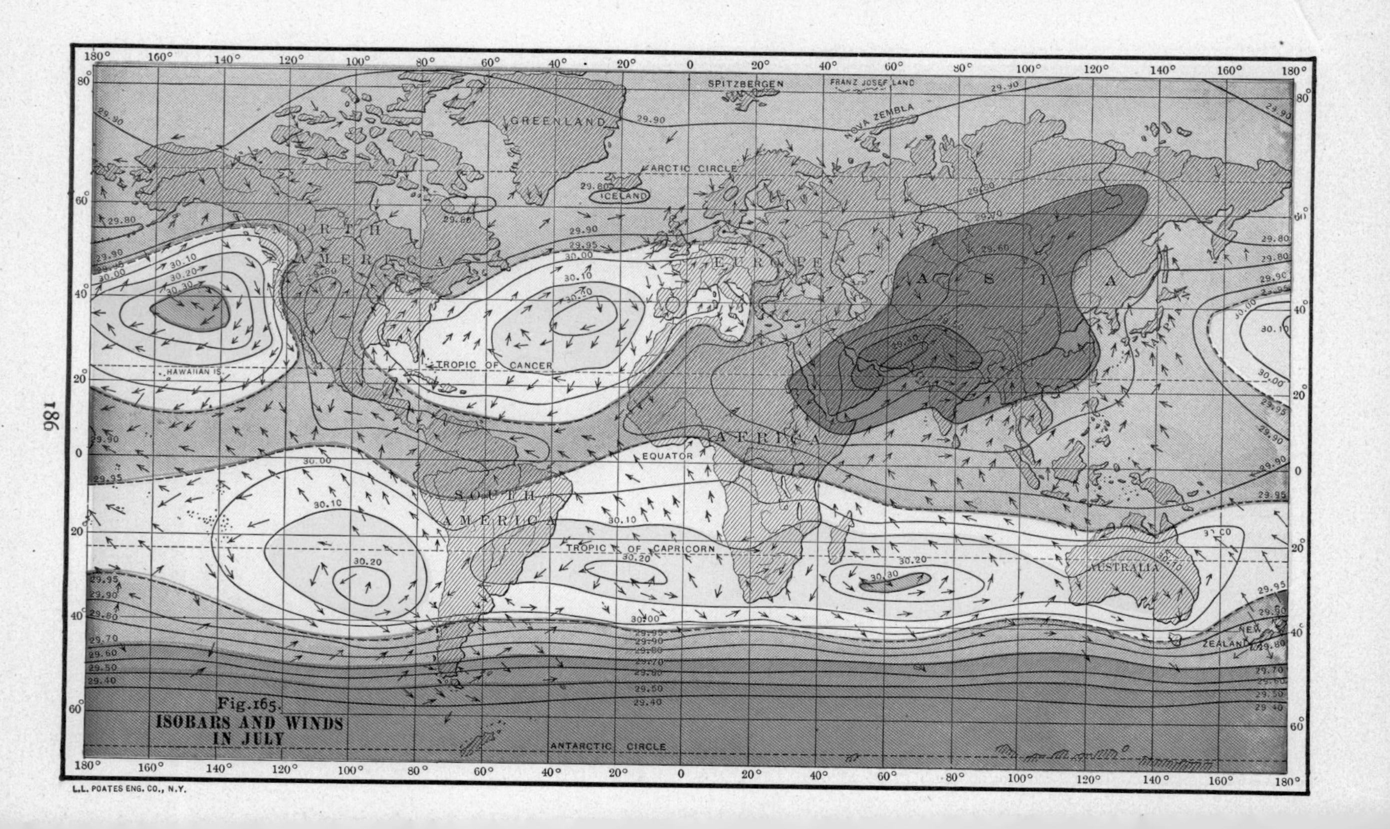

Fig. 165.
ISOBARS AND WINDS IN JULY

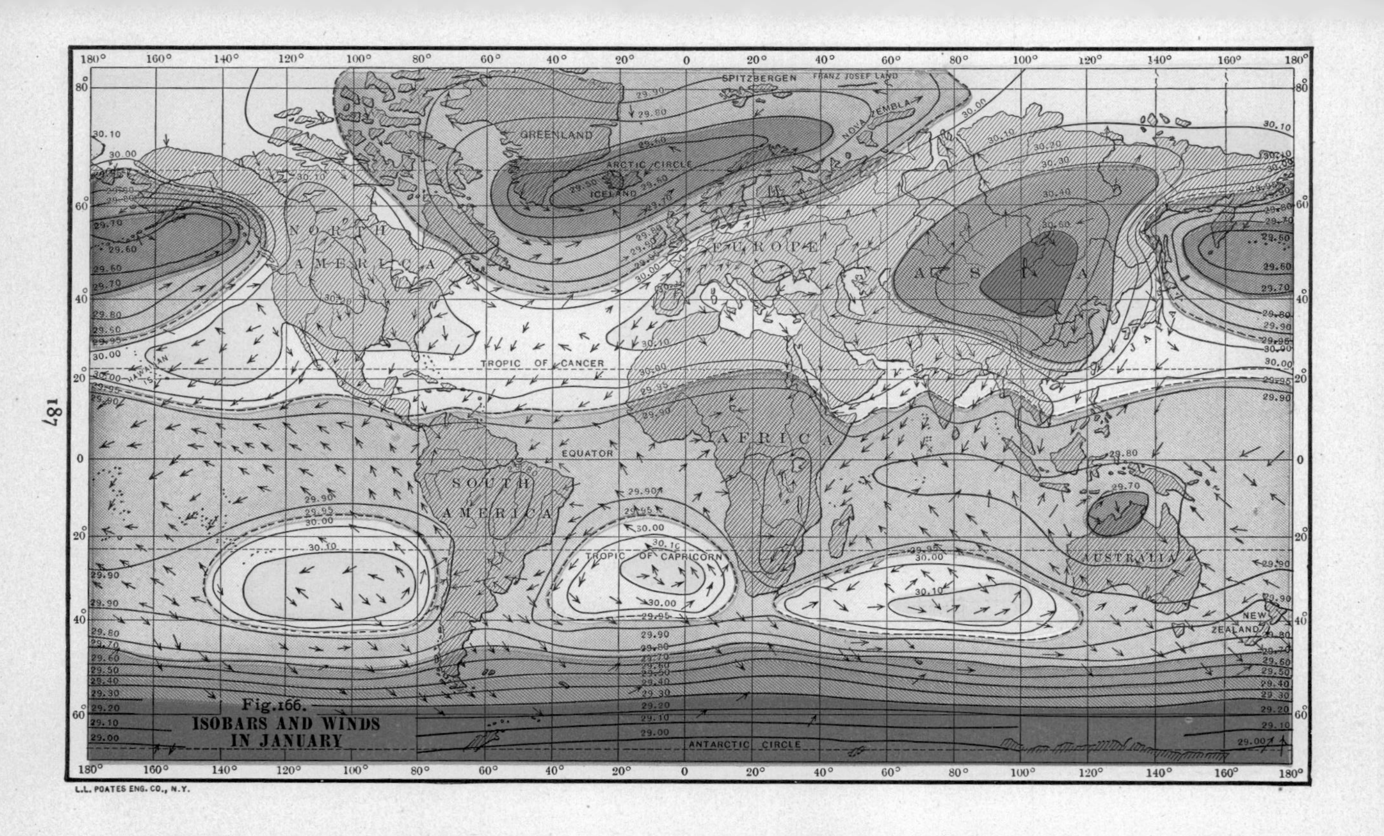

Fig. 166. ISOBARS AND WINDS IN JANUARY

be hundreds or thousands of miles apart, horizontal currents exist which constitute the surface winds. Where the pressure as measured by the barometer is high the air is heavy and settling; where the pressure is low the air is light and rising.

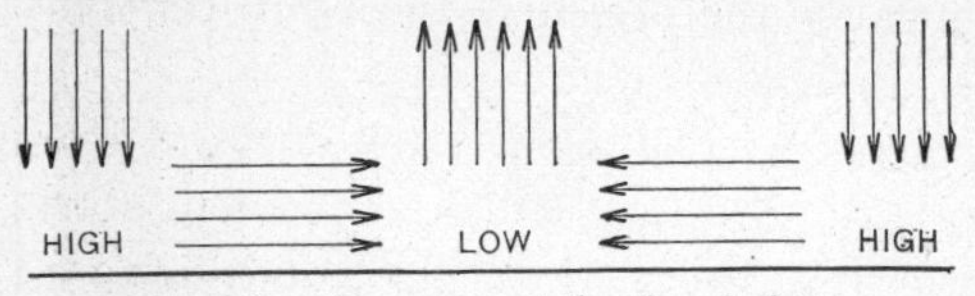

Fig. 167.—Pressure and direction of wind.

Hence the first law: *Winds always blow from regions of high pressure to regions of low pressure* (Figs. 177–180).

Gravitation acting alone would make air move from a region of high pressure to a region of low pressure by the shortest path, crossing the isobars at right angles, just as it makes water flow down a slope by the steepest course; but other influences make the course of the wind less direct. Second law: *The rotation of the earth turns winds blowing from any direction to the right of a direct course in the northern hemisphere, and to the left in the southern.*

The greater the difference of pressure between two regions the faster the air moves. Third law: *Where the isobars are close together the winds are steady and strong, and where the isobars are far apart the winds are light and shifting.*

Distribution of Pressure.—On account of the constantly high temperature near the equator the pressure there is generally low (Figs. 165, 166), but in middle latitudes the land is colder than the water in winter and warmer in summer, and this produces rounded or elliptical areas of high and low pressure which change their positions with the seasons. In the northern winter very high pressures prevail over the interior of Asia and North America, and low pressures over the north Atlantic and Pacific oceans. In summer the conditions are reversed. In the southern hemisphere the land masses never get cold enough to have higher pressures than the oceans. In winter (Fig. 165) a belt of high pressure extends along the southern tropic nearly around the earth, crossing land and sea except a gap in the south Pacific.

In summer (Fig. 166) the heated continents break this belt into three parts, one over each ocean. In spite of the very low temperatures in the polar regions, the pressures there are generally low because there is less air above them.

Cyclones and Anticyclones. — The winds blow outward from centers of high pressure in all directions. The movement starts along radial lines like the spokes of a wheel, but the rotation of

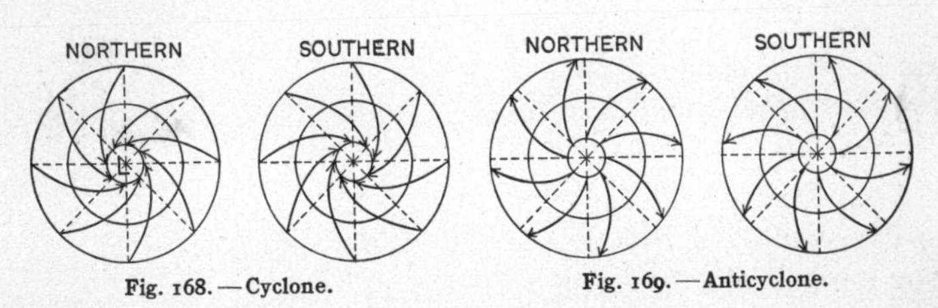

Fig. 168. — Cyclone. Fig. 169. — Anticyclone.

the earth (second law) changes it to a spiral movement clockwise in the northern hemisphere and counterclockwise in the southern (Fig. 169). The winds blow inward toward centers of low pressure from all directions, but the rotation of the earth gives them a spiral motion counterclockwise in the northern hemisphere and clockwise in the southern (Fig. 168). As the winds approach the center, they are crowded into a narrower space, their velocity increases, and their paths become more nearly circular until a whirl or eddy is set up. The movement is like that of water running out through a hole in the bottom of a bowl, only the air escapes upward instead of downward. A mass of air moving spirally inward toward a center of low pressure is called a *cyclone*. The path of the wind in a cyclone in the northern hemisphere is a curve like the figure 6; in the southern hemisphere like a reversed 6. A mass of air moving spirally outward from a center of high pressure is called an *anticyclone*.

Wind Belts. — The prevailing low pressures in the equatorial regions and the presence of areas of high pressure in the tropical regions divide the earth into wind belts, which are more regular in the southern hemisphere than in the northern. Near the equator the air is always warm and rising, a condition which produces a belt of *equatorial calms*. Between the equatorial calms and the southern tropical regions the general movement is toward the equator and westward, producing a belt of constant *southeast trade winds*. South of the southern tropical regions the air moves steadily and strongly eastward in a great spiral whirl around the polar region, producing a belt of almost *constant west winds*. The movement of air within the Antarctic circle is not well known.

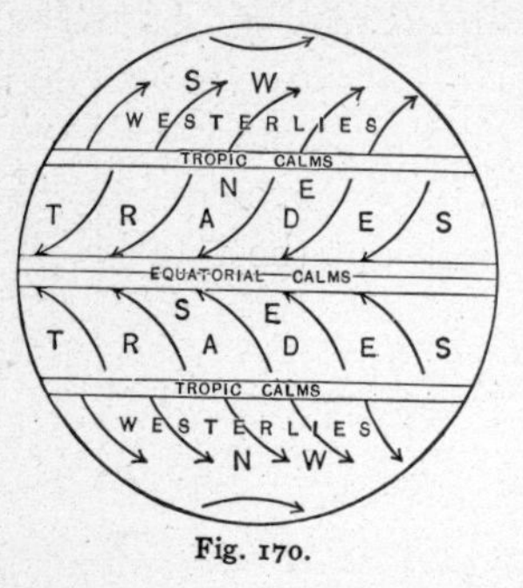

Fig. 170.

Between the equatorial calms and the northern tropical regions is a belt of *northeast trade winds*, but these are not so regular and constant as the southeast trades. North of the northern tropical regions there is a belt of *prevailing westerly winds*, but on account of the large land masses, with their changing temperatures and pressures, these winds are not so regular and constant as the west winds of the southern hemisphere. There is something like a north polar whirl, but it is broken up by the areas of low pressure over the oceans in winter and over the continents in summer. Along the southern tropic and a little north of the northern tropic there are belts of relatively high pressure, where the air is descending, and from which the trades and westerly winds blow. These are called the *tropical calms*. The conditions in the southern hemisphere show what the planetary system of winds would be if the land masses did not interfere. This ideal system, to which the actual system approaches more or less closely, is shown in Fig. 170, which should be carefully studied and used as a key to the actual system.

The wind belts, like the temperature belts, shift north and south with the seasons, following the position of the vertical sun in the heavens (Figs. 165, 166, 171, 172).

Monsoons. — The greatest disturbing influence in the wind system is the large land mass of Asia. In winter it is an area

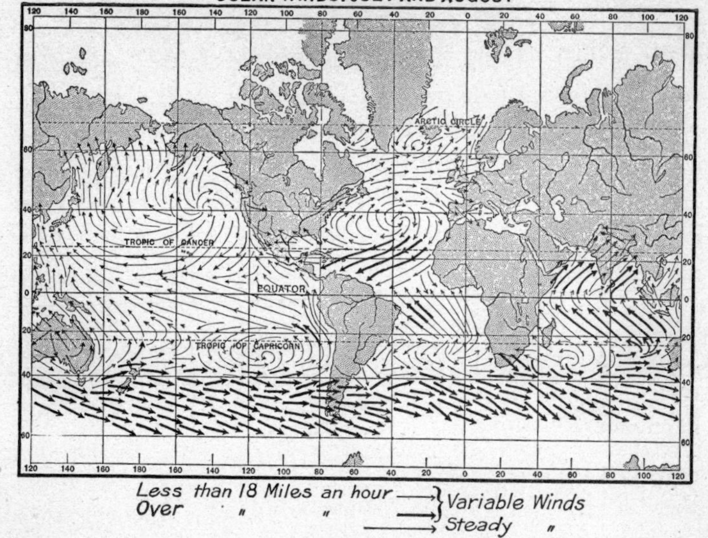

Fig. 171.

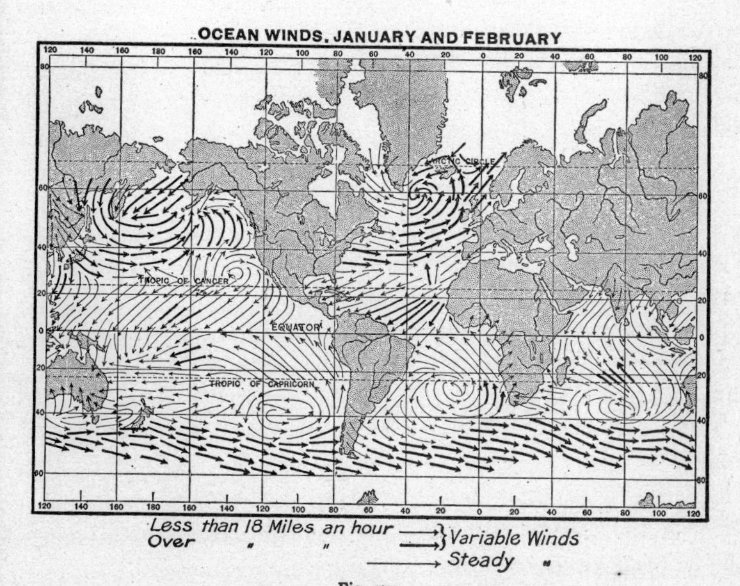

Fig. 172.

of low temperature and very high pressure, from which the winds blow outward in all directions (Fig. 172). In summer it is an area of high temperature and low pressure, which deflects the belt of calms far north of the equator (Fig. 171). At this season the southeast trades over the Indian Ocean cross the equator and, turning eastward, become the *southwest monsoon*, while over the western Pacific the northeast trades become southerly and southeasterly winds (Fig. 171). These directions are opposite to the wind directions in winter. Winds which are thus reversed with the seasons are called *monsoons*. Less important monsoon regions exist upon the west coasts of Africa and South America.

Economic Relations. — Winds are of the greatest importance to the life of plants, animals, and men because they transfer great masses of air from one part of the earth to another. They carry the conditions of temperature and moisture which exist in the regions from which they come to the regions over which they blow, and as they go on they themselves gradually acquire new conditions. Winds blowing over warm waters become warm and laden with water vapor, which they let fall as rain upon the land. Winds from a large land mass are dry and may be the cause of desert conditions in lands to which they blow. Winds moving from a warmer to a colder region bring warm, damp weather, and winds blowing from a colder to a warmer region bring cool, dry weather. Winds blowing from the ocean against a mountain range or plateau bring heavy rainfall to the windward side and little or no rain to the leeward side (Fig. 185). Rising air is always cooled and generally causes cloud to form and rain to fall. Descending air is warmed, and brings clear, dry weather.

Most changes of weather are due to changes in the direction of the wind. Some winds are agreeable and favorable to life; some bring suffering, destruction, and death. Even light breezes effect a continual change of air, which brings more food to plants and animals and removes waste and injurious gases.

CHAPTER XIV

MOISTURE IN THE AIR

Capacity and Humidity. — The atmosphere, as well as the ocean, is a great reservoir of water. Everywhere over the face of the earth the air contains a variable quantity of invisible vapor, which may amount to as much as five per cent. If all the vapor in the air should be condensed and fall as rain, it would be sufficient to cover the whole face of the earth with water to the depth of one inch. Water is constantly evaporating from the sea, lakes, rivers, and land surface. Even ice evaporates, but the higher the temperature of the water the more rapid is the evaporation. The quantity of water vapor which can exist in any given space increases with the temperature of the vapor, whether the space is already filled with air or not. Warm air can contain more vapor than cold air because the air determines the temperature of the vapor in it. When the space or air contains all the vapor it can hold, it is said to be *saturated*. The table on page 194 gives the weight of vapor which can exist in a cubic foot of space or air at various temperatures. These quantities are called the *capacity* for vapor.

When water evaporates it expands instantly to about 1,700 times its liquid volume, and the vapor rapidly diffuses itself through the air in the vicinity. The evaporation and diffusion are hastened by currents of air which carry the vapor away from the evaporating surface. The dryness or dampness of the air is measured not by its *absolute humidity*, or the quantity of vapor actually present in it, but by its *relative humidity*, or the ratio of its absolute humidity to its capacity. If the air out of doors is at a temperature of 32°, and contains two grains of vapor in each cubic foot, it is very damp, because it is nearly saturated; but if the same air is brought into the house and heated to 70°, it becomes very dry, because

GRAINS OF WATER VAPOR IN A CUBIC FOOT OF SATURATED SPACE OR AIR AT VARIOUS TEMPERATURES

10°	.776	34°	2.279	58°	5.370	82°	11.626
12°	.856	36°	2.457	60°	5.745	84°	12.356
14°	.941	38°	2.646	62°	6.142	86°	13.127
16°	1.032	40°	2.849	64°	6.563	88°	13.937
18°	1.128	42°	3.064	66°	7.009	90°	14.790
20°	1.235	44°	3.294	68°	7.480	92°	15.689
22°	1.355	46°	3.539	70°	7.980	94°	16.634
24°	1.483	48°	3.800	72°	8.508	96°	17.626
26°	1.623	50°	4.076	74°	9.066	98°	18.671
28°	1.773	52°	4.372	76°	9.655	100°	19.766
30°	1.935	54°	4.685	78°	10.277	102°	20.917
32°	2.113	56°	5.016	80°	10.934	104°	22.125

it is then only one fourth saturated. This is the reason why air in heated rooms in the winter is generally too dry for comfort and health, and pans of water should be placed where they will supply more moisture.

Unsaturated air is always ready to take up more moisture, but if saturated air at any temperature is cooled a part of the vapor immediately condenses into water. If a bright tin cup is filled half full of warm water, and cold water or ice is added, the cup will generally get cold enough to cause a deposit of dew on the outside. The dew is formed by condensation of vapor from the air. This is the reason why a pitcher or glass of cold water will sometimes "sweat" in warm weather.

If the water in the tin cup is stirred with a thermometer, the temperature observed at the moment of the first appearance of dew is called the *dew point.* It is the temperature of saturation, and from it the absolute humidity may be found by consulting the table. The capacity of the air may be found by noting its temperature and again consulting the table. The absolute humidity divided by the capacity gives the relative humidity. If the temperature of the air is 70°, its capacity is 7.980 grains to the cubic foot. If the dew point is 40°, the absolute humidity of the air is 2.849 grains, and its relative humidity is 2.849 ÷ 7.980, or 35.7 per cent. That is, the air is 35.7 per cent full, and is moderately dry.

Condensation. — When air is cooled below its dew point, some of the vapor condenses into dew, frost, fog, cloud, rain, or snow. The atmosphere is cooled and its vapor condensed by several processes.

1. *Expansion.*— Whenever air rises it expands, and, without any transfer of heat to other bodies, it is cooled one degree for every 183 feet of ascent. As soon as the temperature falls below dew point and condensation begins, cooling is retarded or stopped. Descending air is always warmed by compression one degree for every 183 feet of descent; hence condensation seldom occurs in descending air.

2. *Radiation.* — If the air stands or passes over or near cooler objects, as the ground, the sea, snow, ice, or a mass of cooler air, it radiates its heat, its temperature falls, and condensation may occur. This usually takes place when winds blow from warmer to cooler regions.

3. *Conduction.* — Air in contact with a cooler body loses heat by conduction. This process is less important than is commonly supposed, because air is a poor conductor of heat and only that portion which actually touches a cooler body is cooled in this way. Dew and frost are generally deposited from air in contact with a cold surface.

4. *Mixture.* — When warm air is mixed with cool air, the temperature of the mixture may fall below the dew point and condensation may take place.

Fig. 173.—Fog seen from mountain top above it, California. (U. S. Weather Bureau.)

Clouds. — When water vapor is condensed in the air, it becomes visible as fog or cloud, which is composed of minute particles of liquid water or ice, a sort of water dust. Fog is

Fig. 174. — Upper part of cumulus clouds.

Fig. 175. — Stratus clouds.

formed at or near the surface of land or water, cloud at higher altitudes. Clouds usually settle slowly and, on reaching a layer of warmer or drier air, evaporate. If condensation continues they are renewed above as fast as they evaporate below.

Cumulus clouds are rounded masses which look white in sunlight and dark in shadow. They begin to form at the level where a rising column of air reaches the dew point, and may be piled up to a height of five miles or more. They are common in equatorial regions and on calm summer afternoons, when the air which starts upward in the morning has reached a sufficient height. They often bring showers and thunderstorms and hence are sometimes called " thunder heads."

Fig. 176. — Cirrus clouds.

Cirrus clouds are light, feathery clouds formed at great heights, where the vapor condenses into minute crystals of snow or ice.

Stratus clouds lie in low, horizontal bands, or continuous sheets.

Nimbus or storm clouds are stratus clouds from which rain or snow falls when the sky is overcast.

There are many forms and varieties of cloud intermediate between cumulus, cirrus, and stratus, of which a dozen or more are common and have compound names, such as strato-cumulus, cirro-cumulus, and cirro-stratus.

Precipitation. — When clouds become sufficiently dense the air is no longer able to buoy up or evaporate them, and the water falls as rain, or, if the temperature of the cloud is below freezing, as snow or hail. Snowflakes are formed by the direct condensation of vapor into six-angled crystals of many symmetrical forms, which are usually tangled together before reaching the earth. Hailstones are rounded masses of snow and ice which have passed through several layers of alternating warmer and colder air.

Precipitation is measured by the *rain gauge*. Any open vessel with vertical sides will serve the purpose. The amount of rainfall or precipitation is measured in inches of depth of water caught, snow being first melted. In middle latitudes one inch of rain a day is a large fall, but sometimes an inch falls in an hour. In tropical regions a rainfall of 40 inches has been recorded in a single day. One inch of rain amounts to 113 tons of water on one acre of surface.

Dew and Frost. — Dew and frost are produced by the condensation of vapor upon any cold surface. The deposit is heavier during clear, still nights and upon surfaces which radiate heat freely. On still nights the cooler air settles into valleys and depressions and produces heavier dew or frost there than on elevations. A slight cover, as a tree, or even a piece of paper, may prevent cooling to the dew or frost point.

The dates of the last killing frost in the spring and the first in the fall are very important as limiting the growing season for crops. In central United States the date of the first frost in the fall may vary as much as a month in different years, and its occurrence a month earlier than usual may result in millions of dollars' damage to the corn crop. A temperature near freezing may be destructive to fruits which are in blossom or approaching maturity, and even trees and vines themselves may be killed. Orchards and fields are sometimes protected by a covering of light cloth, like a tent, by ditches or pipes containing hot water, by fires, or by filling the air with smoke which acts as a blanket. The presence of a body of water, even a small pond, may be sufficient to prevent unseasonable warm spells in the spring and early frosts in autumn. For this reason the shores of lakes Ontario, Erie, and Michigan and the Finger Lakes of New York are bordered by belts of vineyards, peaches, and small fruits.

Storms. — Outside the tropics a large part of the rainfall is brought by storms, or temporary disturbances which travel through the atmosphere along definite paths. They bring to the regions over which they pass shifting winds and usually cloudiness and precipitation. If no precipitation occurs they are called wind storms. The winds may be gentle or extremely violent, as in the hurricane and tornado. In nearly all storms the movement of air is spirally inward, toward and around a center of low pressure, and they may be described as traveling cyclones. They may be of any size from a summer dust whirl a few feet in diameter, to a storm which covers half a continent. The whirls travel in the direction of the general air current, but, like eddies in a river, continually take in new air in front as they leave other air behind.

Weather Bureaus and Maps. — Benjamin Franklin was probably the first man to observe that, while long rain storms were brought to New England by winds from the east, they began earlier at points farther west. To account for these facts he conceived the idea of a large whirling storm which passed across the country from west to east. Within the last fifty years the Weather Bureaus of the United States, Canada, and European countries have learned that in the northern belt of prevailing westerly winds there is a continual procession of cyclones moving eastward around the earth. By following their progress from day to day, a Weather Bureau is able to predict their arrival and the kind of weather they will bring.

In America and Europe hundreds of observing stations have been established, from which telegraphic reports are sent to a central station at a given hour twice a day. From these reports weather maps are made, showing the temperature, pressure, wind direction, state of the sky, and precipitation at that hour for the whole country. By means of these maps forecasts are made of what the weather is likely to be for the next 24 or 48 hours. It is sometimes possible to forecast the weather for a week or ten days. The intervals between the cyclones are occupied by areas of relatively high pressure, or anticyclones. As the procession of cyclones and anticyclones passes across the country it brings corresponding changes of weather, a knowledge of which is of the greatest importance to farmers, sailors, boatmen, shippers, and all people whose business or pleasure depends in any degree upon the weather. Figs. 177–180 show typical examples of cyclones and anticyclones, but their study should be continued by the use of the daily weather maps issued by the nearest Weather Bureau station.

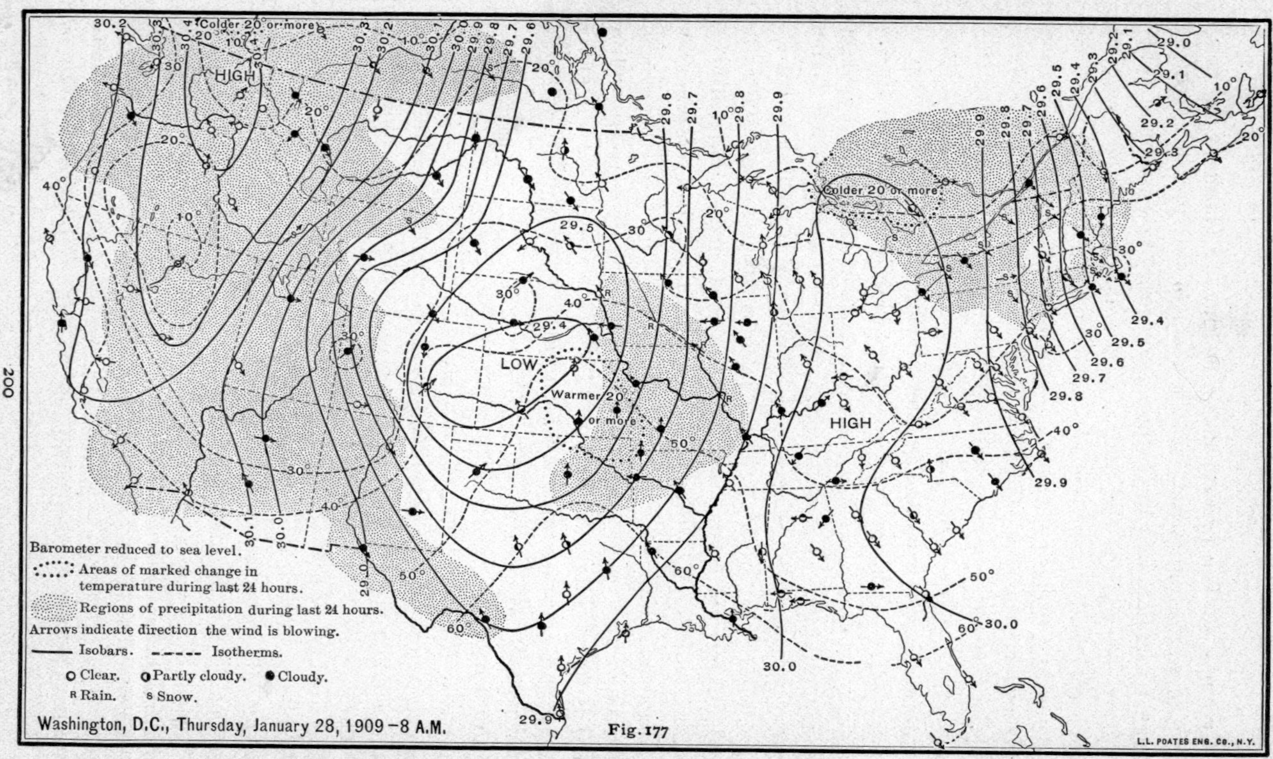
HIGH
LOW
HIGH
Colder 20° or more
Colder 20° or more
Warmer 20° or more
Barometer reduced to sea level.
Areas of marked change in temperature during last 24 hours.
Regions of precipitation during last 24 hours.
Arrows indicate direction the wind is blowing.
Isobars. Isotherms.
Clear. Partly cloudy. Cloudy.
R Rain. S Snow.
Washington, D.C., Thursday, January 28, 1909 – 8 A.M.
L.L. POATES ENG. CO., N.Y.

Fig. 177

Cyclones. — The cyclone shown in Fig. 178 (January 29) is a mass of warm, damp air, and therefore of low pressure, which covers a rounded area more than 1,000 miles in diameter. The pressure is lowest at the center, near Chicago, and increases in every direction toward the circumference. The whole mass is moving in a spiral whirl inward and counterclockwise. In the southern quarter the winds are from the southwest and south, in the eastern quarter from the southeast and east, in the northern quarter from the northeast and north, and in the western quarter from the northwest and west. The southerly and easterly winds bring to the southeast side temperatures above freezing, while on the northwest side northerly winds bring temperatures mostly below freezing. As the air approaches the center it rises and escapes upward. As it rises and whirls it expands and air from all sides is mixed together. By expansion and mixture the warm, damp air from the Gulf and Atlantic is cooled, and its vapor condenses into a layer of cloud which covers nearly the whole area of the cyclone. Snow or rain has been general in the cyclonic area during the past twenty-four hours and is still falling over half of it. The cyclone is moving eastward and carrying with it warm, cloudy, and stormy weather, which clears up as the storm passes.

Anticyclones. — The anticyclone shown in Fig. 180 (January 31) is a mass of cold, dry air, and therefore of high pressure, which covers an area measuring about 1,200 miles east and west and a much greater distance north and south. The pressure is highest, 30.6 inches, at the center from Lake Superior to Texas, and diminishes toward the circumference. It may be compared to a long, smooth ridge upon which heavy rain is falling and the water draining off down the slopes. In like manner the air settles downward and spreads out from the center.

Water would run down the slopes of the hill by the steepest and most direct path, but the rotation of the earth causes the air to move slantingly down the slope of pressure along lines to the right-hand of the shortest path to the bottom. The north-south elongation of the anticyclone causes the principal slopes to be toward the east and west, and accordingly at

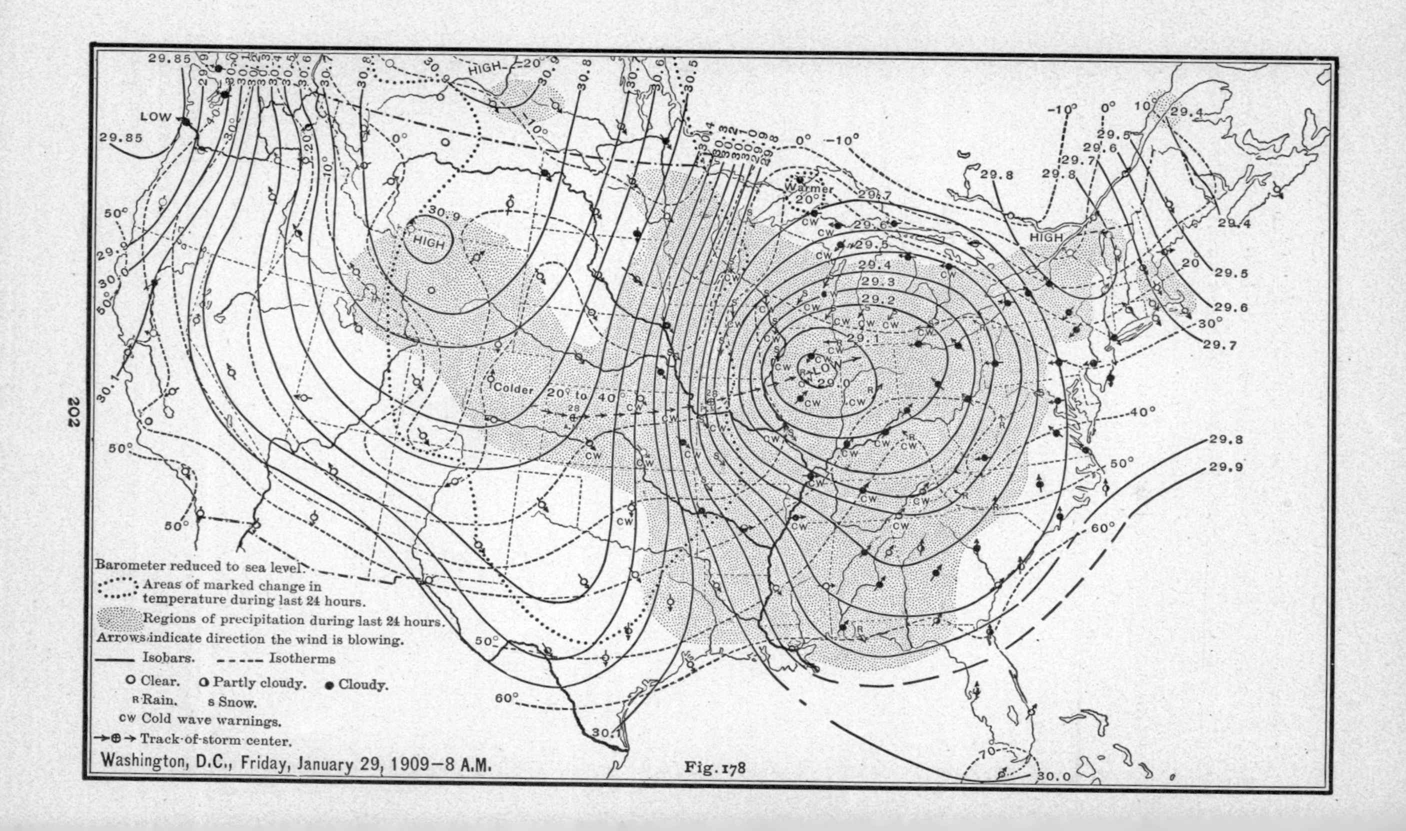
Barometer reduced to sea level.
Areas of marked change in temperature during last 24 hours.
Regions of precipitation during last 24 hours.
Arrows indicate direction the wind is blowing.
Isobars.
Isotherms
O Clear.
Partly cloudy.
Cloudy.
R Rain.
S Snow.
CW Cold wave warnings.
Track of storm center.
Washington, D.C., Friday, January 29, 1909—8 A.M.
LOW
HIGH
Warmer
Colder
20° to 40°
29.0
29.1
29.2
29.3
29.4
29.5
29.6
29.7
29.8
29.9
30.0
30.1
30.5
30.8
30.9
29.85
Fig. 178

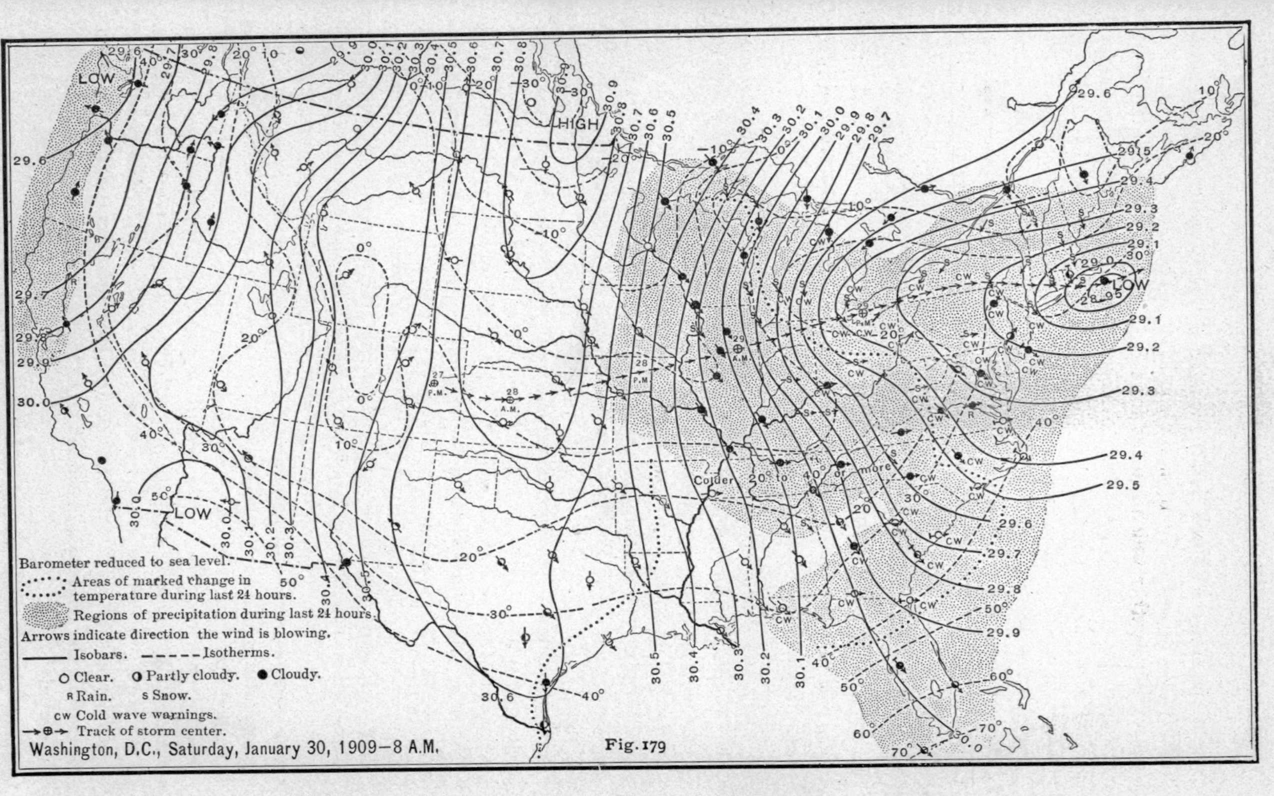

Washington, D.C., Saturday, January 30, 1909—8 A.M.

Fig. 179

most places in the eastern half the winds are from the northwest and north, and in the western half from the southeast. The northerly winds bring clear, cold weather which extends from Port Arthur, where the thermometer stands at 20° below zero, to New Orleans, where the temperature is below freezing. On the west side the temperature rises, and it is as warm in northern Montana as in Florida. The anticyclone brings into the midst of the country dry, clear air, which is cold on account of free radiation, and the temperature changes more rapidly along east-west than along north-south lines. It will move eastward and carry its clear, cold weather to the Atlantic coast. The progress of low temperatures eastward in front of an advancing anticyclone is called a *cold wave*.

Procession of Lows and Highs. — Figs. 177–180 show a regular procession of cyclones and anticyclones moving eastward during four days.

On January 28 a cyclone, or "low," is passing from New England over the Atlantic Ocean. A long ridge of moderately high pressure extends from the upper lakes to Florida, with north and northwest winds and generally clear sky. On the west it descends to a large oval area of low pressure, with spirally inflowing air, general cloudiness, and a patch of rain east of the center. The Pacific states are covered by a feeble anticyclone, or "high."

On January 29 the same elements appear with changed positions, areas, and intensities. The principal center of low pressure has moved from Kansas to Illinois, and the winds have increased in velocity. The force of the winds is indicated by the closeness of the isobars. The barometer at the center has fallen to 29 inches. The air is crowding rapidly in from all sides and streaming upward. It whirls as it rises, and warm, damp air from the Gulf and Atlantic is mixed with cold air from the interior of the continent. Damp air is cooled by expansion and mixture, and condensation takes place, resulting in cloudiness almost everywhere, rain in the southeast quarter, and snow in the north and west. The southerly winds have raised the temperatures in the southeastern states 10 to 20 degrees above those of the previous day. The high on the Pacific coast has expanded and developed until it covers the western half of the country, the pressure at its center in Wyoming being 30.9 inches. The slope to the east is steep, and high northwest winds carry freezing temperatures to New Mexico. The central and southern states are dotted with cold-wave warnings, which mean that the temperature will fall 20 to 40 degrees in the next twenty-four hours.

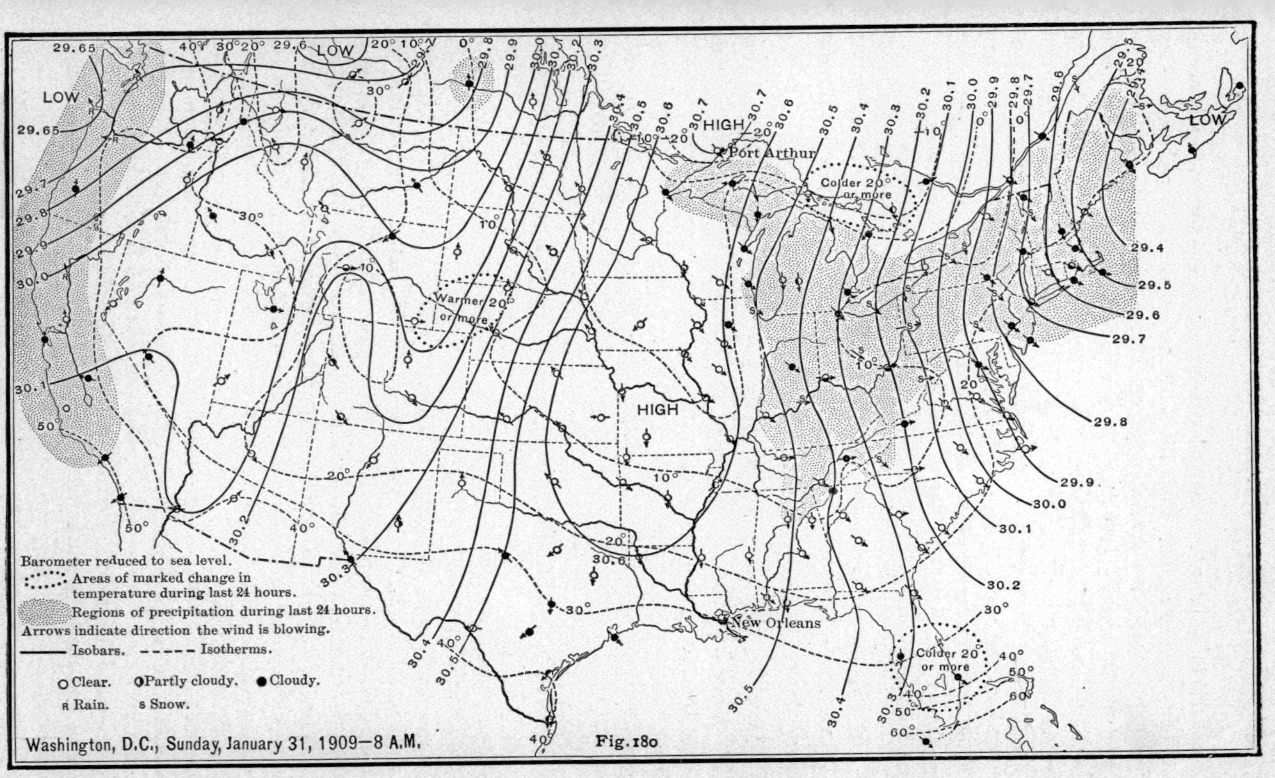

Washington, D.C., Sunday, January 31, 1909—8 A.M.

Fig. 180

On January 30 the principal low center has moved to the southern coast of New England. Across the middle of the country a ridge of very high pressure extends north and south, with steep and regular slopes to the ocean on both sides. Another low is coming in from the Pacific. The winds have a high velocity almost everywhere. In the east they are in accordance with the slopes, but in the west they are more irregular on account of the influence of the mountains. A large area of snowfall extends from Wisconsin to Maine and as far south as Virginia. Over the west of the country clear, cold weather prevails, with temperatures from $-30°$ at Winnipeg to below freezing in the Gulf and southern border states. The highest temperatures are in Florida and along the Pacific coast. The cold-wave warnings have been shifted to the Atlantic coast.

On January 31 the storm center has disappeared over the Gulf of St. Lawrence, and the ridge of high pressure has moved a few hundred miles eastward. The cold wave has reached the extremity of Florida, and nearly the whole country is left with clear, cold, dry, pure, and invigorating air. The rain, snow, and high winds have washed dust from the air and from houses, and the cold air under high pressure has crowded foul gases out of every crack and cranny. At the same time, the low temperatures and blinding snowstorms in the northern states bring more or less hardship and danger to man and beast, and sometimes blockade railroads for many days. Freezing temperatures in the southern states may do vast damage to fruit orchards. On the whole the benefit is probably much greater than the loss or injury. The procession of lows and highs renders the weather very variable, bringing a change from relatively cool, clear, and dry to relatively warm, cloudy, and rainy weather, or the reverse, two or three times a week.

Weather Forecasts and Warnings. — The United States Weather Bureau issues forecasts of the weather every morning, which are published in the principal newspapers and posted at post offices throughout the country. Responsible persons who promise to post the forecasts in a public place may receive them on request free of charge; some newspapers publish also the weather map. They constitute the most trustworthy predictions of the weather that can be made, because they are based upon actual knowledge of the atmospheric conditions which prevail over the continent and surrounding oceans. The forecasts are made for large areas and cannot prove correct in every detail at every locality. The eastward movement of lows and highs is sometimes slower and sometimes faster than usual. Rarely a storm center moves backward to the west for a short distance. Occasionally an area of low pressure divides or dies out or a new one is rapidly formed, and such events cannot be foreseen.

Storm warnings are displayed at all sea and lake ports for the guidance of mariners and shippers, and thus great loss of life and property is prevented. Notice of the advance of a cold wave is given 12 to 36 hours before it arrives, and in consequence millions of dollars' worth of property is protected and saved. Frost and flood warnings are issued whenever occasion requires for the benefit of fruit growers, river men, and owners of property along streams.

Hurricanes. — In tropical and temperate latitudes cyclonic storms occur of such violence as to be among the most destructive of natural agencies. Some of them are so small as to permit their whirling motion to be generally recognized, and are called "cyclones" in popular speech. In late summer and autumn the West Indies are visited by destructive *hurricanes* which arrive from the southeast. They begin in the equatorial calms and increase in size until they reach a diameter of 100 to 300 miles (Fig. 181). On the land they destroy almost everything, — forests, crops, buildings, and people. On the sea they are very dangerous to shipping and pile up the water until it sweeps over the coast lands, flooding fields and towns.

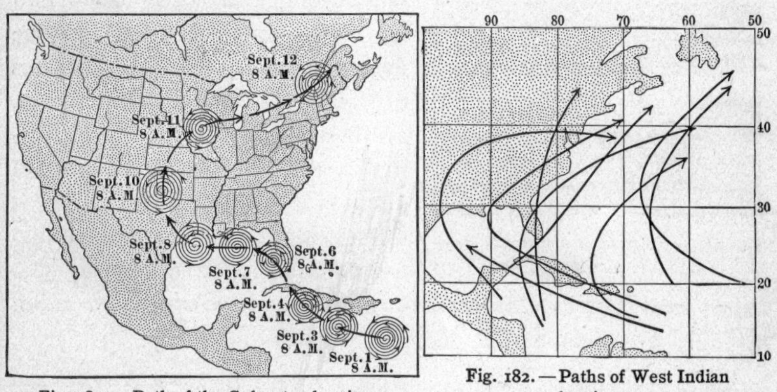

Fig. 181. — Path of the Galveston hurricane.

Fig. 182. — Paths of West Indian hurricanes.

When they approach the coast of the United States they usually turn to the northeast and die away in the north Atlantic Ocean (Fig. 182). Occasionally a hurricane turns westward near Florida and passes over the land, as did the one which destroyed the city of Galveston, Texas, in September, 1900 (Fig. 181). Similar storms occur in the Pacific Ocean near the Philippine

Islands, and in the Indian Ocean both north and south of the equator. In those regions they are called *typhoons*.

Tornadoes.—The tornado or "cyclone" of the western and southern states is even more violent than the hurricane, but fortunately much smaller. It appears as a whirling, funnel-shaped cloud, the small end of which sweeps the ground and overturns or carries away everything in a path from a few rods to a half mile in width. The wind sometimes reaches a velocity of 200 miles an hour and nothing movable can resist it. Although many stories of its power are apparently incredible, it is difficult to exaggerate the truth. Trees of all sizes are uprooted or twisted off, buildings are demolished and their fragments scattered over the neighborhood. Boulders, masses of iron, and even railroad engines, are lifted from their places. Animals and human beings are whirled about and carried long distances, often being torn in pieces or killed by collision with other objects. Wires and straws driven into hard wood testify even more strongly to the incredible violence of the wind.

Fig. 183.—Progress of a tornado, Newcastle, Neb., April 30, 1898.

The tornado travels about 40 miles an hour and seldom lasts more than two hours. The average number in the United States is about 150 a year. They are most frequent in Kansas, Iowa, Missouri, Illinois, and Georgia, but may occur anywhere east of the meridian of 100° and south of the parallel of 45°. In some states people dig holes in the ground, called "cyclone cellars," into which they may retreat for safety on the approach of a tornado.

Fig. 184. — Effects of a tornado, Illinois.

Thunderstorms. — Thunderstorms are seldom cyclonic, but result from the rapid rising of currents of warm air until heavy cumulus clouds are formed at the top. They bring violent gusts and squalls of wind and a downpour of rain, which leave the air cool, clear, and bracing. In the United States a thunderstorm moves eastward at the rate of 20 to 50 miles an hour, and grows larger as it progresses. It may attain a length, from side to side, of 100 miles, and a breadth, from front to rear, of 30 miles, and continue from 2 to 12 hours.

Rainfall. — There is probably no spot on the face of the earth where it never rains or snows. The mean annual rainfall, as far as measured, varies from less than one inch to more than 400 inches. Less than 10 inches in any region means a desert or tundra. At least 20 inches are generally necessary for forests and for agriculture without irrigation. The lands most favorable for human occupation have from 20 to 60 or 80 inches (Fig. 185), while 100 inches or more may be counted as undesirable excess.

Even a small amount of rain falling during the growing season is of more value for grass and crops than a large amount falling in the autumn and winter. A good crop of corn has been raised in Kansas with a rainfall of only eight inches for the year, but most of it fell in spring and early

MEAN A

80°
60°
40°
20°
0
160°
140°
120°
100°
80°
60
40°
20°
20°
40°
60°
80
More than 60 in.
20 to 60 in.

RAINFALL

n

summer. Winter rains supply ground water, fill wells, springs, and streams, and saturate the subsoil from which trees draw most of their water supply. On a map showing regions of small (less than 20 inches), medium (20 to 60 inches) and large (more than 60 inches) rainfall (Fig. 185) several general laws of rainfall appear.

Laws of Rainfall. — 1. *Disregarding small patches, the principal rainfall regions extend north and south, cutting across the temperature zones.* This is due to the fact that the large land masses extend north and south across the path of the prevailing winds.

2. *The coasts of the continents receive more rain than the interior, and windward coasts receive more than leeward.* Most of the rainfall is first evaporated from the oceans, carried as vapor by the winds, and condensed as it is cooled by rising over the lands.

3. *Highlands act as screens which stop most of the moisture on the windward side and cut it off from the regions on the leeward side, producing a rain shadow,* just as opaque bodies cut off light and cast dark shadows.

4. *In the equatorial zone as a whole, the rainfall is much heavier than in higher latitudes.* This is the result of two causes. Air at a temperature of 70° can contain and carry nearly twice as much vapor as air at 50°, and more than four times as much as air at 30° (see table, p. 194). Warm, damp air is lighter than cool, dry air, and is compelled to rise by the pressure of heavier air around it, and by rising the vapor is cooled and condensed. Somewhere between the tropics, swinging north and south with the changing position of the sun in the heavens, is the *heat equator* (Figs. 159, 160), or line passing through the point of highest temperature on each meridian. The heat equator carries with it a belt of calms and rising air, in which copious rain falls in the afternoon and evening every day. This belt of daily rains crosses the geographical equator twice a year, and touches the northern tropic in July and the southern in January. Thus the regions of heavy rainfall stretch across the lands from tropic to tropic, and have one or two rainy seasons, each of which lasts a month or more. During the rest of the year the trade

winds blow, bringing more or less rain from the ocean to east coasts and slopes and unprotected lands of the interior (Figs. 186, 187). Where the trade winds blow from large land masses or over highlands they bring a dry season, or in some cases a desert is the result. In monsoon regions, like southeastern Asia from India to Japan, the winds bring rain from the ocean in summer and dry weather from the land in winter (Figs. 186, 187).

5. *The subtropical zones, as a whole, receive less rainfall than any other part of the land, outside the polar regions, and may be called the desert belts.* This is due in part to the high pressure which exists there, especially in winter. The general movement of the air is downward and outward to the north and south. Descending air is warmed by compression and hence cannot bring rain. In north Africa and southwestern Asia, the winds blow from Eurasia and are dry. Here the Sahara, Arabian, and Persian deserts stretch from the Atlantic to India, covering an area larger than the whole of Europe. In southwestern United States and northern Mexico, desert conditions are intensified and extended by mountain ranges which shut out the moisture from the Pacific and Gulf of Mexico. In South America the deserts of Peru and Chile are rendered almost rainless by the lofty chain of the Andes on the east. The Kalahari desert in southwest Africa and the desert of central Australia lie in the rain shadow of the highlands on the east.

6. *In the temperate zones the prevailing winds from the west bring copious rains to the west coasts* of North America, Europe, southern South America, and New Zealand. In central Europe the rains extend halfway across the continent, but in northern Europe and North and South America they are stopped by mountain ranges near the coast.

7. *The eastern half of North America, from the Gulf to Hudson Bay, is saved from being a desert by the cyclonic winds which bring rain from the Gulf and Atlantic.* The interior of North America is dry because the high mountains shut out rain from the west, and the cyclonic winds from the southeast lose most of their

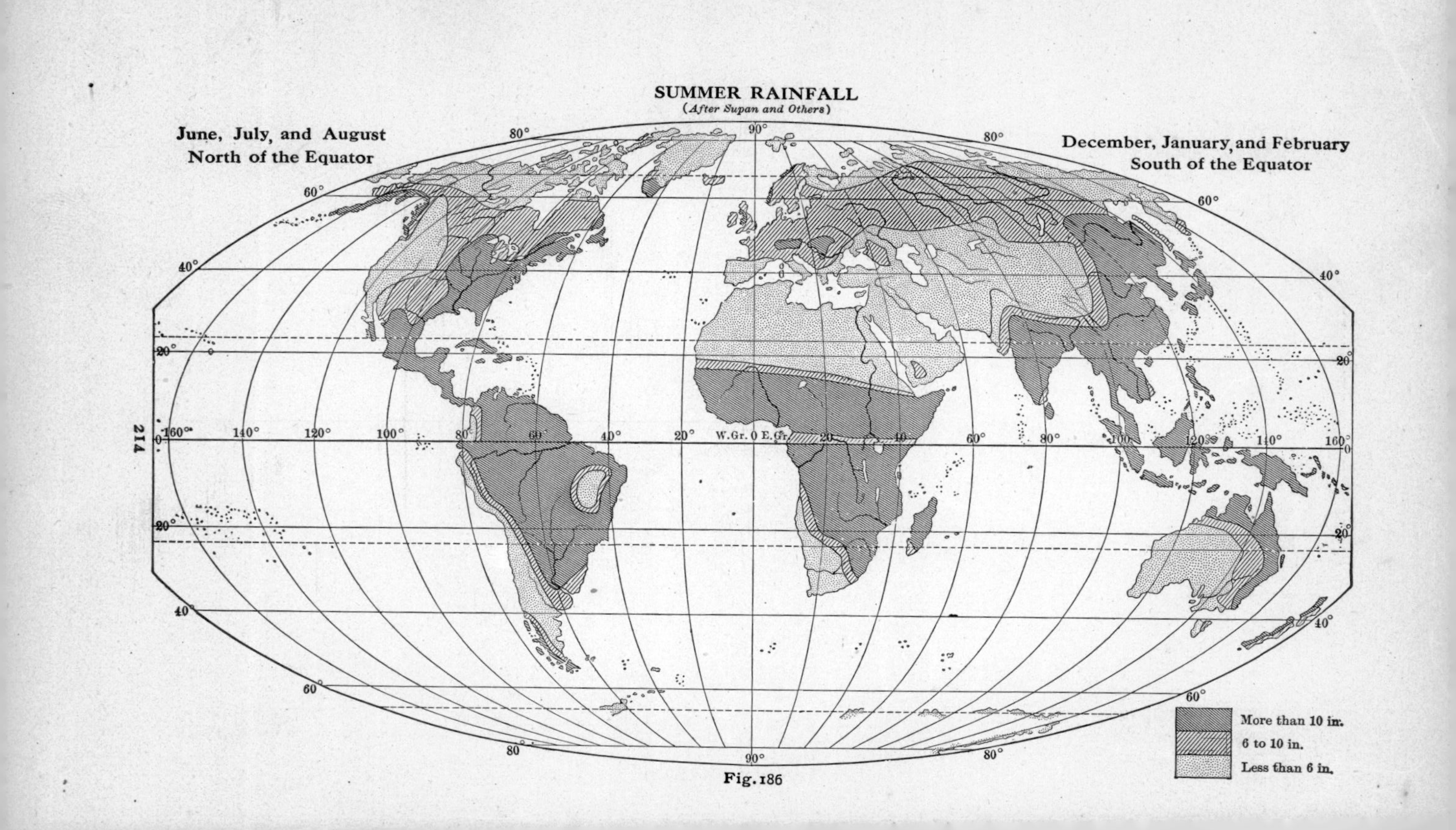
SUMMER RAINFALL
(After Supan and Others)
June, July, and August
North of the Equator
December, January, and February
South of the Equator
W.Gr. 0 E.Gr.
More than 10 in.
6 to 10 in.
Less than 6 in.

Fig. 186

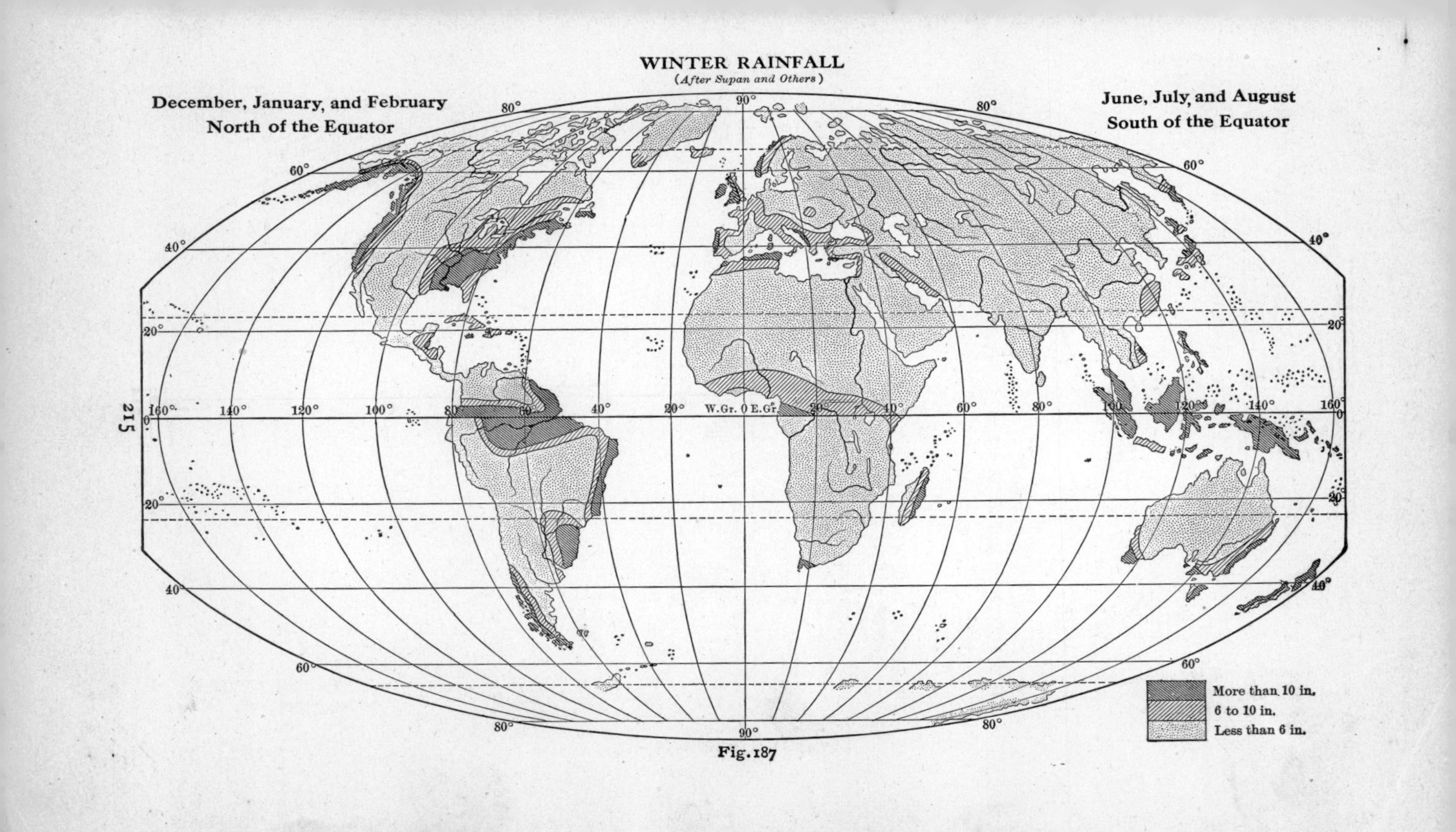
WINTER RAINFALL
(After Supan and Others)
December, January, and February
North of the Equator
June, July, and August
South of the Equator
W.Gr. 0 E.Gr.
More than 10 in.
6 to 10 in.
Less than 6 in.

Fig. 187

moisture before they reach so far inland. Central Eurasia is dry because it is too far from the Atlantic, and the monsoon rains from the Indian and Pacific are shut out by lofty mountains, which inclose the deserts of Tibet, Gobi, and the Ural-Caspian basin.

8. *The polar caps have little rainfall because the air is too cold to carry much vapor.*

About half of all the land receives too little rainfall to support more than a scanty population. Only about one third of the land receives between 20 and 60 inches of rain, the amount most favorable for thriving, civilized communities.

The maps of seasonal rainfall, Figs. 186, 187, show that very few places in the world receive heavy rainfall in winter.

CHAPTER XV

CLIMATE

Factors of Climate. — Climate includes all those conditions of the atmosphere which affect plant and animal life, among which temperature and moisture are the prime factors. The presence of dust and disease germs affects the healthfulness of the air and forms a factor of climate. The climate of any region is determined by its latitude, relief, prevailing winds, and position in relation to the great features of land and sea, and is thus a resultant and expression of all the physical influences and conditions which exist there. It is mainly climate which, in turn, controls, directly or indirectly, the life of plants, animals, and men. Therefore climate may be regarded as the middle link in the chain of geographical causes and consequences. It furnishes the key to a full understanding of geographical conditions.

The Equatorial or Tropical Zone. — In equatorial lowlands the temperature is constantly high with small range, and the rainfall is generally heavy. As the belt of calms, with low pressure and ascending air, follows the vertical rays of the sun northward and southward, it brings a rainy season in spring and fall near the equator and in summer near the tropics. Near the tropic the two rainy seasons may overlap, and on highlands exposed to trade winds from the ocean the rainfall is well distributed throughout the year.

Equatorial regions where all seasons are sufficiently wet are occupied by dense evergreen forests (Figs. 192, 193). In regions where, on account of elevation or protection by highlands, the rainfall is moderate or there is a strongly marked dry season, the forests thin out or disappear and give place to *savannas* covered with coarse grass and scattered trees (Fig. 200). In the monsoon region of southeastern Asia there is a hot summer with heavy rainfall, and a cool, dry winter. The monsoon forests are almost as luxuriant as the equatorial, but are nearly leafless in winter.

The Subtropical Zones. — In the subtropical zones of high pressure and descending air, and extending into the temperate zones, vast tracts of arid lands occupy about half the land surface of the globe. On account of the dryness and clearness of the air, arid regions are subject to extremes of temperature, the deserts of Africa, Arabia, North America, and Australia being the hottest regions of the world. The daily range is sometimes from above 100° in the daytime to near freezing at night.

In the deserts vegetation is confined to scattered thorny bushes which are often leafless (Figs. 191, 192, 204, 205). The deserts are bordered by savannas or steppes, where a thin growth of bunch grass furnishes pasturage (Figs. 192, 201, 202, 203). The soil needs only water to make it productive, and wherever sufficient ground water exists oases of dense vegetation arise (Fig. 206).

Mediterranean Climates. — Some regions in or near the belt of tropical calms have a climate which is transitional between that of the subtropical zone and that of the temperate zone. The rainfall is generally small, but not so little as to produce desert conditions. The summers are too dry to be favorable for grass, and pasturage is relatively poor. Frost rarely occurs, and the range of temperature is small. The climate is characterized by uniformly mild, dry weather, free from sudden or great changes. The skies are generally clear, and warm days alternate with cool nights.

In these regions people can live most of the time out of doors, and the climate is probably the most agreeable and healthful in the world. Hence they are noted as health and pleasure resorts. These conditions prevail in most of the coast lands and islands of the Mediterranean Sea, and constitute what is often called the Mediterranean climate.

Conditions similar to those of the Mediterranean region prevail in California, central Chile, south Africa, and southwest Australia (Fig. 188).

The Temperate Zones. — The so-called temperate zone in the northern hemisphere is broken up by the land masses and mountains into regions which have diversified and even strongly contrasted climates. Nearly all parts of North America and Asia between 30° and 50° N. Lat. are characterized by hot summers and cold winters, less than half the year being really temperate. The interiors of North America and Eurasia have an extreme continental climate of great range of temperature and small rainfall, which, in areas screened by mountains, is so intensified as to produce bleak steppes and deserts almost as barren as the Sahara (Fig. 192). The mid-continental ranges of temperature are carried by the prevailing westerly winds over the east coast lands of North America and Asia, but cyclonic winds from the Gulf of Mexico and Atlantic and the summer monsoons from the Pacific bring a moderate rainfall (Figs. 185, 186).

East Coast Climates. — Those parts of the United States and southern Canada lying east of the meridian of 100° have a continental climate with four strongly marked seasons and a large range of temperature (Figs. 161, 164). On the Gulf coast these conditions are modified by nearness to the ocean and the tropic. Throughout the region the climate is made changeable by the frequency of cyclones and anticyclones, especially in winter, when alternations of cold, clear weather, and mild, cloudy weather with rain or snow, occur every three or four days.

Northwest winds, blowing out from an advancing center of high pressure, bring a cold wave with zero temperatures as far south as St. Louis and Philadelphia, and freezing temperatures in Florida. Southerly winds blowing toward a center of low pressure carry cloud and rain, changing to snow in the north, across the country to and beyond the Great Lakes (Figs. 177–180). These irregular changes are very noticeable in spring, when alternations of almost summer weather with wintry spells occur from March to May. In summer the cyclonic changes are much feebler and less frequent. In autumn the change of seasons is more gradual than in spring, and clear, mild days and frosty nights may persist without notable storms until December.

Almost everywhere east of the meridian of 100° the annual rainfall is above 20 inches, increasing from northwest to southeast to above 50 inches on the Gulf coast. It is well distributed throughout the year, with a maximum in spring and early summer when crops are growing. Midsummer and early autumn are usually dry and favorable for harvest (Figs. 185, 186, 187).

Most of this region was originally covered with a heavy forest of deciduous trees, green in summer and bare in winter. Toward the north and on the Appalachian highlands the forests are partly or wholly of evergreen coniferous trees (Fig. 192). Towards the west the forests pass gradually into *prairies*, or tracts on which grasses form a dense, continuous sod or turf, trees being absent except along the streams.

In Asia the countries which most nearly resemble eastern United States in climate and products are Manchuria, Korea, northern China, and Japan.

West Coast Climates. — The west coast lands of North America and Europe are exposed to the westerly winds from the ocean and have a truly temperate, oceanic climate, almost as equable as that of the equatorial zone. The narrow strip of country between the mountains and the Pacific in Alaska, British Columbia, Washington, and Oregon has a mild, moist climate, with heavy precipitation in winter (Figs. 185–187). In the north the summers also are rainy and the snowfall is sufficient to maintain large glaciers upon all the mountains. The strip is covered with dense forests of pine, fir, spruce, cedar, and redwood, which yield a greater value of timber to the square mile than any other in the world (Fig. 192).

The countries of western Europe belong to the same climatic belt as the Pacific states of America. They are exposed to the westerly winds blowing from the north Atlantic, the waters of which are abnormally warm for their latitude on account of the drift of the Gulf Stream from tropical regions. The winds themselves are the chief cause of the ocean drift, and are therefore both directly and indirectly the cause of the mild climate. Their influence is greatest on the west coast and diminishes gradually inland, but south of Norway there are no mountains to shut out moisture from the interior.

In winter the winds are stronger and more southwesterly in direction, and the isotherms extend almost north and south, the temperature decreasing from west to east (Figs. 160, 171, 172). The range of temperature is small, and the rainfall large, with excess in autumn and winter. The air is constantly damp, and rain falls on more than half the days in the year. In autumn and winter fog and drizzling rain prevail. The winds from the ocean and the cloudiness combine to prevent great or sudden changes of temperature. Cyclones and anticyclones pass across these countries from west to east, but bring much smaller contrasts of weather than in eastern America. Spells of freezing weather are not prolonged or severe, and occasional falls of snow on the lowlands do not remain long upon the ground. Hardy plants blossom out of doors all winter, and work in the fields can be carried on every month in the year. The frequent rains are very favorable for grass, which covers unplowed ground with a thick sod even among the trees of the forest. The country looks fresh and green at all seasons. The Mediterranean countries have a climate like that of California, the British Isles like that of Oregon and Washington, and Norway resembles British Columbia and southern Alaska. The small range of temperature and large rainfall, with excess in autumn and winter, change gradually eastward to continental conditions of large range and small rainfall, with excess in summer. In general the climate of central Europe resembles that of eastern United States, with the direction of east-west change reversed A person traveling from France to central Russia would notice the same kind of changes as in traveling from Maryland to Colorado. A traveler from southern France to Sweden would experience changes similar to those from Florida to Quebec. The natural vegetation and cultivated crops of Europe have about the same range as in the United States, with local variations.

Climate and Civilization. — The middle latitudes of North America, Europe, and eastern Asia are the homes of the most advanced and progressive peoples of the world. The climate is not oppressive and overpowering as in the equatorial and polar regions. The contrast of seasons is stimulating to human effort, which must be expended in the summer to provide food and shelter for the winter, while the winter brings a period of comparative leisure and rest. The energy received from the sun can be utilized to greater advantage than elsewhere to supply human wants. Conditions of climate and vegetation are more capable of human control than in the regions of perpetual heat or perpetual cold, and human intelligence and labor bring a greater return of wealth than anywhere else in the world.

In the southern hemisphere the only lands which resemble the United States and Europe in climate and products are Chile, Argentina, Uruguay, eastern Australia, and New Zealand. Their natural resources and future possibilities are great, but for the most part they lack development for the want of sufficient population.

Cold Temperate Zones. — The northern cold temperate zone extends across North America and Eurasia. The climate is that of continental lands in high latitudes. The winter temperatures are the lowest in the world, except in Antarctica; the summers are cool and the range of temperature is very large (Figs. 159, 160, 161). The long days of summer, during which the period of sunshine varies from 16 to 24 hours, compensate for the low altitude of the sun above the horizon, and days with temperatures above 70° occur. The growing season is short, but may be warm enough to ripen wheat even on the Arctic circle. The rainfall is generally less than 20 inches (Fig. 185), but is more efficient than an equal amount in lower latitudes because evaporation is less. During more than half the year the ground is covered with snow, which plays an important part in protecting the roots of trees from severe frost.

A belt of coniferous forest extends across the continents from ocean to ocean, interrupted by patches of "muskeg" swamp and prairie (Figs. 192, 197, 199).

In the southern cold temperate zone, the narrow extremity of South America presents two strongly contrasted regions. The west coast resembles southern Alaska in small range of temperature, heavy rainfall, and dense coniferous forest. In Tierra del Fuego the climate is stormy and inclement at all seasons, and snow falls every month in the year. East of the mountains the rainfall is too scanty for forests, and Patagonia is an arid steppe (Fig. 185).

The Polar Caps. — In the north polar regions the climate is still more severe than in the cold temperate zones. The winters are not colder but longer, and the cool growing season is reduced to two months or less. During the winter the sun does not rise at all for a period of from one day to six months. The sky is generally clear, but violent storms of wind are frequent. There is no spring, but winter holds with slight mitigation until June, when the ice begins to break up and summer comes on with a rush. The summers are cold and foggy, and in September winter sets in again with full severity. The annual precipitation is less than 10 inches, but there is so little melting that on moderate elevations snow and ice accumulate from year to year. The ground is permanently frozen to great depths and never thaws for more than a few feet on top.

The Arctic borderlands of America and Eurasia are occupied by *tundras* (Figs. 192, 208), where the only vegetation consists of lichens, mosses, grasses, and stunted shrubs, which never grow higher than the level of the snow surface in winter.

Greenland and Antarctica are buried under vast sheets of ice, upon which no living thing exists. Bare land appears around the shores, where sea-birds, mammals, and in the north a few thousand Eskimos find means of support.

Alpine Climate. — The climate of lofty mountains and plateaus resembles that of the polar caps. Between the tropics, surfaces above about 15,000 feet in elevation are covered with permanent snow and ice. In middle latitudes perpetual snow descends to about 10,000 feet, and in polar regions nearly to sea level. The height of the snow line varies not only with the temperature but with the amount of snowfall, and is different on the windward and leeward sides, and on north and south slopes, of the same range. The rainfall generally increases with the altitude to a height which varies on different mountains and then diminishes. The belt of heaviest rainfall below the snow line is generally forested (Fig. 198).

Tropical plateaus between 5,000 and 13,000 feet in elevation are generally more healthful and suitable for human occupation than the lowlands. In the northern Andes and Mexico nearly all the cities and areas of dense population are found upon the highlands. In Mexico the traveler can ascend in a distance of 100 miles from the hot, damp coast land to a temperate plateau and cold mountain heights, through as many belts of climate as he would traverse in traveling from the tropic to the polar circle.

Climatic Regions. — The map, Fig. 188, shows how the land areas may be divided into regions bounded approximately by isotherms and lines of equal rainfall, in each of which the principal factors of climate are nearly uniform. These are grouped under twelve types, and all the regions be-

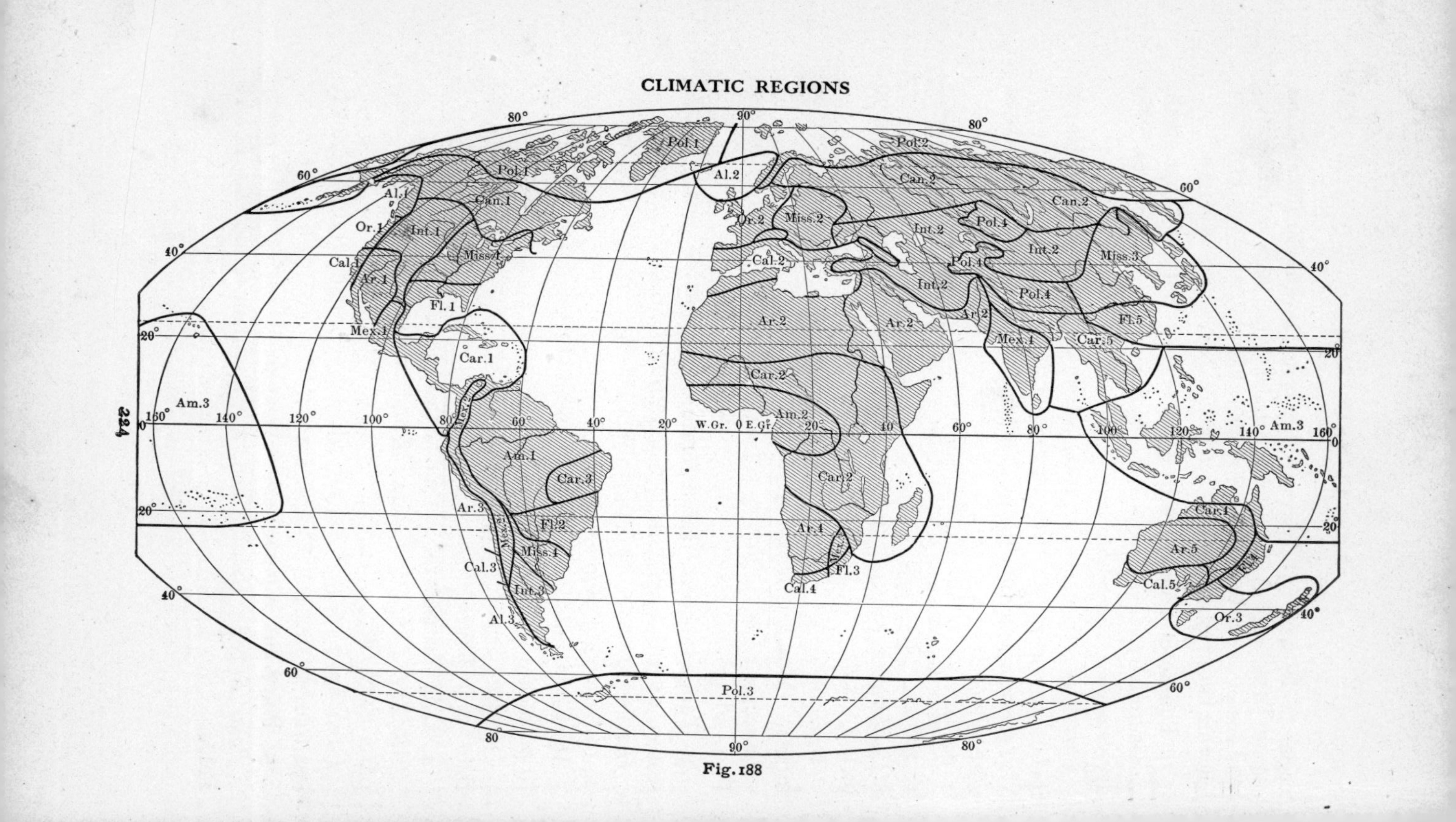

CLIMATIC REGIONS
Pol.1
Al.2
Pol.2
Pol.1
Can.1
Can.2
Can.2
Al.1
Or.1
Int.1
Or.2
Miss.2
Int.2
Pol.4
Miss.1
Cal.1
Ar.1
Cal.2
Int.2
Pol.4
Int.2
Miss.3
Fl.1
Pol.4
Mex.1
Ar.2
Ar.2
Ar.2
Fl.5
Mex.1
Car.5
Car.1
Car.2
Am.3
Am.2
Am.3
W.Gr.
E.Gr.
Am.1
Car.3
Car.2
Ar.3
Fl.2
Ar.4
Car.1
Ar.5
Miss.4
Cal.3
Fl.3
Cal.4
Cal.5
Int.3
Al.3
Or.3
Pol.3

Fig. 188

longing to the same type, wherever they occur, have essentially the same climate. This map should be compared with the maps of temperature belts and of annual and seasonal rainfall (Figs. 164, 185, 186, 187). The following table explains the map and briefly characterizes each type.

1. **Equatorial and Tropical.** — All seasons hot and range small.

Amazon Type. — Equatorial. Rainfall above 60 inches. No dry season. Am. 1 – Am. 3.

Caribbean Type. — Tropical. Rainfall generally 20 to 60 inches (except in 5). Dry winter. Car. 1 – Car. 5.

2. **Subtropical and Warm Temperate.** — Always temperate or with a hot season.

Arizonan Type. — Always dry. Rainfall generally less than 10 inches. Ar. 1 – Ar. 5.

Californian Type. — Dry summer. Rainfall generally 20 to 60 inches. Cal. 1 – Cal. 5.

Mexican Type. — Dry winter. Rainfall generally less than 60 inches. Mex. 1 – Mex. 4.

Floridan Type. — No dry season. Rainfall less than 80 inches. Fl. 1 – Fl. 5.

3. **Temperate and Intemperate.** — Temperate, with a cold season, or with a cold and a hot season.

Oregon Type. — Oceanic. Small range. Rainfall generally 20 to 60 inches. Or. 1 – Or. 3.

Mississippian Type. — Continental. Large range. Rainfall 20 to 60 inches. Miss. 1 – Miss. 4.

Interior Type. — Continental. Large range. Rainfall less than 20 inches. Int. 1 – Int. 3.

4. **Cold Temperate.** — Cold with a temperate season.

Alaskan Type. — Oceanic. Small range. Rainfall in some parts above 60 inches. Al. 1 – Al. 3.

Canadian Type. — Continental. Large range. Rainfall mostly less than 20 inches. Can. 1 – Can. 2.

5. **Polar and Alpine.** — Always cold.

Polar Type. — Rainfall generally less than 10 inches. Pol. 1 – Pol. 4.

CHAPTER XVI

PLANT REGIONS

The Distribution of Plants. — The distribution of plants over the face of the earth and the kind of vegetation found in any region are nicely adjusted to a combination of conditions, of which air, light, water, soil, and temperature are the most important. Green plants absorb about 75 per cent of their weight from the air in the form of oxygen and carbon dioxide. The

Fig. 189. — Zonal arrangement of plants.

absorption of carbon dioxide is done by the leaves and other green parts in the sunlight and cannot take place in the dark. Plants absorb from the soil through their roots large quantities of water containing compounds of nitrogen, potash, phosphorus, lime, and other elements in solution. Most of the water, after circulating through the plant, evaporates from the leaves. For all plants there is a certain range of temperature within which they are able to survive, and a smaller range within which they grow vigorously. Hence plants are arranged in zones, roughly corresponding to the zones of temperature. Within the zones of temperature the distribution of plant societies is determined largely by the available soil water. Thus the variations of soil water break up the plant zones into plant regions, just as the rainfall breaks up the temperature zones into climatic regions. The natural vegetation of any region is a striking and intelligible expression of the physical conditions of structure, relief, and climate which prevail there, and, consequently, of the natural influences exerted upon animal and human activities. Vegetation is a key which unlocks the chain of geographic causes and consequences.

Water Plants. — A large class of plants flourish only in water or in very wet soil. (1) Floating or submerged plants are characterized by thin walls through which water is absorbed by all parts of the plant. Roots, being unnecessary, are absent or used for anchorage only. The plant is supported by the water, and has no need of stiffness; hence it is soft and flexible. Numerous species of seaweed belong to this class, some of which attain such dimensions as to rival the largest of land plants. Bladderworts and duckweeds are common floating plants in fresh-water lakes and ponds. (2) Many plants are rooted to the soil, but have submerged or floating leaves; for example, pondweeds and water lilies. The submerged leaves are commonly narrow and threadlike; the floating ones very broad (Fig. 190).

Fig. 190. — Water plants.

(3) Swamp or marsh plants are rooted in water or very wet soil, while their stems and leaves are exposed to the air. Many societies of them are common in temperate climates; among them may be found cat-tail flags, reed grass, sedges, willows, alders, tamarack, and cypress.

Fig. 191. — Drouth plants. Barrel cactus, Mexico. (Desert Botanical Lab.)

Drouth Plants are adapted to thrive in a dry soil and climate. They generally have an extensive root system in proportion to the size of the plant, a small leaf surface, and a thickened epidermis. Many plants survive regular periods of drouth by the disappearance of root, stem, and leaves, and the reduction of the individual plant to seeds, bulbs, or tubers. The shedding of leaves is a provision against destruction by the dry as well as the cold season. The reduction of the leaves to threads or needles, as in the pine and other species of coniferous trees, and the total absence of leaves, as in the cactus, are efficient means of withstanding drouth. The perfection of these adaptations is probably found in the melon cactus, in which the whole plant is reduced to a spiny, thick-skinned, globular mass.

Intermediate Plants. — The class of plants adapted to a medium supply of water comprises about 80 per cent of all known forms and constitutes the more common vegetation of temperate regions.

Salt Plants. — Some species of plants are able to grow where the soil water is impregnated with common salt or alkali, which would be fatal to most plants. Salt plants are found along the seashore, in tidal marshes, around salt lakes, and in arid regions.

Plant Regions. — The land surface may be divided according to its vegetative covering into woodland, grassland, and desert.

1. *Woodland.* — Trees are deep-rooted and their growth is not dependent on frequent rain or a rainy growing season, but

on the presence of water within reach of the deep roots. They require a warm growing season, a moist subsoil, and calm, damp air in winter. They may thrive where long seasons of drouth recur periodically. They are not limited by low temperature in winter, if protected by a snow covering, but suffer from dry winds when the ground water is frozen.

2. *Grassland.* — Grasses are shallow-rooted and their growth is dependent upon a moist superficial soil. They require frequent, even if small, rainfall during the growing season. They endure extreme drouth during the season of rest.

3. *Desert.* — Deserts are due to dryness of the ground or low temperature. Except on ice caps, vegetation is not absent but sparse. There is always much vacant space, and the plants do not struggle against one another for room, but against unfavorable conditions of soil and climate. Fig. 192 shows the distribution of the principal types of vegetation. It should be compared with the map of climatic regions (Fig. 188).

Wet Woodland. — *Tropical Rain Forest.* — In the climatic regions of the Amazon type, where the temperature is constantly high and the rainfall above 60 inches, the growth of vegetation is luxuriant. Dense forests of very tall trees, overgrown with climbing plants and air plants, and crowded with underbrush, occupy the country and almost shut out large animals and men. The trees have large, thin leaves with smooth, glossy skin to shed water, and are green all the year round. The number of species growing together is very large, but palms and tree ferns are characteristic. This woodland can hardly be penetrated except by way of the streams, and is more difficult to cross than a desert.

If men, with great labor, make a little clearing in it to plant crops, the native vegetation springs up again so rankly that the work of clearing must be done over again every year. The heavy rainfall leaches and washes away the soil, which is soon exhausted. The hot, damp air is unhealthful and oppressive, and the scattered inhabitants, overcome by the forces of nature, are unable to rise above a state of savagery. These conditions prevail in a large part of the Amazon basin, in west equatorial

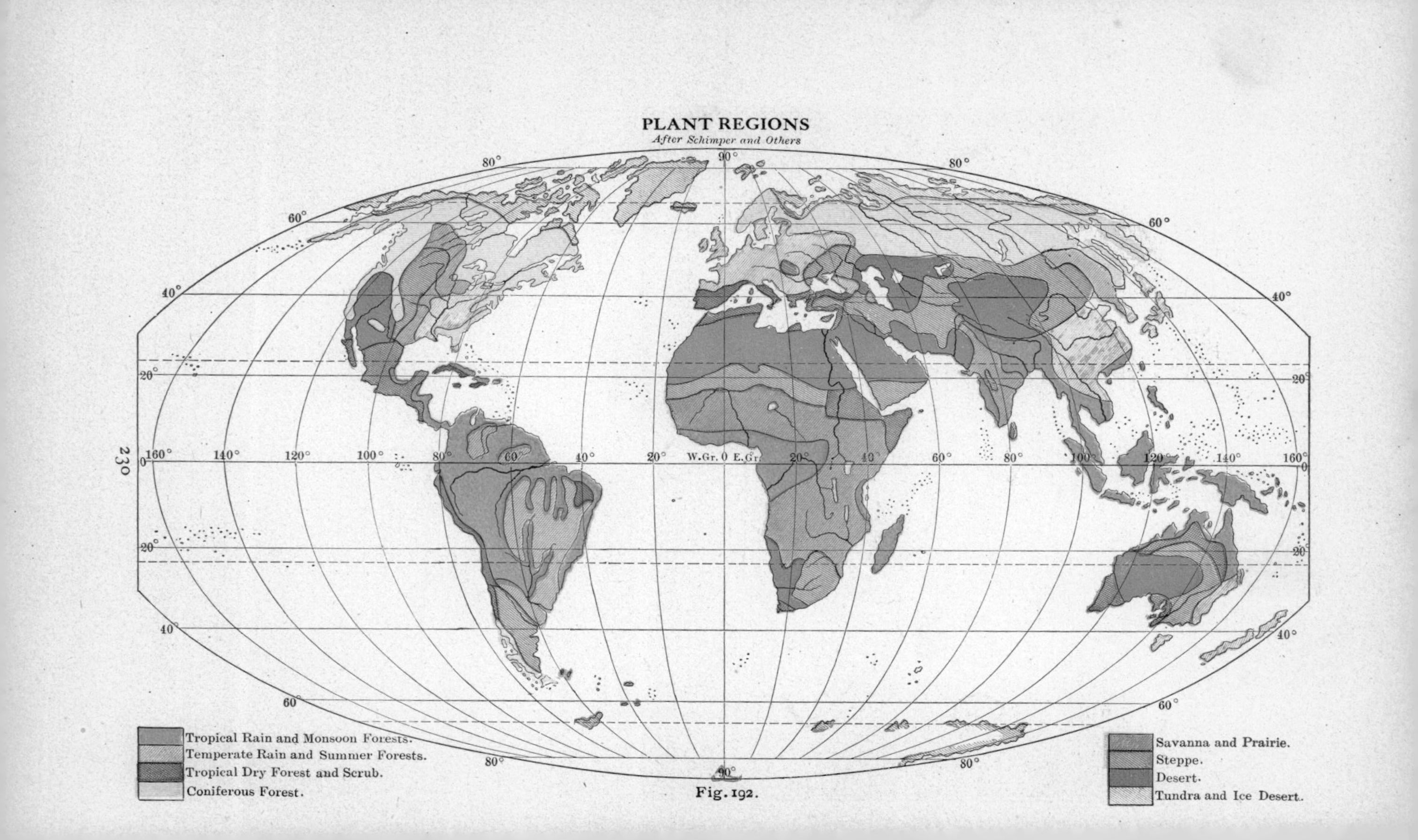
PLANT REGIONS
After Schimper and Others
W.Gr. 0 E.Gr.
Tropical Rain and Monsoon Forests.
Temperate Rain and Summer Forests.
Tropical Dry Forest and Scrub.
Coniferous Forest.
Savanna and Prairie.
Steppe.
Desert.
Tundra and Ice Desert.

Fig. 192.

Africa, and in the East Indies. European peoples have made some progress in establishing colonies in all these regions, and have stimulated the natives to gather and grow valuable tropical products, such as rubber, sugar, coffee, spices, chocolate, tapioca, tobacco, fruits, oils, and medicines.

Fig. 193. — Tropical rain forest, Java. (Schimper, *Plant-Geography*.)

Monsoon Forests. — In some parts of the monsoon region of southeastern Asia the rainfall is more than 60 inches, but occurs mostly in summer, while the winters are relatively cool and dry. In the rainy season the forests are much like the tropical rain forest, but in the dry season are leafless.

Temperate Rain Forest. — In the climatic regions of the Floridan type the conditions are similar to those of the tropical rain forest, except that the temperatures are not so high and the rainfall is not so heavy. They are occupied by a mixed forest of evergreen and deciduous trees. Climbing and air plants, ferns, and tree ferns are abundant. The multiplicity of species is very great. The camphor tree of Formosa, the eucalyptus of Australia, and the palmetto and live oak of Florida are characteristic. These forests are much less formidable than the tropical rain forests. They have been largely cleared and the lands now support a moderate or dense population of civilized people. The principal crops are rice, corn, wheat, sugar cane, cotton, semi-tropical fruits, and, in China, tea.

Fig. 194.—Temperate rain forest, Florida. (Schimper, *Plant-Geography*.)

Temperate Summer Forest.—The climatic regions of the Oregon and Mississippian types are very favorable to the growth of trees which have broad, soft, thin leaves in summer and are bare in winter. The oak, beech, maple, elm, chestnut, ash, linden, and sycamore are characteristic and widely distributed. Climbing plants and air plants are rare, but grasses and herbaceous plants growing among the trees are relatively abundant.

These forests furnish the world's supply of hardwood timber for fuel and construction. In the United States and Europe they have been largely destroyed to clear the land for agriculture. The combination of forest and grassland, natural or artificial, affords good conditions for agriculture and stock raising, and makes these regions preëminent in the production of foodstuffs and the homes of the richest and most progressive peoples.

Fig. 195. — Temperate summer forest, North Carolina. (U.S.G.S.)

Dry Woodland. — *Tropical Dry Forest.* — In the climatic regions of the Californian type and some of the Mexican type trees grow in clumps rather than in forests. The leaves are evergreen, small and thick, with a leathery skin. The myrtle, holly, laurel, box, cork oak, oleander, cypress, and olive are characteristic species. Lilies, tulips, hyacinths, and other herbaceous plants growing from bulbs and tubers are numerous. Grass is scanty and poor, and sheep and goats are kept in preference to cattle. In the Mediterranean region olive oil largely takes the place of meat and butter. Grapes and tropical fruits flourish, while grain is grown in the cool, moist season or by means of irrigation.

The plateau of the Dekkan (Mex. 4, Fig. 188) is protected by bordering heights from the excessive monsoon rains. Two or more crops a year are often raised, some suitable to the hot, wet season (June to October), and others to the cool, dry season (November to March). Thus the same area may produce large crops of wheat, rice, and cotton. The monsoon rains are so variable from year to year that the crops often fail, and on account of the dense population a dry year may bring a serious famine in which thousands starve to death. Irrigation is practiced, and India is dotted with storage tanks and wells. About 50,000 miles of canals carry off flood waters, and in the dry season distribute water to the fields.

Fig. 196. — Tropical dry forest, Mexico.

Extreme forms of tropical dry forest are *thorn forest* and *thorn scrub*, in which all woody plants are dwarfed, scraggy, thorny, and tangled, forming thickets difficult to penetrate (Fig. 196). The dwarf oak, acacia, and mesquite are characteristic. Thorn forests occur in scattered patches in the borderlands around deserts and grasslands. It is called *chapparal* in North America, *catinga* in Brazil, and *scrub* in Australia (Fig. 203).

Temperate Dry Forest (*Coniferous*). — Climatic regions of the Alaskan and Canadian types are generally occupied by evergreen coniferous forests. Most of the species have a central trunk, with horizontal or pendent branches in whorls, and their fruit is a cone. The needle-shaped or scale-shaped leaves, with a hard skin, are adapted to dry and frozen soils and strong winds. The pine, fir, spruce, cedar, and larch extend throughout the cold temperate belts and on mountain sides in all latitudes, and furnish the world's supply of soft-wood timber.

The valuable products are timber, as yet largely unavailable for want of means of transportation, and the furs of numerous small animals, such as

Fig. 197. — Coniferous forest, Great Bear Lake, Canada. (U.S. Biol. Surv.)

Fig. 198. — Spruce forest, Colorado.

the fox, sable, marten, mink, otter, badger, beaver, and muskrat. Canada and Siberia have been for centuries the chief sources of furs, and there is no indication that the supply is diminishing. The population is generally very sparse. Coniferous forests sometimes occur on poor, porous soils, in wet, warm regions, as the long-leaved pine of the southern United States.

Fig. 199. — Cedar forest, Oregon. (U.S.G.S.)

Grassland. — *Savanna.* — In climatic regions of the Caribbean type, the vegetation consists chiefly of tall, stiff grasses growing in dense tufts. Low, deciduous trees with parasol-shaped tops are scattered about and give the landscape a parklike aspect (Fig. 200). A large part of central Africa is occupied by such savannas, the home of immense numbers of large animals, — the elephant, rhinoceros, hippopotamus, giraffe, lion, leopard, buffalo, zebra, and nearly one hundred species of antelopes. It is the finest country in the world for "big game."

The abundance of animal life has been a serious hindrance to human occupation and control, but is itself an evidence of what might be done there with domestic animals. The success of native agriculture, carried on with rude implements and methods, in raising corn, bananas, millet, beans, sheep, goats, and cattle, suggests great possibilities for the future. Under the control of Europeans the black natives are prevented from robbing and killing one another, and are settling down into peaceful and orderly industrial communities. The natural conditions are favorable for their redemption from primeval savagery and for the occupation of the country by civilized peoples.

Fig. 200. — Savanna with fringing forest, East Africa. (De Martonne.)

A part of Brazil is a plateau with moderate rainfall, and the forests are replaced by *campos*, or undulating grassy tracts, with clumps of trees in the valleys. In Venezuela the rain shadow of the Guiana highlands produces the *llanos*, which have a warm, rainless winter of five months, during which all vegetation apparently dies. When the summer rains appear grass and herbaceous plants spring up and grow luxuriantly. In swampy depressions and along streams oases of stunted trees rise like islands from the sea.

Prairie. — In the drier parts of climatic regions of the Mississippian type, forests give place to prairies, or open tracts of meadow, covered with a thick, continuous sod of grasses and other herbaceous plants. Fringing forests of small trees along the streams do not occupy more than 20 per cent of the area. The soil is especially fertile and easily worked. Such lands lie all ready for human occupancy, and are at once available with small expenditure of labor. The American prairies are one of the most productive agricultural regions in the world.

Steppe. — Climatic regions of the Interior type, and other

Fig. 201. — Bunch grass. (U.S.G.S.)

temperate regions with a rainfall between 10 and 20 inches, are covered with bunch grass, which does not form a continuous sod or grow very high. It cures on the ground into a nutritious hay. Trees are very rare. Vast areas of this kind exist in the interior of Eurasia, where they are called steppes. They have been for many centuries the home of nomad peoples, who have no fixed habitation, but wander about with flocks and herds of cattle, horses, camels, sheep, and goats in search of pasture. The similar regions of North America have been ranged over by herds of cattle under the care of "cowboys," but are now being divided up and fenced into cattle and sheep ranches. By irrigation and

Fig. 202. — Steppe, South Dakota. (U.S.G.S.)

dry farming agriculture is gradually encroaching upon the areas of pasture.

Fig. 203. — Steppe and thorn scrub, South Africa.

The *pampas* of Argentina include prairie and steppe lands, hitherto used for raising sheep and cattle for wool and hides. As railroads are extended they are being converted into wheat fields. The *veldt* of the Transvaal, in South Africa, is a similar region, where cattle raising is combined with some agriculture (Fig. 203). The Australian *bush* between the desert and the eastern mountains, belongs to the same class, and supports millions of sheep and cattle. Steppe lands are "belts of herbage strown between the desert and the sown," and will always be important sources of meat, wool, and hides.

Fig. 204. — Sage brush desert, Arizona.

Deserts. — In desert regions the rainfall is generally less than 10 inches, but desert conditions may occur where the rainfall is much larger if rapid evaporation or subterranean drainage leaves the soil and subsoil too dry. Great deserts occur in climatic regions of the Arizonan, Interior, and Polar types.

Warm Deserts. — In tropical and temperate deserts vegetation is limited to drouth and salt plants only. The root system is large and shallow, and the leaf surface is greatly reduced. There are few leaves at once, and in many forms no leaves at all, their functions being performed by the stems. Desert plants respond quickly to a slight fall of rain, and pass through their stages of leaf, flower, and fruit rapidly. They are characterized by thick skin, hairs, spines, resins, and spongy tissue for storing water. The cactus, agave, sage brush, and creosote bush are typical forms. Where sufficient ground water exists, permanently or temporarily, oases occur and support a sparse population. The air of the desert is pure and stimulating, and acts directly, along with the hard conditions of life, to render animals and men lean, hardy, restless, and fierce.

Fig. 205. — Giant cactus, Arizona.

Polar and Alpine Deserts. — Along the polar borders of coniferous forests and above the timber line on mountains, the growing season is short and plant growth is very rapid. Patches of herbaceous plants have rosettes of leaves next to the ground and send up short stems bearing bright-colored flowers. Trees,

Fig. 206. — **Date palm oasis, Sahara.** Note flat-roofed houses. (Robin.)

when present, are stunted, scraggy, and twisted. Shrubs spread out close to the ground in dense mats.

Tundras. — In high latitudes and altitudes the ground is perpetually frozen, thawing only to the depth of a few inches in

Fig. 207. — **Alpine desert, Bolivia.** (Schimper.)

summer. The principal vegetation consists of lichens and mosses, upon which caribou, reindeer, musk oxen, and hares find subsistence. Willows, larches, and junipers occur in the form of

Fig. 208. — Tundra, Lapland. (Schimper.)

dense cushions, which do not rise above the level of the snow surface of winter.

Ice Deserts. — Ice caps are entirely devoid of vegetation, except the occasional appearance of microscopic algæ known as "red snow."

In cold deserts the possibilities of human life are reduced to the lowest limits. In Europe the Laplanders maintain a semicivilized life by keeping herds of reindeer. In Asia the Chukchis, and in America the Eskimos, depend largely upon the sea, in which fish, birds, seals, and walrus abound.

CHAPTER XVII

THE GEOGRAPHY OF ANIMALS

Water Breathers and Air Breathers. — The most important distinction among animals due to adaptation to geographical environment is that between those which absorb oxygen from solution in water and soon die out of water, and those which absorb oxygen from the air and soon die when immersed in water. The conditions of life in the water are more simple and less varied than in the air. The water furnishes nearly uniform pressure on all sides of the body, and little energy is expended in supporting weight; hence the form and surface of the body, the structure of the skeleton and muscular system, and the character and arrangement of the limbs are adapted to propulsion through the medium. A comparison of a fish and a cat will show a remarkable contrast in these particulars. The water breathers include all fish, most shellfish, such as oysters and clams, most crustaceans, such as crabs and lobsters, and a vast number of lower and less familiar forms of animal life. The temperature of water is uniform over wide areas, and far less changeable than that of the air. Food supply is more generally diffused in water than on land, and many aquatic animals are fixed to one spot and have their food brought to them by currents. Hence the water breathers belong entirely to the less highly developed classes. The demands upon them are comparatively few and simple, and their lives do not require the numerous and complex activities and abilities of life in the air.

Marine animals depend directly or indirectly for food upon the vegetation which flourishes in the sea or the organic matter brought by rivers from the land. Life in the sea is most abundant in the shallow waters of the continental shelf (p. 24), which are penetrated by the heat and light of the sun, and where the bottom is covered with mud from the land. The open sea is inhabited near the surface by great schools of fish and swarms of invertebrate animals, many of which are minute in size. The abundance of mineral matter in solution, the volume of sunlight, and the uniformity of temperature are favorable to the growth of microscopic plants in such numbers as to furnish an ample food supply for all.

The sea is probably rather densely inhabited at all depths, but those animals which live constantly below a few hundred feet are difficult to catch, and our knowledge of them is imperfect. Deep-sea animals exist

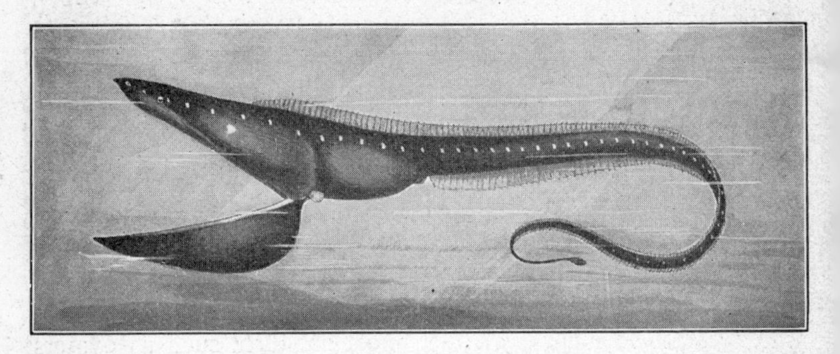

Fig. 209.—Deep-sea fish, with lanterns.

under conditions of great pressure, low and unchanging temperature, and absolute darkness. Most of them are degenerate descendants of surface and shallow water forms. Some are eyeless and some are provided with lantern organs which generate a dim light. Owing to the great area and depth of inhabited waters, the number of marine animals probably exceeds all others.

Some animals are amphibious, spending a part of their lives in water and a part in the air. Many insects are hatched and pass their larval stage in water, but live their adult life in air. Tadpoles have gills and are true water breathers, but change into frogs, toads, or salamanders, which are air breathers. A few animals have both gills and lungs throughout life and can live in either medium. Among the higher animals some assume the aquatic form and habit, but are not water breathers. Among birds the

Fig. 210. — Marine mammals.

penguins swim vigorously under water in pursuit of fish. Even some mammals, which suckle their young and cannot live more than a few minutes under water, have assumed the aquatic form and habit. Such are the whale, dolphin, porpoise, sea cow, seal, and walrus. The last two are ice-riding animals, vigorous swimmers which spend a part of the time on the polar ice.

Fig. 211. — Penguins. Wings are used for swimming. (Shackleton's *The Heart of the Antarctic.*)

Fliers and Walkers. — Another distinction among animals, scarcely less important geographically, is the division of air breathers into fliers and walkers or crawlers. Most birds and insects and a few mammals have become highly specialized for locomotion in the air. The buoyancy and resistance of the air are slight compared with water, and flying requires a more complex body structure than swimming. The insect body is small and very light, with a thin outer shell, provided with one or two pairs of delicate wings. The muscles inside the shell are capable of moving the wings at a high speed, amounting in the house fly to 330 strokes a second. The bones of the bird are hollow and filled with air for lightness, the fore limbs are provided with a complex arrangement of interlocking and folding feather vanes, the breast bone and muscles are strongly developed for moving the wings, and the tail feathers act as a rudder.

Fig. 212. — Soaring bird.

Among the more powerful birds, flight has attained the climax of natural locomotion. The passenger pigeon can fly 100 miles an hour, the eagle and condor can rise to great heights and soar almost without effort, while the albatross and frigate bird make journeys of thousands of miles across the sea. Yet no animal can live in the air indefinitely without alighting on land or water for rest and food.

Animal Adaptations. — The adaptations of animals to food supply, climate, enemies, and breeding are innumerable. A few of the more striking cases may be noticed.

Most insects are vegetable eaters and live upon the juices and leaves of plants. Many eat dead animal matter or are parasitic on live animals.

The large majority of birds live on seeds, fruits, and insects. Sea birds are fish eaters, and birds of prey catch land animals alive. A few are scavengers of carrion.

Mammals, with few exceptions, are land animals and walk, run, or jump. A few species swim (p. 245). Bats are the only mammals that really fly. Most mammals are plant eaters (herbivorous) or flesh eaters (carnivorous), but bears, swine, and men eat all kinds of food. Plant eaters have cutting teeth for cropping herbage, and flat grinders for chewing it. The large ones are hoofed animals, including cattle, sheep, goats, deer, antelopes, the giraffe, camel, horse, hog, hippopotamus, rhinoceros, and elephant. The small plant eaters are gnawers (rodents), such as the squirrel, prairie dog, beaver, rat, mouse, guinea pig, and rabbit. The flesh eaters live mostly upon the plant eaters and generally have claws and sharp teeth for catching, holding, and tearing their prey. The large ones are bold and fierce, with keen senses and quick intelligence, as shown by the cat, lion, tiger, leopard, panther, dog, fox, wolf, bear, otter, and weasel. The small ones live chiefly upon insects, as the mole and the bat. The plant eaters in a wild state are in constant danger of attack from the flesh eaters, and few of them have adequate means of defense. Their safety lies in flight or concealment; hence the majority have keen senses and are slender, agile, and built for speed.

Fig. 213.—Plant eater: caribou.

Fig. 214.—Flesh eater: lion.

A few are able to maintain themselves by strength, mass, and tough skin, as the bison, rhinoceros, hippopotamus, and elephant. The rodents are in danger from birds as well as beasts of prey, and find refuge by burrowing in the ground, in hollow trees, or about buildings.

Fig. 215.—Hippopotamus. Lives mostly in water with only eyes and nostrils above the surface.

Many animals of all classes are favored by protective coloration which makes them almost invisible in their usual haunts. Cases of this kind are most numerous among insects and birds, but the lion on the sand, the leopard, zebra, and giraffe in the forest, and the Arctic fox, hare, and ptarmigan on the snow, are striking examples.

Shelter.—The higher animals generally make use of some kind of a shelter, nest, or house, at least for the purpose of rest and rearing their young. Aquatic animals are generally homeless, but fur seals swim hundreds of miles to reach the islands where they annually congregate to bring forth their cubs. On land, animals burrow in the ground and make use of natural rock houses or dens. Beasts of prey find shelter and a sleeping place in some thicket. The hippopotamus spends the day in the water, with only his nostrils visible. The large plant eaters are generally homeless and their young are "precocious," or able to run with their mothers soon after birth. Constructive ability reaches a high development among birds, whose nests are often marvels of skill in the choice of site and in the adaptation of materials to home building. Yet the palm for such achievement must be given not to any bird, but to the beaver and the bee. The beaver gnaws down trees, builds an elaborate dam with timber and mud, raises his house of reeds above the surface of the pond, and enters it through a tunnel opening under water. Bees construct in a hollow tree a comb made of their own wax, in a form which gives a maximum of storage space with a minimum of material, and fill it with honey and pollen.

It is notable, however, that such feats are accomplished only by an organized community which rivals human society.

Distribution of Animals. — Animals are so much more mobile than plants that they have become more widely diffused, and the earth cannot be divided into animal regions so clearly distinguished as the plant regions. It may be said that every species of animal would be found in every part of the earth suitable for its maintenance, if it were not prevented by barriers of some sort which its individuals are unable to cross. The principal barriers to animal migration are water, climate, mountains, deserts, forests, lack of food supply, and enemies. Marine animals are generally limited to salt water, but some sea fish run up rivers to spawn and feed. The barriers in the sea are differences of temperature, pressure, and food supply. Shallow-water forms never venture far into the open sea because of lack of food. Deep-sea forms die when brought to the surface because of reduction of pressure. Those which swarm in warm surface waters would perish in waters a few degrees colder.

On land the most widely distributed animals are birds, bats, and some insects on account of their powers of flight. Those of smallest range are found among fresh-water fishes, which cannot cross from one stream system to another and are stopped by high falls, and snails, which are very poor travelers. For most land animals except fliers the sea is an absolute barrier to migration, and each land mass would have a fauna in most respects unlike every other if there had never been any land connection with some other mass. Mountain ranges are barriers more on account of climate and limited food supply than height and steepness. If they were not cold and barren most animals would be able to climb and cross them. Deserts are nearly as efficient barriers as the sea because they are almost equally foodless. Grazing animals cannot cross a wide belt of dense forest because of want of grass, and forest animals do not flourish in grassland. Although warm-blooded animals have the power to maintain their bodily temperature above that of the surrounding air and are generally protected by a coat of hair, wool, feathers, or fat, these things are not sufficient to enable them to live in all climates. Domestic cattle would soon perish in Greenland, where the musk ox seems not to suffer at temperatures of eighty degrees below zero. Polar bears brought to temperate regions must be constantly supplied with ice.

Fig. 216. — Musk ox.

Animal Realms. — *The Northern Realm.* — The northern continents are close together, and in the past have been so connected as to give a continuous land area from Norway eastward around to Labrador. The bulk of these continents lies in temperate regions between the tropic and the polar circle, and there is no impassable north-south mountain barrier. Consequently the fauna throughout this vast area presents a striking similarity, with a multitude of minor differences. It is especially the home of the hoofed grass eaters, — cattle, deer, sheep, goats, horses, and camels. While beasts of prey are not absent, the species are relatively few in num-

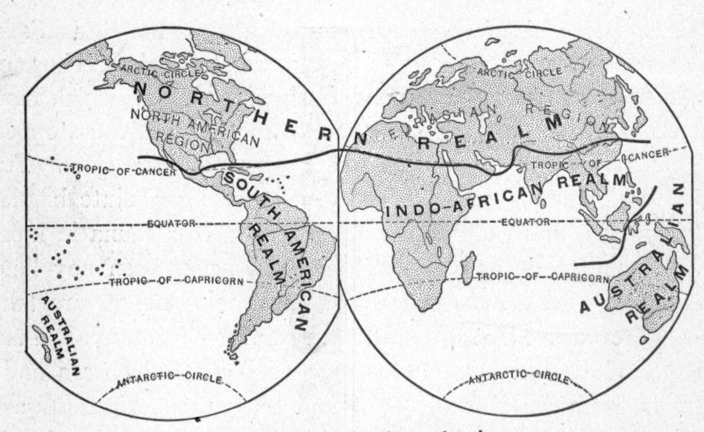

Fig. 217. — Animal realms and regions.

ber and inferior in size. These natural conditions have been intensified by man, who has killed the flesh eaters and bred the grass eaters. North Africa has recently been connected by land bridges with Europe, and belongs to the Northern realm, which finds its southern land boundaries along the tropic in the natural barriers of the Mexican plateau, the Sahara and Arabian deserts, and the great mountain ranges of southern Asia.

Fig. 218. — Zebra.

The Indo-African Realm lies between the tropics and includes Africa south of the Sahara, Asia south of the Himalayas, and most of the islands of the East Indies. It is far richer in number and variety of species than the Northern realm. The plant eaters are well represented by wild cattle, asses, and horses in Asia and by antelopes and zebras in Africa; but the flesh eaters are even more conspicuous,

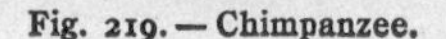

Fig. 219. — Chimpanzee.

Fig. 220. — Giraffes.

including the lion, tiger, leopard, and panther, the largest and most ferocious of their class. It is the home of the largest land animals, — the rhinoceros, hippopotamus, and elephant, — and of the tallest, — the giraffe. It is well supplied with four-handed folk, containing all the manlike apes, the gorilla, chimpanzee, and orang, and all the tailless monkeys, besides baboons, gibbons, and lemurs. Among its birds are eagles, vultures, ostriches, guinea fowls, peafowls, pheasants, and the jungle cock. Crocodiles and venomous serpents abound. More than half its mammals and birds do not occur elsewhere. In number, variety, and beauty of butterflies and beetles it is unrivaled. Central Africa is now the richest region in the world for big game, but white men will soon exterminate many of the species unless they are protected by law.

Fig. 221. — Ostriches.

The South American Realm is almost wholly tropical and includes the most extensive and luxuriant forests in the world. Large animals of the higher classes are singularly few. Notwithstanding the existence of the pampas, llanos, and campos (pp. 237, 239), which are vast seas of grass, the hoofed grass eaters are poorly represented by a few deer, the llama and three other small species of the camel family, the peccary, and the tapir. Horses, cattle, and sheep have been introduced from Europe. The beasts of prey are the puma, panther, and jaguar, the latter a match for the lion. Among animals peculiar to this realm are the little arma-

Fig. 222. — Llama.

dillos, the sluggish sloths, the toothless anteaters, and the long-tailed monkeys. Yet it is surpassingly rich in the lower forms of life, and is the paradise of naturalists. In birds, reptiles, fishes, and insects it is the most populous part of the world. Five sixths of the birds do not occur elsewhere. There are 400 species of humming birds. Among its serpents are the anaconda and boa constrictor, the largest of their kind; and turtles, crocodiles, and alligators abound.

Fig. 223. — Tapir.

Fig. 224. — Monkey.

Most of the animals in the world would thrive in South America if they could get there.

The Australian Realm, including Australia, New Zealand, New Guinea, and some small islands, presents the poorest and strangest assemblage of animals in the world. Most of its mammals belong to the small and unique group which carry their young in an abdominal pouch formed by a fold of skin. The largest is the kangaroo, as tall as a man, and making prodigious leaps with its powerful hind legs and tail. These and several species of large and almost wingless birds, the emus and cassowaries, are the most prominent of the native inhabitants.

Fig. 225. — Emu.

Fig. 226.—Kangaroo.

Flesh eaters are represented only by dogs. These lands have been long separated from the other continents by deep water, which has kept out all the larger and higher forms, including beasts and birds of prey. They are a sort of museum in which weak and inferior species, long ago destroyed in other lands, have been protected from enemies and preserved. The thoroughness of this protection is shown by the fact that rabbits introduced from Europe have so multiplied in the absence of enemies as to become a serious pest.

Islands are poor in species of both animals and plants in proportion to their distance from the continents. Mammals are often entirely wanting. Birds and insects, which can fly, and reptiles, whose eggs are not killed by salt water, are more numerous.

CHAPTER XVIII

THE HUMAN SPECIES

Man as an Animal. — Compared with the animals which are physically best equipped for the struggle for existence, man is in most respects inferior. He cannot fly, is a slow and awkward swimmer, and is easily outstripped in running. For defense he has no horns, or hoofs, or beak, or claws, and his teeth are small. His skin is soft, thin, and almost naked. The young require parental care for many years. His structure indicates descent from ancestors of apelike habits, living in trees, and on fruits. The physical characters which render him superior to all other animals pertain chiefly to the feet, hands, and skull. The feet and limbs are used for locomotion only, and he can stand and walk erect. The hands and arms are highly perfected and left free for use solely as organs for grasping, holding, and performing delicate and complex movements. The cranium has more than twice the capacity of that of any ape. Its bones do not unite for twenty years or more, thus enabling the brain to attain a weight in proportion to the total body weight superior to that of most other intelligent animals. The long period of growth, and the size and complexity of the brain, render possible a development of the mental powers which sets the human species apart from

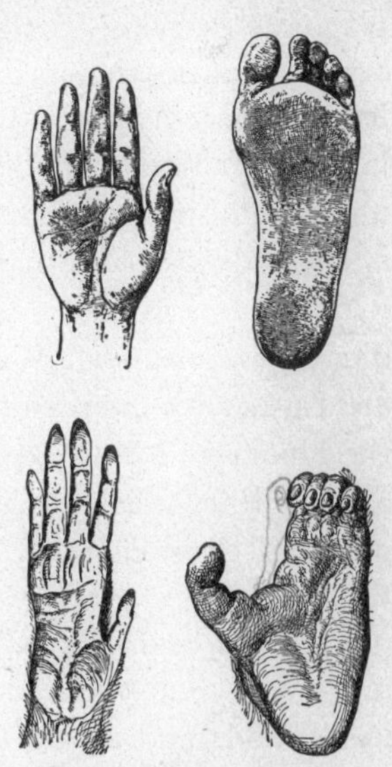

Fig. 227. — Hand and foot of the chimpanzee and of man.

all the other inhabitants of the earth, and almost immeasurably superior to them. With few exceptions, man is the only species in which the individuals coöperate in a complex way for the benefit of the community. It is by living in societies that man has become educated and civilized. "Man has not made society, but society has made man." All those things which are the result of human thought constitute a realm by itself, which may be called the *mind sphere* (*psychosphere*).

Enemies. — Man's worst enemies are no longer beasts of prey and venomous serpents, although these are still formidable in Africa and India, but the minute organisms which infect his body with disease. Many tribes of American Indians have been exterminated by smallpox and measles. To-day parts of central Africa are being depopulated by sleeping sickness. The plague is carrying off the people of India by the hundred thousand. Asiatic cholera and yellow fever, bred in the tropics, have repeatedly carried death into temperate countries. Malarial fever renders many parts of the equatorial regions almost uninhabitable by white men. Yet no one of these diseases is more destructive than the "white plague" of tuberculosis, which causes as many deaths in the United States every year as did the whole Civil War. All these diseases and many more are caused by microscopic plants or animals which multiply in the blood, and have been unrecognized until recently. Medical and sanitary science has discovered means of defense against many of these enemies, and may be expected to conquer all of them in time.

Varieties and Races. — Of all species of animals, man is the most widely distributed. His intelligence enables him to live in all lands and all climates between Greenland and Tierra del Fuego, and from marshes and islands near sea level to the high Andes and Himalayas. From his cradle land, which was probably in southern Asia, he seems to have migrated in all directions, without definite purpose or destination, wherever the land connections of those remote times furnished a road. Led on by the pursuit of food, or driven from place to place by enemies, he penetrated every unoccupied land, and while still in a very rude stage of culture took possession of most of the habitable world. In the struggle for existence under such a great variety of conditions, men, like other animals, necessarily developed differently and unequally. Hence arose four distinct races, differing in physical and mental characteristics. The hot, moist equatorial forests of central Africa produced a *black race* (Ethiopian), which spread over tropical Africa and the whole of Australia, which formed a new center, where men of a somewhat different and lower type were developed. The high, arid

Fig. 228. — Ethiopian race.

Fig. 229. — Mongolian race.

Fig. 230. — American race.

plateaus of central Asia produced a *yellow race* (Mongolian), which spread over nearly the whole of Asia and the neighboring islands. The American continent produced a *red race* (American), perhaps originally a branch of the yellow, which occupied its whole area for many centuries without interference from the rest of the world. North Africa and western Europe gave birth to a *white*

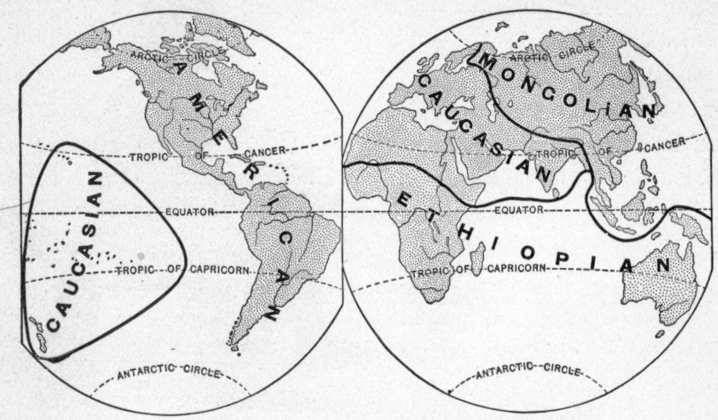

Fig. 231.—Distribution of races previous to modern migrations.

race (Caucasian), which, in historic times, has spread thence over northern and southern Asia, America, south Africa, and Australia, dispossessing or gaining control of the aboriginal races. Fig. 231 shows the distribution of the four races as it was previous to the modern migrations which began in the sixteenth century. The table on page 259 shows their distinctive characteristics and present distribution.

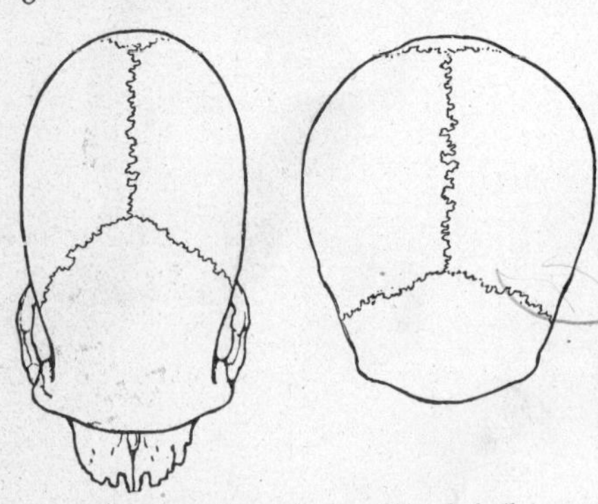

Fig. 232.—Long skull and broad skull.

Types of the Caucasian Race. — The peoples of each race, though alike in the characteristics mentioned on page 259, differ in many minor details. Among the peoples of the Caucasian race there are three well-marked types, Baltic, Alpine and Mediterranean:

	Ethiopian or Black Race (Fig. 228)	Mongolian or Yellow Race (Fig. 229)	A[illegible]d Race (F[illegible])	Caucasian or White Race (Figs. 233–235)
Home	Central Africa.	Central Asia.	America.	Europe, north Africa.
Color	Chocolate to black.	Yellowish to brown.	Coppery red.	Pale white to nearly black.
Hair	Black; frizzly, woolly, or shaggy.	Black, long, straight, coarse; beard scanty.	Black, long, straight, coarse; beard scanty.	Flaxen, red, brown, or black; straight, wavy, or curly; beard heavy.
Skull	Long and narrow.	Broad and round.	Variable.	Variable.
Jaws	Projecting.	Slightly projecting.	Massive.	Not projecting, small.
Lips	Thick and rolling.	Rather thin.	Medium.	Thin, or rather full.
Nose	Broad and flat.	Small and concave.	Large; straight, or aquiline.	Straight and narrow, with high bridge.
Eyes	Large, round, black; yellowish cornea.	Small, black, and oblique.	Small, black, and deep-set.	Blue, gray, brown, or black.
Culture	Very low; no science or letters; arts confined to agriculture, weaving, pottery, woodwork, and the use of simple implements of iron.	Ranges from savagery to civilization; agriculture and some arts well developed; letters common, but science and literature stagnant.	Ranges from the lowest savagery to low civilization; agriculture and the arts moderately developed in the highest; letters and science rudimentary.	Civilized, or enlightened; arts, industries, science, literature, and social institutions highly developed.
Present range	Africa, United States, West Indies, Brazil, Peru, Guiana, Australia, New Guinea, and neighboring islands.	All Asia, except India, Persia, Arabia, and Afghanistan; East Indies and Asiatic islands; northeastern Europe, Turkey.	Most of South and Central America, Mexico, Alaska, and Canada, and some small areas of the United States.	Europe, north and south Africa, northern and southern Asia, India, America, Australia, New Zealand, and many other islands.

1. *Baltic.* — Blond or florid, with flaxen or reddish glossy hair, blue eyes, long skull, and tall stature. Scandinavians, North Germans, Dutch, English, Scotch, Irish, and their descendants in America, Australia, and south Africa; West Persians, Afghans, many Hindus, and some other peoples of southwest Asia.

Fig. 233. — Baltic type. Darwin.

Fig. 234. — Alpine type. Pasteur.

Fig. 235. — Mediterranean type. — A Sicilian.

2. *Alpine.* — Light brown or swarthy, with brown, wavy dull hair, brown, gray, or black eyes, broad skull, and medium stature. Most French and Welsh, South Germans, Swiss, Russians, Poles, Bohemians, and other peoples of southeastern Europe; Armenians, East Persians, and the peoples of the eastern Pacific islands.

3. *Mediterranean.* — Olive brown to almost black, with dark

PART II. ECONOMIC GEOGRAPHY

CHAPTER XIX

NATURAL RESOURCES AND FOOD SUPPLY

Natural Resources. — Wherever and however men live, they are dependent upon the natural resources of the earth for a living. A naturalist on the coast of Australia relates how he came across a band of "black fellows," as the natives are called, at their camp, or rather lying-down place, for they had no huts or shelter of any kind. He hired them to show him the nests of a certain species of bird, promising to give them plenty of biscuit after they had shown the nests. They were all clothed in natural attire, the brown-black skin in which they were born, with the addition of a thick coat of white clay and red and yellow ochre on their faces and chests. Each man carried one or two spears, which he threw at the birds flying overhead. One climbed a tree, tore off some onion-like plants growing on the upper limbs, and threw them down to his companions, who ate them all up before he got down to claim his share. Along a stretch of rocky shore were many crabs, which the blacks caught and ate raw and alive. They also found sea snails with shells three or four inches long, which they strung on a reed stem to hang in the sun until the animal should die and putrefy, so that it could be drawn out and eaten. Some bulbs like Indian turnip were dug up and tied in their hair, to be cooked in the future. A lizard and a grub six inches long were tussled for, torn in pieces, and swallowed on the spot. The nests having been found and the biscuits handed over, the blacks filled themselves and lay down to sleep. They cared no more for the traveler or his biscuit. One had a short pipe tied to his arm, and was persuaded by the promise of tobacco to pilot the traveler back to the shore.

The wants of these savages are almost as simple as those of the animals around them, and they exercise but little more fore- than the animals iding for them. ropean colonists ir descendants living in the same country make use of a hundred natural resources of which the savages never dreamed. They grow wheat, corn, grapes, oranges, and other fruit, raise sheep and cattle, and mine coal, gold, copper, and tin. They have abundance of bread, meat, and fruit to eat, and clothing to wear. They use stone, brick, timber, and iron in constructing houses, vehicles, and ships. They travel with horses, steam cars, and automobiles. They use gold and silver for ornament and coinage. They exchange their own products with all the rest of the world for comforts and luxuries which they do not find at home. Their wants increase as the means of supply increase, and there is no limit to the number of things they can use. Yet the civilized man is as dependent upon natural resources as the savage.

Fig. 237. — Australian natives. (Ratzel.)

Utilization of Natural Resources. — Most natural resources must be worked over and utilized by human labor. Crude minerals are manufactured into implements and machinery, soils are made to yield food products, forests are converted into houses and ships. Man's desire to consume and his ability to produce have increased together with the progress of civilization. The earth is not only the home of man but also his workshop and school — a great "manual-training high school." While he has made it more habitable, comfortable, and luxurious, it has made him civilized. The study of those natural resources which are useful to man, and of the uses which men make of them, constitutes the science of *economic geography*.[1] It discusses the *influence* of natural environment upon human activities, and the conscious *reaction* of man upon his environment. It recognizes the relationship between nature and human welfare, and considers how the earth is fitted for the development of civilization.

The economic progress of man means his ability to make a better living, and depends upon natural resources and human faculty. Natural resources are practically unchangeable from age to age, but man, through the experience of thousands of years and by his increasing knowledge of nature, may improve his condition indefinitely.

Chief Natural Factors. — The chief natural factors of economic geography are (1) *the substratum*, or *ground*, including minerals, soils, and ground water, (2) *climate*, (3) *plants*, and (4) *animals*. Each of these factors contributes to human welfare directly, and also through its influence on the other factors.

Soil and ground water combine with climate to determine the character of vegetation. Plants manufacture food for animals, and both for man. Plants and animals are our neighbors and kinsmen, closely related to us physiologically, and more remotely by descent from common ancestors. They have developed with man, and their control and conquest have been comparatively easy.

Some natural resources essential for the existence of man are almost everywhere present, and so abundant as to require little or no attention.

[1] Economy means literally *housekeeping*, or household management.

Among these are air, water, insolation, and land. We live at the bottom of an ocean of air, which penetrates water and solid earth to great depths. The supply is inexhaustible, and it is difficult to shut it out; yet in mines and tunnels, fans and pumps are employed to insure safety, and in crowded rooms, houses, and cities a sufficient supply of good air is a serious problem. On the sea and in deserts the traveler must continually look to his water supply or pay the penalty with his life, and water for irrigation is a costly commodity. In well-watered regions some energy and expense are generally necessary to secure good water for domestic use, and in cities one of the largest items of public expenditure is for water. Insolation, or radiant energy from the sun, penetrates the atmosphere, and furnishes heat and light to every part of the face of the earth during half of each year. It makes plants grow, enables animals to live, and supplies all the power available for human industries.

Land, as *terra firma*, or a ground upon which men can stand, walk, live, and work, is abundant and, as yet, largely unoccupied. There is room enough in the state of Texas to contain all the people in the world and to give every man, woman, and child a space as large as an ordinary city lot. Most of the land is covered by some kind of soil which is workable and fertilizable, and its total productive capacity is sufficient to support many times the present population of the world. The substratum is only superficially known and used except in mining, which is limited in depth to about one mile. Its surface is generally traversable by roads.

Food Supply.—The only absolutely necessary thing which man must procure to live is food. A part of this is easily obtained from the mineral world in the form of air, water, and common salt, but man cannot live upon mineral food alone. He must depend upon plants to convert mineral matter, air, water, and salts into organic substances which he can assimilate. Generally he robs plants of the food which they have stored up for the next season or the next generation. Bulbs, thickened roots, tubers, fruits, nuts, and grains are local concentrations of food stuff in the plant which form staple articles of diet for men almost everywhere. The animal body contains still more concentrated food stuff, and almost every part of it except hair, feathers, and bones are eaten by men. Shellfish, fish, worms, reptiles, birds, and all the higher animals are caught, hunted, or bred. Materials provided by animals for the support of their young, such as eggs and milk, are of special value because they can be used without killing the animal which produces them.

Collective Economy. — The simplest way of getting a living is that in which men make no effort to produce anything, but live by *plucking* or collecting whatever nature provides, as in the case of the Australian black fellows. This is, of course, very inefficient, but in tropical countries nature is so prolific that people can live with little effort.

On the coral islands of the Pacific a few coconut trees will support a large family. No implements, or only very simple ones, are required. There is no incentive to stimulate discovery and invention, and men remain in a state of savagery. Tropical forests, savannas, and oceanic islands are most favorable for plant collection on account of the abundance and variety of edible fruits and nuts. Various species of palms, such as the oil palm, date palm, sago palm, and coconut palm, are important sources of food supply. The yam, a root resembling the sweet potato, and the banana, the most prolific of all food plants, flourish spontaneously and render labor almost unnecessary.

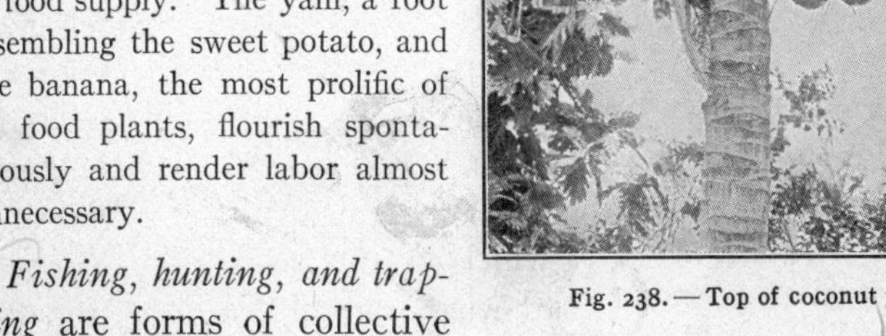

Fig. 238. — Top of coconut palm.

Fishing, hunting, and trapping are forms of collective economy which require considerable effort and skill. Implements and weapons, such as fishhooks, lines, nets, spears, harpoons, bows and arrows, must be designed and made, and the successful chase of the larger animals demands trained powers of body and mind.

Hunting furnishes a limited and precarious food supply, abundant at one time and scanty at another. A large territory is necessary to support a few people. The North American Indians of Columbus's time depended

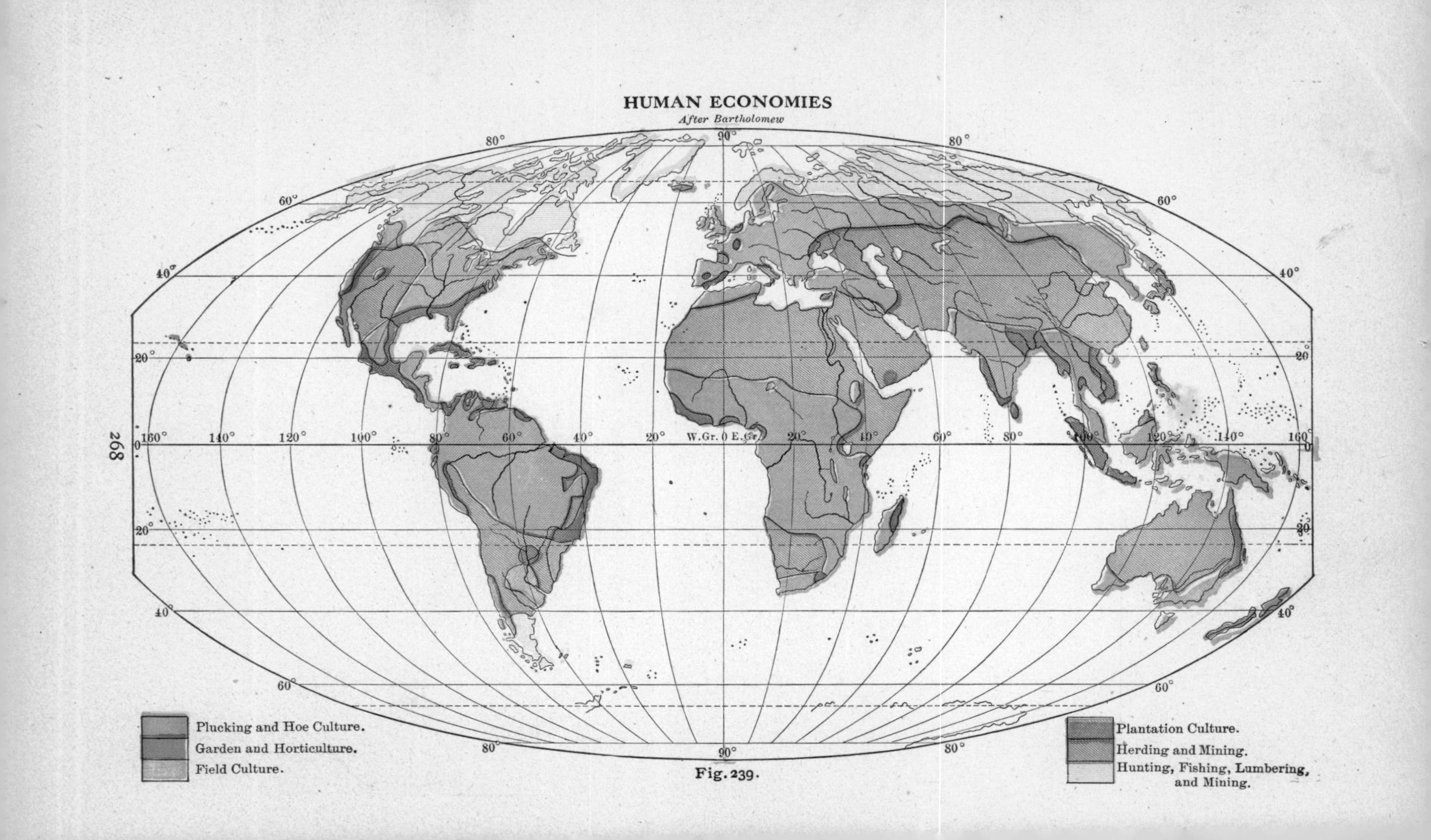
HUMAN ECONOMIES
After Bartholomew
W. Gr. 0 E. Gr.
Plucking and Hoe Culture.
Garden and Horticulture.
Field Culture.
Plantation Culture.
Herding and Mining.
Hunting, Fishing, Lumbering, and Mining.

Fig. 239.

upon the chase, and there were probably not more than one million of them on the continent north of Mexico. Hunting, trapping, and fishing survive and continue among highly civilized peoples. They are still the chief occupations in the great forest belts of the cold temperate zone. Fishing is carried on in favorable coast waters in all latitudes, but is most productive on both shores of the north Atlantic and north Pacific.

Fig. 240. — Hoe culture. (After Ratzel.)

Agriculture. — The domestication of plants is a long step toward a large and regular food supply. It was at first haphazard from seed accidentally sown. The planting and care of cultivated plants was begun and carried on entirely by women, who loosened the soil in favorable spots with a stick, planted seed, and cultivated the growing crop with rude hoes. This was the beginning of *hoe culture*, which now prevails in the equatorial forests and savannas of South America, Africa, and the East Indies. The banana, manioc, and yam are the staple crops (Fig. 249). As hoe culture becomes more efficient it develops into *garden culture*, which is intensive agriculture in small plots, the work being done mostly by hand. With heavy fertilization, several crops a year and a maximum production are possible. It prevails in densely populated subtropical countries where labor is cheap, as in China, Japan, India, Egypt, and some parts of France,

Fig. 241. — Garden culture.

Spain, and Italy. The value of the land is sometimes as high as $1,000 an acre. Special crops, such as celery, onions, vegetables, small fruits, and flowers are grown by improved methods of garden culture in many parts of the world.

Agriculture could not reach its highest stage of efficiency until animals were domesticated and trained for draft. Then a heavy, crotched stick could be used as a plow, from which the many forms of plows and cultivators now in use have been evolved. Thus has arisen the prevalent and, on the whole, the highest form of agriculture, *field culture*, carried on in fields and

Fig. 242. — Field culture.

farms of moderate size, largely by the use of animal power. A variety of crops are grown, and domestic animals are bred for food as well as for power. Field culture is general in the temperate regions of North America and Europe, and in smaller areas in the other continents. Labor is relatively costly. The laborers are free, and often independent owners of the land they cultivate, with small or moderate capital.

In *plantation culture* (Figs. 245, 248, 260, 261) special crops, such as cotton, sugar cane, coffee, tea, and rubber, are grown on large tracts. The laborers are often of inferior native or imported races, and under some form of servitude; ownership and control being in the hands of foreign proprietors with large capital.

This is the only practicable way, it is said, of utilizing the labor supply and developing the agricultural resources of tropical countries. Natives of such countries will not work steadily even for large wages, and are made to work, if at all, under some sort of compulsion. White men, as a rule, can not work in tropical countries; the proprietors find, therefore, that forced native labor, or none at all, are the only alternatives.

Cereal Grains. — The most valuable domesticated food plants are the cereal grains, — wheat, corn (maize), rice, oats, rye, and barley, — all of which are species of grass, and have been greatly modified and improved over the original wild forms.

Wheat probably originated in the highlands of western Asia. It is now extensively grown in the temperate and cool temperate regions of North

Fig. 243. — Harvesting wheat.

America and Europe, but is profitable on tropical plateaus and even on tropical lowlands as a winter crop. It requires a cool, moist growing season and a warm, dry ripening season. There are hundreds of varieties each adapted to special conditions of soil and climate; hence its range is very wide, extending from the tropic to the polar circle. The world's wheat crop is now 3,700 million bushels annually. Of this one third is raised in temperate Europe, and more than one fourth in temperate North

America. The subtropical countries of Europe and Asia produce about one fourth. There was a total increase of nearly one fifth in the ten years 1900–1910, which is approximately equal to the increase of population in wheat-eating countries. The average yield per acre is from eight bushels in Russia to thirty bushels in France, and could be doubled by more scientific farming. The possible world's wheat crop of the future is closely connected with the available supply of nitrogen and phosphorus (p. 145). The possibilities of wheat growing in southern South America are great, but as yet slightly developed. The United States, Canada, Russia, Ukraine, Roumania, Hungary, India, and Argentina raise wheat to sell, of which Great Britain is the largest purchaser. The people of France, United States, Great Britain, Austria, and Hungary consume the most wheat per capita.

Corn. — Indian corn [1] or maize originated in the subtropical plateaus of America. It was the only cereal known to the American Indians, and is the one best fitted for primitive hoe culture. Next to rice it is now the largest of the world's cereal crops and probably the largest of all food crops. It requires a longer and warmer growing season than wheat, and many days of bright sunshine to ripen it. Hence its range is from middle temperate to subtropical latitudes, and it is excluded from oceanic climates of cool summers and much cloudiness, such as that of the British Isles. The world's crop is about 4,000 million bushels, of which the United States produces about 3,000 million bushels. It is grown in southern Europe, Argentina, Mexico, India, Egypt, and south Africa. More than half the corn crop is fed to animals, chiefly swine and cattle, and thus converted into pork and beef. It is also extensively used in the manufacture of starch, grape sugar, beer, and alcohol. The stalks and leaves furnish excellent fodder for cattle. The direct use of the grain for human food is increasing, but in this it still falls far short of wheat.

Fig. 244. — Corn field.

[1] Corn is the common name of maize in the United States, but in Great Britain corn is a general name for all grains. In England the word usually means wheat, and in Scotland oats.

Oats. — The second largest cereal crop in temperate climates is oats, nearly 4,000 million bushels, of which the United States and Russia produce more than 1,000 million bushels each, and Germany half as much. Oats thrive in a cooler and damper climate than wheat, and hence have a larger range. Most of the crop is fed to horses, but it is excellent for human food and its use is increasing.

Rye. — Rye is a hardier grain than wheat, and can be grown with profit on soils where wheat cannot. It is used extensively by the peasants of Russia and Germany as a substitute for wheat in making "black bread," and in many countries in the manufacture of distilled liquors. The world's crop is about 1,500 million bushels, of which Russia produces one half and Germany one fourth.

Barley. — Barley has a wider range of latitude than any other cereal. It was once the chief breadstuff of the civilized world, but is now mostly fed to stock and converted into malt for brewing beer. The world's crop is nearly 1,500 million bushels, one fourth grown in Russia and the rest well distributed throughout the grain-producing countries.

Rice. — The chief cereal grain of warm, wet climates is rice. It is the principal food crop of southeastern Asia from India to Japan, and the

Fig. 245. — Rice field.

breadstuff of nearly one third the human race. There are several varieties, but those extensively grown are water plants and require flooded fields during most of the season. Hence alluvial and delta lands with abundant water under control are most favorable. The grain is not generally ground to flour, but the processes of hulling and polishing to remove chaff and skin are complex and costly. With the use of improved machinery, similar to that used for wheat, the rice crop of southern United States is increasing rapidly and now amounts to 40 million bushels a year. It is impossible to ascertain the total world's crop, but it probably exceeds that of any other grain.

Fig. 246. — Potato field.

Root Crops. — Root crops are well adapted for hoe culture, and are generally indicative of a lower stage of civilization than grain crops.

In tropical countries the yam, sweet potato, manioc (cassava), and taro can be raised with little labor and furnish a large amount of bulky food. The manioc of the Amazon basin is the source of tapioca used in temperate countries for desserts, and is being grown in the United States as food for cattle. The most valuable root crops are potatoes and sugar beets. The potato originated in the high plateaus of tropical South America, but from its common use in Ireland has acquired the name of Irish potato. The world's crop is about 5,500 million bushels, of which Germany and Russia produce more than half. Potatoes are used in Europe as a source of starch and alcohol.

Fig. 247. — Sugar beets.

Sugar Beets are grown chiefly in Europe. Germany, Austria, Hungary, Russia, and France produce four fifths of the world's crop. Seven million tons of sugar, or one third the world's supply, are made from beets. They are profitable in cool, dry climates, and supplement the tropical supply of sugar from the cane. The pulp from which most of the sugar has been extracted is used to fatten swine.

Fig. 248. — Cutting sugar cane, Louisiana.

Sugar Cane. — Sugar is not merely a luxury and a condiment, but a valuable and stimulating food. Its use has grown in a few centuries to enormous proportions. The source of the largest supply is the sugar cane, a species of tropical grass. It is grown from cuttings planted in deep, rich, moist, but well-drained soil, and requires a hot season of seven or eight months to mature. The canes are cut and passed between rollers, which press out the juice. The liquid is purified and evaporated until the sugar crystallizes. It is afterwards refined to remove the coloring matter and again crystallized into white sugar. Cuba, India, Java, Hawaii, and Porto Rico produce three fourths of the world's supply of cane sugar.

Fig. 249. — Banana and manioc. (Schimper.)

Fruits. — In tropical countries fruits are the mainstay of life; in temperate countries they are in some degree superfluities and luxuries. The

Fig. 250. —Date palms.

quantity and variety of tropical fruits spontaneously produced encourage collective economy only.

The banana and its near relative, the plantain, are the most prolific of all food plants and will support five times as many people per acre as grain. In the East Indies the mango and breadfruit, and in the oases and irrigated tracts of the subtropical deserts the date palm, are in themselves sufficient to feed a dense population. In the Mediterranean region the olive takes the place of butter and meat. The citrus fruits, including many varieties of the orange, lemon, and lime, have become plentiful in the principal markets of the world. The grape has a wider range than the fruits above mentioned, and is common both fresh and in the form of raisins and wine. France produces more wine than any other country. Of the strictly temperate climate fruits, apples are the most important, with pears, peaches, and plums as a secondary crop. Cold storage and rapid transportation bring the fruits of all climes to every civilized man's door, and at almost all seasons. Fruit raising partakes of the character of both plucking and agriculture, but in the temperate zones it is fast becoming a highly specialized branch of scientific agriculture.

Fig. 251.—Vineyard, New York.

The Domestication of Animals. — The domestication of animals was as important a step in human progress as the domestication of plants. One and perhaps the chief cause of the backward condition of the American Indians before their contact with Europeans was the lack of domestic animals: the only animals which they domesticated were small species of the camel family in the Andes, and the dog. In well-populated countries the dangerous, destructive, and least useful animals have been exterminated, and many of the useful wild animals nearly so. Domestic animals have been bred, spread, multiplied, diversified, and improved until they have lost to a large extent their ancestral characters.

Herding. — In Eurasia domestic animals have been bred since prehistoric times. A lasso stage, in which wild animals

Fig. 252. — **Herding in Asia.** Tents and utensils are easily moved.

are caught alive, is intermediate between hunting and breeding. The vast steppe regions of central Eurasia have been for thousands of years the home of peoples whose chief occupation is herding. Their wealth consists of flocks and herds of cattle, horses, sheep, goats, and camels, which are driven from place to place in search of fresh pasturage. Hence the people are nomadic, having no fixed home, and their houses, usually tents, and domestic utensils are all designed to be easily movable. Political organization and centralized government are almost impossible, and the place of both is filled by patriarchal rule, in which the head of the family exercises control over a group, consisting of a family of blood relatives, with their wives, children, servants, and dependents. The story of Abraham, Isaac, Jacob, and Joseph in the book of Genesis gives a vivid picture of nomadic, patriarchal life as it was three thousand years ago, and as it still exists to-day.

Cattle. — Of all the domestic animals, horned cattle are the most important and valuable for their flesh, milk, and labor. A damp, temperate climate, with quick-growing grass, is most favorable for cattle. Mountainous and oceanic lands produce the best milk, steppe regions the best meat. The Mediterranean climates, with dry summers, are distinctly unfavorable. In some parts of Africa cattle cannot exist on account of a disease communicated by the bite of the tzetze fly.

Fig. 253. — Herding cattle, United States.

Cattle are numerous in all the good agricultural countries of the world, and number about 460 millions. Europe has about 125 millions, India 140 millions, the United States 68 millions, and Argentina 25 millions. In the "Great Plains" or steppe region of North America the vast herds of wild bison, or buffaloes, which once occupied them, have been displaced by domestic cattle under the care of "cowboys." The cattle thrive on the nutritious bunch grass, which cures spontaneously on the ground, and some live out all winter by scraping away the snow with their hoofs. When the grass is covered with ice and sleet the losses from cold and starvation are very large. The former free range on public lands is now generally broken up and fenced into large ranches under private ownership, and the cattle are fed in the winter with cut hay. The farmers of the middle western states buy large numbers of young cattle from the ranches to fatten on corn and fodder. Kansas City, Omaha, St. Louis, and Chicago are the principal cattle markets and slaughtering and packing centers of the world.

The pampas of the Plata region of South America furnish a vast extent of pasturage which has never been fully utilized. Herds of cattle have been bred there and slaughtered for their hides only, but with cold storage and improved means of transportation the flesh is also marketed. South Africa, Australia, and New Zealand are also favorable regions for cattle raising. Eastern United States and Canada, Ireland, the Netherlands, Denmark, Sweden, Finland, France, and Switzerland are the leading dairy countries.

The zebu or humped cattle of India are adapted to savannas, and the water buffalo (Fig. 254), the principal beast of burden and draft in China, Japan, and the Philippines, where it is known as the carabao, is as well adapted for service in tropical swamps as the camel for the desert. On the plateaus and mountains of Asia, above 6,000 feet, the yak is the most hardy beast of burden, and is used also for milk and flesh.

Sheep.—The sheep is a steppe animal and does best in dry subtropical and temperate lands (Fig. 202). Sheep will live upon short, scanty pasturage where cattle would starve, and if permitted will do serious injury to grazing grounds. Large,

Fig. 254. — Water buffalo, Siam.

coarse-wooled sheep are bred for mutton, and smaller, fine-wooled animals for wool. In a wet climate the wool is poor, and in a hot climate it is scanty. Australia, the Plata countries, Russia, and the United States lead in the production of wool, mutton, and hides. Frozen mutton is shipped from Australia and New Zealand to Europe. The total number of sheep in the world is estimated at more than 575 millions.

Fig. 255. — Goat, Switzerland.

Goats are hardy animals, and will pick up a good living from coarse, rough herbage which cattle and sheep would not eat. In mountainous countries and regions of scant summer rain, they are bred for their flesh and their milk, which is very rich. Goat and kid skins are used extensively in the manufacture of gloves.

Horses. — The horse attains his highest perfection on the steppes, where he is admirably adapted for riding, and is used in the chase, in herding, and in war. Eastern Europe and north Africa have been repeatedly invaded and overrun by horsemen from the Asiatic steppes. The horse's leg is a combination of levers which makes it mechanically the most efficient of animal motor machines. In Asia mares are bred for their milk, which forms the staple food of many nomad peoples. The flesh is sometimes eaten. The horse is most used among the most advanced peoples, and may be regarded as the characteristic animal of civilization.

Many varieties have been developed for speed, beauty, and strength and used for riding, driving, and draft. Horse racing is a favorite sport among British, French, and American people. No other animal is so intimately related to human activities, and in spite of the multiplication of other means of locomotion, the horse is not likely to lose his place as the most useful servant of mankind. The number of horses in the world is about 95 millions.

The *ass*, or donkey, or burro, is less intelligent than the horse, but more hardy and sure-footed. He thrives on coarse fodder, is strong in proportion to his size, and is very useful as a beast of burden in rough countries. The *mule*, a cross between the ass and the mare, inherits the good qualities of both parents, and will perform hard service in rough and hot countries where the horse would fail. In 1898 it was found necessary to supply the British army in South Africa with mules shipped from the United States at a cost of $1,000 a head.

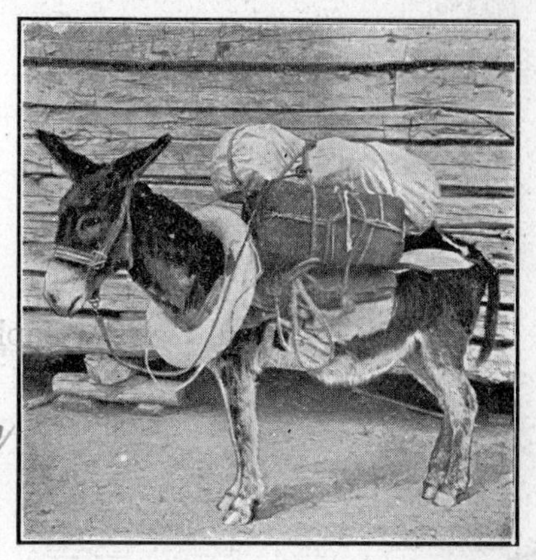

Fig. 256. — Burro.

Swine. — Pork has come to be second only to beef in the meat supply of the world. The hog is omnivorous in his diet and never-failing in appetite. He is the only animal that, beginning at birth, can gain, on the average, a pound a day in weight for 250 days. He is the poor man's animal, because he can subsist largely upon the waste products of the forest and farm. In China swine are the only large domestic animals, and pork is the only flesh food used by the common people, except birds and fish. More swine are raised in the United States than in any other country, and a large part of the corn crop is converted into pork. There are not less than 180 million swine in the world.

Camels. — The camel (Fig. 293) is the domestic animal of the warm deserts, to which he is wonderfully well adapted. His feet are expanded into large pads, which prevent his sinking into the sand. His stomach is triple and can hold several gallons of water. His nostrils are slits which can be voluntarily closed when the air is full of wind-driven sand. His hump is a mass of fat, which is absorbed when food is insufficient. He can carry a load of 400 to 1,000 pounds, drink brackish water, and go a month without drinking. In the deserts of Asia and north Africa he is the indispensable beast of burden. In disposition he is stupid and vicious.

Four small species of the camel family are natives of the Andes mountains. The *llama* (Fig. 222) is used in Peru and Bolivia as a beast of burden, but will carry a load of only 80 pounds. The *vicuña* and *guanaco* are raised for flesh and wool, and the *alpaca* furnishes a hair of considerable value for dress goods.

Reindeer. — The reindeer bears the same relation to the tundra as the camel to the warm deserts. Its foot is adapted to snow as the camel's to sand. It is bred in northern Eurasia for milk, flesh, and draft. A Lapland family may keep a herd of 500 reindeer. They have recently been introduced into Alaska and are found very serviceable.

Dogs. — The dog was originally a wolf which hung around human habitations to steal food. He was at first tolerated and finally adopted as a domestic parasite. He is the only animal except the cat which man has come to regard as a member of the family. He has been found useful as a scavenger, for food, herding, hunting, and draft; but the large majority of dogs are of no use except as pets and companions. In ice deserts, tundras, and cold temperate forests in winter, dogs are indispensable draft animals, all travel and transportation being by dog sledge. The Arctic or Eskimo dog is but little better than a wolf in disposition, but he is strong and hardy, can live on frozen fish, and can sleep out of doors in any weather.

Fig. 257. — Elephant.

Elephants. — The elephant is kept in domestication in India and Siam and used for riding, hunting, and display. His strength and intelligence render him valuable in more menial employments, such as hauling and piling timber. The wild African elephant has been hunted for pleasure and for his tusks, which furnish ivory, until the species is threatened with extinction.

Fig. 258. — Poultry.

Poultry. — The domestic birds include the common fowl, goose, duck, pigeon, turkey, guinea fowl, peafowl, and ostrich. The common barnyard fowl, descended from the wild jungle cock of India, is one of the most valuable of animals. Many varieties have been developed by breeding and have spread to nearly all parts of the habitable world. The flesh and eggs are so palatable and nutritious as to be generally esteemed as semi-luxuries. The total value of poultry and eggs produced in the United States annually is about $1,200,000,000.

Geese and ducks are waterfowl bred for flesh, eggs, and feathers. Domestic pigeons are largely "fancy" birds, bred to many fantastic forms and used to a limited extent as food. The turkey, the only domestic bird native to America, is scarcely known elsewhere. The guinea fowl from Africa and the peafowl from Asia are more ornamental than useful. The African ostrich (Fig. 221) is valuable for his plumes.

Insects. — The only domesticated insects are the silkworm and the bee.

The breeding and care of the *honey bee* has become a highly specialized art in nearly all civilized countries. The honey is made by the bees from the nectar of flowers and stored in combs or cells of wax for their own use and for feeding the young. With proper management a swarm of bees will produce a large surplus beyond their own needs.

The *silkworm* is the caterpillar of a moth which spins a cocoon yielding the fiber of raw silk. The caterpillars are hatched and fed upon the leaves of mulberry trees which are grown for the purpose.

Fig. 259. — Feeding silkworms.
The silkworms are the white objects in the trays.

China, Japan, and Italy furnish 95 per cent of all the raw silk that is produced.

Physiological Luxuries and Medicines. — There is a large class of substances, mostly of vegetable origin, which have little or no value as food, but which men use internally for various purposes. They include spices, condiments, and flavors which give food an agreeable taste or stimulate digestion, stimulants and narcotics which produce agreeable sensations, and medicines which relieve pain or assist in the cure of disease.

Condiments and Spices. — In the Middle Ages, spices were among the most valuable goods which could be marketed in Europe, because they rendered dried and salted meats and poorly cooked food more palatable. Arabia was called "the land of spices" because the supply came through that country from the Far East. The blockade of the caravan routes by the Turks stimulated efforts to open a sea route to the "spice islands" and led directly to the voyages of Da Gama around Africa and of Columbus to America.

Mustard is now the most important condiment and the most widely distributed. It is made from the seed of several plants grown in Europe, the United States, Asia, and the East Indies. *Vinegar*, made from cider, wine, and other alcoholic liquors, is in common use in all civilized countries.

Spices are tropical products grown in India, Ceylon, China, the East and West Indies, Zanzibar, Mexico, and South America. Pepper is made from dried berries, cloves from flower buds, nutmegs from fruit stones, cinnamon from bark, and ginger from roots. Cayenne or red pepper and vanilla are the fruits of plants grown chiefly in Mexico.

Stimulants and Narcotics. — *Alcoholic liquors* are used by people of nearly all races, countries, and classes. Their use is prohibited among the believers of the Mohammedan religion. They are made by the fermentation of sugar derived from fruits, grains, roots, or any material containing starch. The yeast plant, a microscopic organism, is the only agent known by which sugar can be converted into alcohol cheaply and on a large scale. The yeast is added to a solution containing sugar or allowed to grow from spores everywhere present in the air.

Wines of many varieties are made from the fermentation of grape juice, and are the common beverage in the warm temperate regions of Europe. *Beer* is made from barley or corn and is a favorite drink in northern Europe. Distilled liquors contain a much higher percentage of alcohol than wine or beer. *Whisky* is distilled from corn, rye, and potatoes, *brandy* from wine, and *rum* from sugar cane. In Japan *sakê* is made from rice, in Mexico *pulquê* from the century plant, and in India *toddy* from the coconut palm. From any of these sources pure alcohol may be obtained by careful distillation, and is manufactured in large quantities, not for drinking, but as a chemical product used in many important arts and for fuel. Alcohol has no direct food value, but is a stimulant and intoxicant, more or less injurious to body and mind.

Fig. 260. — Coffee plantation, Straits Settlements.

Coffee, *tea*, *matê*, and *cocoa* are mild stimulants, not intoxicating, and generally harmless. *Coffee* is the seed of a small tree grown by the plantation system chiefly in Brazil, and in smaller quantities in Venezuela, Central America, Java, Mexico, and the West Indies.

Brazil furnishes about two thirds of the 2,600 million pounds exported annually. It is used more largely in the United States than in any other country.

Fig. 261. — Picking tea.

Tea is the dried young leaves of a shrub which yields best on tropical highlands with warm, rainy summers. China and Japan have had until recently a monopoly of tea growing, but now the plantations of India and Ceylon furnish three fifths of the 770 million pounds exported. Russia and Great Britain are the largest consumers of tea. *Yerba maté*, or Paraguay tea, consists of the dried leaves of a tree growing wild in southern South America and possesses the same stimulating qualities as tea. Its use is local, very little being exported.

Cocoa and *chocolate* are prepared from cacao beans, the seeds of a tree which grows in the lowlands of tropical America, the East Indies, and west Africa. They contain a mild stimulant and a large percentage of oil, starch, and albuminoids which render them highly nutritious.

Tobacco and *opium* are narcotic stimulants possessing decided physiological and medicinal properties. Tobacco, originally a native of America, has in the last 300 years ex-

Fig. 262. — Cacao tree.

tended over the entire world, and has come into general use among all kinds of people. Naturally a semi-tropical plant, it is now grown as far north as Connecticut, Wisconsin, and Germany. Its quality, flavor, and value are greatly modified by soil, climate, cultivation, and curing. It requires a growing season at least as long as corn, but is much more exhausting to the soil.

Fig. 263. — Tobacco field.

The whole plant is cut and hung up to dry, the leaves are stripped off and slightly "sweated" or fermented, the stems are removed and the blades rolled into cigars or put up in various forms for smoking and chewing. The "seed leaf" used for cigar wrappers is grown in Sumatra, the Philippines, and the Connecticut valley, where the gross value of the crop is sometimes $10,000 an acre. The relation of tobacco to the human race is unique. Purely a luxury, and with no beneficial effect upon the system, it is a mild narcotic which, though usually injurious, is not ruinous, and has an attraction for people of all classes, from the most degraded to the most refined, possessed by no other substance except, perhaps, alcohol. The United States produces about one half the crop of 2,200 million pounds.

Opium is the dried juice of the white poppy grown in India, China, Persia, and Turkey. It is smoked in small pipes as a narcotic by the Chinese and other Oriental peoples. Its effects are much more serious than those of tobacco, and opium smoking in China has become a national danger. Morphine, laudanum, and other derivatives of opium are extensively used in medicine to relieve pain, but should never be taken except under the direction of a physician, since there is grave danger of acquiring the opium habit, which is very difficult to cure.

Medicines. — Medicines are largely extracted from crude drugs, or the dried bark, leaves, and seeds of plants. The varieties in common use are very numerous, and most of them are of great value for the relief and cure of disease. Of substances which are purely medicinal, wholly beneficial, and almost invaluable to man, *quinine* may be taken as a type. It is obtained from the bark of the cinchona tree, a native of the tropical South American forest. The natural supply has long been insufficient, and the cinchona plantations of Java now furnish 86 per cent of the 17 million pounds of bark required to supply the world. Quinine is the only safe and efficient antidote to malaria, and without it the occupation of the tropics by white men would have been impossible.

CHAPTER XX

CLOTHING AND CONSTRUCTIVE MATERIALS

Clothing. — After food, the object for which the greatest amount of human energy is expended is clothing. Clothes are not naturally as important as they seem. They are not required and are not worn for protection by half the people in the world. The natives of Tierra del Fuego in 55° S. Lat. go naked and do not appear to suffer. In tropical regions the common people wear very little clothing, and that chiefly for ornament. Civilized people are prevented from going naked by a sense of modesty, and a sense of what is becoming or in fashion determines the material, cut, style, color, and other details. The simplest of all dress is the coat of clay and mineral paint used by the Australian black fellow, or the mixture of grease and soot with which a Central African belle anoints herself. They are regarded as ornamental, and they furnish some protection against insects. Some articles of clothing have come into use for convenience in carrying small articles, as the belt around the waist, and bands around the arms. Simple clothing is often made of leaves, bark, grass, or straw, more or less skillfully braided or woven together. In regions of cold winters, men rob animals of their fur, feathers, and skins.

All these things are obtainable by collective economy, but herding and agriculture are necessary to supply light, pliable, comfortable, and durable garments, which are generally woven from some kind of fiber, and are therefore called *textiles*. The principal vegetable fibers are cotton and linen, and the principal animal fibers are wool and silk.

Cotton. — The hairs which cover the seeds and fill the bolls of the cotton plant furnish the best fiber known for cloth and small cordage. It is strong, soft, fine, flexible, and easily dyed and washed, — an almost ideal combination of qualities. Cotton produces the best fiber in a tropical climate near salt water. It is grown from seed, cultivated like corn, and picked usually

Fig. 264. — Cotton field, South Carolina.

by hand. The seeds are separated from the fiber by a machine called a gin, and contain an oil valuable for food and for soap making.

On account of the large amount of hand labor required, cotton has generally been grown by the plantation system. The invention of the gin, the spinning jenny, and the power loom, in the latter part of the eighteenth century, made it possible to utilize large quantities of the fiber, which stimulated production and increased the supply until cotton became the cheapest and most plentiful of all textiles. The invention of a successful machine for picking cotton will put cotton cloth practically within reach of every human being. The world's cotton crop is about 10,000 million pounds, of which the United States produces one half, India one fifth, and Asiatic Russia one twelfth.

Linen. — Linen is made from the fiber of the stem of the flax plant. The process of separating it from the wood and preparing it for spinning is long and difficult. Hence linen is far more expensive than cotton, and is used for laces, napkins, and articles of luxury. Flaxseed furnishes linseed oil, which is indispensable in mixing good paint. Russia produces about four fifths of the world's supply of flax.

Wool. — The animal fibers most useful for cloth are obtained from sheep, goats, and camels, including the alpaca and vicuña. Sheep's wool is used in all cold countries for heavy clothing, especially that worn by men. Australia and Argentina produce about half the wool exported.

Silk. — The silkworm spins a cocoon of fine, lustrous, elastic threads which form the raw silk of commerce. A large amount of hand labor is required in feeding and caring for the worms, unwinding the threads, and preparing them for the loom, hence the industry is confined to countries where wages are low.

Artificial silk, but little inferior to the natural fiber and much cheaper, is now being manufactured. For serviceable clothing silk is inferior to cotton and wool, but is superior in beauty. It is used extensively for laces, ribbons, and velvets.

Fig. 265. — Rubber trees.
The marks on the trees are cuts in the bark, from which to collect the sap.

Rubber. — The milky juice (*latex*) of various species of tropical plants forms a gummy mass when dried, and is used to render textiles waterproof. The supply obtained from native wild plants in Brazil is now small compared with that from cultivated plantations in the Straits Settlements, Malay States, and Ceylon.

Furs and Leather. — The skins of animals have always formed an important part of human clothing, either cured with the fur on or converted into leather. Deerskin was the chief reliance of the North American Indian, as sealskin is of the Eskimo, and sheepskin of the shepherd peoples of Eurasia.

Among highly civilized peoples furs have become articles of luxury, and some, such as seal, otter, ermine, marten, sable, beaver, and silver fox, command fabulous prices. Canada and Russia are the principal fur-producing countries. Leather, made by soaking hides in a solution of tanbark or other chemical agent which renders them tough and impervious to water, has become an indispensable article for shoes and gloves. Thus men protect their extremities which are most exposed to rough usage. Leather is made from the skins of cattle, horses, swine, sheep, goats, dogs, and many other animals.

Fig. 266. — Straw hut, Hawaii.

Shelter. — Few, if any, human beings live so simply as never to need shelter of any kind. Some kind of a lair is necessary as a place for rest and sleep. A tree, forest, overhanging rock, or cave may furnish shelter from heat, cold, wild animals, or enemies, and men soon learn to improve these natural advantages. Sticks, grass, leaves, and boughs are among the most easily available materials, and a large part of the human race still live in more or less elaborate huts made from them. With the progress of the mechanic arts men have become able to use trees for timber and to construct from them commodious and luxurious homes. Hence have arisen all the refinements of lumbering, carpentry, and cabinet work.

Fig. 267. — Log house.

Among the early inhabitants of Europe were the cave men, who inhabited the natural limestone caverns, furnished them with the skins of wild beasts, and even decorated their walls with paintings. In some parts of France inhabited houses and even churches are still made by enlarging and improving natural caverns. In China thousands of people live in houses dug out of the soft but firm deposits of loess (p. 144), and the pioneer in the American prairies and steppes often lives at first in a "dugout"

Fig. 268. — Rock house, France. (Robin.)

Fig. 269. — Sod house. (U.S.G.S.)

or in a sod house. The Eskimo finds chunks of frozen snow cut to proper shape the best material for building a hut adapted to his needs in an Arctic climate. In countries of small rainfall and with alluvial or adobe soils, sun-dried bricks are easily made and built into huts or houses which are comfortable and permanent.

Copyright by Doubleday, Page & Co.

Fig. 270. — Igloo or Eskimo snow house.

In most parts of the world clay is plentiful, from which bricks can be made and hardened by burning into excellent building materials. Many kinds of rock, such as sandstone, limestone, granite, and slate, are quarried and used to construct the most substantial and imposing buildings. For many thousand years various ores, especially those of iron, have been mined and smelted and the extracted metals used in all sorts of construction. Hence the industries of quarrying, mining, and metallurgy have grown to enormous proportions. These industries belong to scientific collective economy, since they collect and utilize natural materials, but do not produce them as in agriculture or stock raising.

Fig. 271. — Redwoods.
200 to 300 feet high.

Timber. — Of all materials for construction wood is the most generally useful, and for most purposes that furnished by the coniferous forests (pp. 234–236) is the best.

Pine, spruce, fir, hemlock, larch, cedar, and redwood lumber is light, strong, durable, and easily worked, and can be had in pieces of large dimensions. None is better than the white pine of North America, which is ten times as strong as steel of equal weight. The yellow or hard pine of the southern states is full of resin, from which turpentine, rosin, and tar are extracted. The timber is hard, strong, durable, and fit for heavy construction, while its beautiful color and grain make it desirable for inside work in houses. The Douglas fir of the Pacific coast of North America is especially valuable in ship-building on account of the length and size of timbers which can be cut from it. California redwood, a near relative of the Sequoias, or "big trees," is famous for the size of the individual trees and the yield of merchantable lumber per acre. Redwoods grow from 200 to 300 feet high, with a diameter of

10 to 20 feet, and so close together that it is difficult to drive a wagon between them. The redwood forests are confined to the Coast Ranges of California and Oregon, and at the present rate of cutting are likely to disappear at an early date. White spruce is being cut at a rapid rate for the manufacture of paper pulp. White cedars are used largely for posts, telegraph poles, and shingles; and red cedar, or juniper, is familiar in lead pencils. These cedars are well distributed throughout the forest regions of the United States and Canada. The hemlock of the north and the cypress of the south are inferior to the pine as timber trees, but are used as a substitute for it. The Norway spruce, the European pine, fir, and larch, and the Indian cypress and deodar are among the chief timber trees of their respective countries. The area of coniferous forests in northern North America and Eurasia is very large (Fig. 192). No part of it is more valuable than that on the Pacific coast from California to Alaska.

The broad-leaved and generally deciduous timber trees are more widely distributed and of greater variety than the coniferous trees.

The tulip tree, poplar, and linden, or basswood, common in eastern United States, furnish soft, light wood easily worked. The linden is common in Europe. Of close-grained hardwoods the maple, beech, birch, and sycamore, or plane tree, exist in many species throughout temperate North America and Europe. Among the coarse-grained hardwoods the oaks hold the first place in number of species, wide distribution, and value of timber.

Fig. 272. — Floating logs to a sawmill. (U.S.G.S.)

They are the most abundant timber trees of eastern North America and Europe, and extend across south central Asia to Japan. Cork is the bark of a species of oak growing in the Mediterranean region. The ash, chestnut, elm, hickory, locust, and many other less important trees furnish wood of much value for various purposes. Among the woods famous for their beauty of color and grain, and commanding high prices for furniture, cabinet work, and interior finish, the black walnut, butternut, cherry, and gum are native to eastern United States. Still more highly prized is mahogany, imported from tropical America and west Africa to Europe and the United States. Rosewood and ebony are tropical woods used entirely for fancy or ornamental purposes. One of the most valuable of all woods for heavy construction is the teak of India, Indo-China, and the East Indies. The gum or eucalyptus trees of Australia are not much inferior to teak.

Fig. 273. — Sawmill, North Carolina. (U.S.G.S.)

Lumbering. — Lumbering is a form of specialized collective economy, which consists in cutting trees into logs and transporting them by sled, wagon, rail, or water to mills to be sawed, planed, and otherwise elaborated for particular uses.

Fig. 274. — Burned forest, Washington. (U.S.G.S.)

The people of Europe and the United States have destroyed their native forests to such an extent that timber has become scarce and high-priced.

The future supply must be largely imported from the northern forests, or much of the land originally timbered must be reforested. The conservation of forests, which includes the cutting of timber without unnecessary waste, the prevention of forest fires, and the replanting of tracts of little value for other purposes, is one of the most important problems of present-day economics. The science of forestry has been highly developed in Germany and is being taken up in the United States.

Fig. 275. — Result of deforestation, China. The land has been ruined by erosion. (Carnegie Institution, *Research in China.*)

Paper. — Paper is made from various vegetable fibers by grinding and digesting to a pulp, which is then rolled into sheets. Fine book and writing papers are made from linen, coarse wrapping paper from straw, and newspaper from wood pulp. The spruce forests of North America are being rapidly used up in the manufacture of wood pulp.

Clay. — Of all minerals used in construction, clay is the most widely diffused and readily available. It is a product of the decay of feldspar. By mixing, molding, and heating, common

Fig. 276. — Clay works.

clay is made into building, paving, and fire brick, tiling, sewer pipe, and pottery. Pure clay, or *kaolin*, is mixed with other materials to make fine porcelain and chinaware.

Cement. — Mortar made of quicklime and sand is generally used to bind brick and stone work together. In recent years, owing partly to the increasing cost of wood, hydraulic or Portland cement, made by heating and grinding a mixture of clay and lime, has come into general use. The mixture of cement, sand, and gravel or broken stone called *concrete* is really an artificial conglomerate, and is displacing brick and other materials in paving and house building. When reinforced by an imbedded framework of steel, concrete is superior to steel or stone alone for bridge construction.

Fig. 277. — Quarrying granite, New Hampshire.

Building Stone. — Stone is used the world over for foundations, bridge piers, docks, breakwaters, pavements, public buildings, and costly private structures. Its value depends upon many factors, such as ease of quarrying and working, strength under a crushing load, hardness, color, and resistance to weather.

Probably limestone is most extensively used, but sandstone, granite, and volcanic rocks of various kinds are valuable. Metamorphic limestone, or marble, on account of its beautiful colors and the high polish of which it is capable, is a favorite ornamental stone for buildings, monuments, statuary, and furniture.

Quartz, the most abundant of all solid minerals, occurs in massive quartzite and sandstone, in common sand, and in transparent crystals. It has many colors.

Agate, amethyst, onyx, chalcedony, carnelian, chrysoprase, heliotrope, jasper, opal, and many other varieties of quartz are semi-precious stones prized for their color and luster. Millstones, grindstones, and whetstones are fine-grained sandstones. Flint is a hard variety of quartz which was used all over the world before the discovery of iron for weapons and cutting implements. *Glass* is made by heating a mixture of pure quartz sand and soda ash to a very high temperature. Most glass articles are shaped by blowing air into melted glass through a metal tube. Various ingredients are added to give color, luster, and other special qualities.

Ores and Metals. — An ore is a mineral from which a metal may be profitably extracted. Most ores have been deposited by solution in ground water which rises from the depths of the earth, and occur in fissures called veins, lodes, and leads; consequently valuable deposits of ore are found chiefly in mountainous regions, where the earth crust has been broken, and in old, worn-down plains (pp. 44, 53, 58) from which a great thickness of the crust has been removed by erosion.

Fig. 278. — Iron mine, Minnesota.

Iron. — Of all the metals, iron is the most useful to mankind. No people have ever been able to attain a high state of civilization without the use of iron. It is the physical basis of modern industry. Its extraction from the ore is difficult and requires such a high temperature that the progress of the human race was delayed thousands of years for lack of it.

As long as all implements and tools were made of wood, with points and cutting edges of stone, no great material civilization was possible. Iron is supreme because it is abundant, strong, and workable. When hot it can be hammered into shape, when melted it can be cast in molds, and in the form of steel it can be given a high degree of hardness and elasticity. If kept dry it is very durable, but if damp it rapidly rusts.

Iron ores are smelted with charcoal or coke, and limestone to absorb impurities, in a furnace which is raised by a blast of hot air to a tempera-

Fig. 279. — Blast furnaces, Gary, Ind.

ture of nearly 3,000 degrees. The liquid metal drawn from the furnace is pig or cast iron, which is moderately hard and relatively brittle, but can be cast in molds of almost any desired size and shape. Cast iron, when purified, forms wrought iron, which is soft and flexible but tough and malleable. By various processes cast iron can be converted into steel, which possesses all the best qualities of iron. It can be cast, hammered, rolled into railroad rails, bars, beams, girders, and sheets, and tempered for cutting tools and springs.

Iron is the most widely diffused of metals, and iron ores are found in every land; but the best ores, which furnish most of the world's supply, are mined in the Lake Superior region of the United States and Canada, in Great Britain, Germany, Belgium, and Spain. Sweden has immense masses of high-grade ore not yet fully developed. The United States is far in advance of all other countries in the production of iron ore, pig iron, and steel, with Germany and Great Britain as second and third in rank. The quantity of iron used is the best measure of industrial progress.

Copper. — Next to iron, copper is probably the most important metal. It is workable, durable, and moderately hard. Before the discovery of iron smelting, bronze, an alloy of copper and tin, played the part now taken by iron and steel, and it is still used for statuary and ornamental work.

Brass is an alloy of copper and zinc. The peculiar value of copper lies in the fact that it is one of the best known conductors of heat and electricity, and can be drawn into strong wire. Hence it is indispensable in the development of modern electrical industry. The mines of Arizona, Montana, and Michigan produce more than half of all the copper mined. Japan, Chile, and Canada rank next after the United States.

Lead. — Lead is a soft, heavy metal easily melted or shaped in the cold. It is used for shot, bullets, roofing, and plumbers' work. Solder, pewter, and type metal are alloys of lead.

White lead, a compound of the metal, is one of the essential ingredients of good paint. Lead occurs with silver in Idaho, Utah, and Colorado, and with zinc in Missouri. The United States, Spain, Germany, and Australia produce three fourths of the world's supply.

Zinc. — Zinc is a hard, white metal which is not corroded by air or water. It is extensively used as a coating for sheet steel to prevent it from rusting. Such sheets, under the name of galvanized iron, are used for tanks, roofing, cornices, spouts, water pipes, and domestic utensils. The United States, Germany, and Belgium yield four fifths of the world's supply.

Tin. — Tin is a soft, white metal which was once semi-precious on account of its scarcity and the demand for it in making bronze. It is very useful in the form of tin plate, which consists of sheets of iron coated with tin and used for roofing and "tinware." The tin mines of Cornwall, England, have been worked for 2,500 years, but the Malay Peninsula and neighboring islands and Bolivia now furnish three fourths of the supply.

Aluminum. — Aluminum, the lightest of the commercial metals, is also the most abundant, being the base of all clays and forming eight per cent of the earth crust. The difficulty of extraction from its ores makes it costly. In color, luster, and polish it resembles tin. It does not corrode, is workable, and is a good conductor of electricity. It is about one third as heavy as iron and may be substituted for it in places where lightness and strength are desirable. Its workable ores are rare. The metal is extracted at Niagara Falls and Massena, N. Y., and Badin, N. C.

Mercury. — Mercury, the only metal liquid at ordinary temperatures, is invaluable in the extraction of gold from its ores, in the manufacture of thermometers, barometers, and other scientific instruments, and in silvering mirrors. Italy, Austria, Spain, and California furnish 85 per cent of the supply.

Precious Metals. — Gold and silver are known as precious metals on account of their high value. An ounce of gold is worth a little over twenty dollars, and an ounce of silver from fifty cents to one dollar. For use in the arts gold is inferior to copper, and silver is inferior to tin. Their value depends essentially upon their beauty, which makes them desired for ornament; hence gold is the common material used for jewelry, and silver for tableware. Gold has a rich yellow color and a brilliant luster which does not readily tarnish. It is easily workable, but too soft for use unless alloyed with copper or silver to harden it. Silver is white, less lustrous than gold, and more easily tarnished; hence it is far inferior in value, although more useful in the arts. Gold has become the standard of value and a medium of exchange of the civilized world and is used chiefly for coinage, while silver is the metal for coins of less value.

Fig. 280. — Washing gold, Guiana. (Robin.)

Gold is found disseminated in veins, lodes, or reefs of quartz and other minerals, and in alluvial sands and gravels. It is separated by crushing the ore, when necessary, washing out impurities with running water, and dissolving the gold with mercury. Gold is extracted from low-grade ores by a solution of potassium cyanide. The world's output of gold is about $460,000,000 annually, of which South Africa produces about two fifths, the United States one fifth, and Australia one twelfth.

Silver is obtained largely from lead and gold ores, as well as from ores worked for silver alone. Its extraction is difficult and complicated. The amount mined is largely in excess of gold, but its total value is less. The United States produces one half and Canada and Mexico about one third of the world's product.

Tools. — Man is the only animal that uses tools. It is doubtful if apes and monkeys, who have hands and could use tools, ever spontaneously use even a stick or a stone for any purpose. Primitive tools were of the simplest character. A stick, smoothed, straightened, and pointed, with the end hardened in the fire or tipped with an animal tooth, developed into the spear and harpoon. A stone thrown from the hand or from a sling of bark or hide, a club weighted at one end or made more effective by the insertion of sharp teeth or stones, a flake of flint or broken volcanic glass with a cutting edge, were the rude forerunners of the rifle, cannon, ax, sword, scythe, knife, and razor.

Fig. 281. — Primitive tools and weapons.

The invention of the bow and arrow gave their possessors such an advantage in range and accuracy of aim as to rank in importance with the discovery of gunpowder. The invention of pottery, made at first by daubing a basket with clay, then molding the clay without the basket, made it possible to store and carry liquids and to cook food by boiling. The smelting of iron ore put into men's hands at once a superior material for all sorts of implements, weapons, and utensils, enabled them to work wood into boats, houses, and furniture, and vastly to improve their agriculture. Chiefly by the utilization of wood and iron man has arrived at his present stage of economic development, in which by the use of machines he has increased production in an incalculable ratio beyond what he could do with his bare hands. The grain binder and thresher, the steam plow, the cotton gin, the power loom, the linotype, the cylinder press, the pipe organ, the electric crane, the steel steamship, the steam turbine, the gas engine, the dynamo, the trolley car, the automobile, and the aeroplane are only complex tools for doing work efficiently and on a large scale. They are extensions and improvements of the natural machines, — the human leg and arm.

Technical Materials. — The complex activities of civilized men require a vast variety of materials for a vast variety of purposes. They are derived from many natural sources and are artificially made. To describe them and their uses in detail would require a large volume. The following are some of the most important in each class.

Fertilizers. — The natural supply of plant food in good soils is generally sufficient except in nitrogen, phosphorus, and potash (p. 145). Hence these elements are important ingredients of artificial fertilizers, and in old and densely populated countries their supply is a serious problem.

Nitrogen is furnished by animal matter, and is a constituent of common stable manure. Guano is the dung of fish-eating sea birds, which has accumulated upon islands in the almost rainless region off the coast of Peru, in some places to the depth of 200 feet. It contains large percentages of both nitrogen and phosphorus, and many million tons have been shipped to England and other countries of western Europe. Bat guano, obtained from caves, is used for the same purpose. Chile saltpeter (sodium nitrate), containing a large percentage of nitrogen, occurs in extensive deposits in the desert of Atacama (Peru and Chile), and has been mined and exported to Europe for many years. The supplies of guano and nitrate are limited and exhaustible, but the nitrogen of the air is inexhaustible. It has been discovered that clover, alfalfa, peas, beans, and other plants of the same family, have upon their roots nodules containing bacteria, or microscopic plants, which absorb and assimilate nitrogen from the air. When the roots decay the nitrogen becomes available for the next crop. Artificial nitrate is now being made from air and lime by electricity in Norway, where water power is cheap. **Thus the nitrogen problem seems to be definitely solved.**

Fig. 282. — Tubercles on the roots of soy bean. (Fletcher's *Soils*.)

Phosphorus. — Animal matter generally contains phosphorus as well as nitrogen, but it is present in large proportions in fish and in the bones of herbivorous animals. Near the seashore fish which are not fit for food are caught in nets and liberally applied to the land. Beds of phosphate rock in southern United States and other localities are composed largely of the teeth and bones of marine animals. Such deposits are of greater real value to the human race than gold mines. The phosphorus in them is in an insoluble form, and must be chemically treated to make it available for plant food. Large quantities of phosphatic fertilizer are made from slaughterhouse refuse and the bones of domestic animals.

Potash. — Wood ashes contain considerable quantities of potash salts, which are leached out with water and used in making fertilizers, glass, and soap. Potash salts are mined in Germany and France.

Salt. — Many chemical compounds are found in nature which can be utilized in their natural state. The most important is common salt (sodium chloride). It is obtained by the evaporation of sea water and of other natural brines, such as the water of the Caspian Sea, Great Salt Lake in Utah, and the Salton Lake of California.

Strata of rock salt, left by the evaporation of ancient seas, sometimes 1,000 feet thick, occur in the earth crust. The solid salt is sometimes mined like coal, but since it is frequently impure it is often cheaper to dissolve the salt in water and evaporate the brine. There are famous salt mines in Poland, Germany, Roumania, Spain, England, New York, and Louisiana. Salt is used almost universally as a food and as a preservative. It is also the source from which many compounds are manufactured, among which soda ash, used in making soap, glass, and baking powder, is the most important.

Fig. 283. — Salt works, France.

Sulphur is often obtained from volcanic regions, where it sublimes from the hot rock, and by roasting pyrite, a mineral common in coal mines. Sicily, Louisiana, and Japan are the chief sources. It is one of the most important of chemicals, indispensable in the manufacture of matches, gunpowder, and vulcanized rubber. The fumes of burning sulphur are a cheap and efficient bleaching agent and disinfectant. It is the basis of manufacture of sulphuric acid and a long series of derivative compounds which rival in number and variety of uses those derived from common salt.

Pigments. — Substances used to give color to paint are in some cases natural minerals and in others artificial products. The ochres are yellow, brown, and red compounds of iron, both natural and artificial. White lead, red lead, litharge, and chrome yellow are made from lead, zinc white from zinc, vermilion from mercury, and chrome red from chromium.

Oils. — There are many vegetable oils in use for food for men and animals, for soap and candle making, lubrication, illumination, and dressing skins. Olive oil is the most valuable and takes the place of animal fat and flesh in the Mediterranean countries. Palm and coconut oil are products of tropical regions, and cottonseed and maize oils of temperate. The most important animal fats and oils are lard from hogs and tallow from cattle and sheep, used for food and for making soap and candles. Oil is obtained from the menhaden fish, and the whale fishery was once the chief source of illuminating oils. Right whales are now nearly exterminated. Soap is made from vegetable and animal fats by boiling them with lye (caustic soda or caustic potash). Glycerin is a by-product.

Essential Oils are not fats, will not make soap, and are soluble in water. They are distilled from various plants and are in common use as medicines and flavoring extracts. Camphor is the only solid essential oil, and is obtained entirely from the Japanese island of Formosa. Oil of peppermint, lemon, vanilla, wintergreen, sassafras, bitter almonds, anise, cloves, and many others are well known.

Resins and Gums. — Resins and gums are vegetable products used in making soap, paint, varnish, and mucilage. Crude turpentine from the hard pine tree is the most important. It is separated by distillation into spirits of turpentine, used for mixing paints, and rosin, an ingredient of many soaps.

Gum arabic, from the savannas of Africa, is the base of mucilage. Copal, dammar, and lac, which is produced by an insect, make fine varnishes. Chicle, produced only in Yucatan and used only in the United States, forms the body of chewing gum. Amber is a fossil gum from the shores of the Baltic Sea, used for ornament and the mouthpieces of pipes.

Dyestuffs. — Dyestuffs are mostly of vegetable origin. Indigo, madder, and logwood are the most important. The natural supply is now almost entirely superseded by artificial dyes, made in great variety from coal tar.

The number of useful commodities, natural and artificial, has probably never been estimated, but would run into the tens of thousands. The number of kinds of articles procurable in any civilized town of 50,000 inhabitants, not including medicines, is not less than 1,000.

CHAPTER XXI

HEAT, LIGHT, AND POWER

Heat. — The development of civilization is characterized not only by a vastly increased utilization of material resources, but no less by growing dependence upon immaterial resources, especially heat, light, and power. The discovery of the use of fire, at first accidental from lightning or a volcano, was a step second in importance to none in the rise of man.

The invention of methods for kindling fire when wanted has exercised a marked influence upon human progress. The savage rubs two sticks together until they ignite, — a thing not easy to do. Our ancestors of only a century ago depended upon sparks struck by flint and steel, while with us lucifer matches are the cheapest and most abundant of devices. While artificial heat is not needed for comfort in tropical regions, fire enables men to cook food, and this will always be its prime function. The use of fire to maintain bodily temperature became necessary as men migrated into higher latitudes and altitudes. The burning of brick and pottery, the smelting of ores, the working of metals, and the manufacture of glass require the highest temperatures attainable by the use of fuel. Some modern industries, such as the extraction of aluminum, are made possible only by the electric arc at 6,000°.

Fig. 284. — Savage kindling a fire.

Light. — Artificial light is an unappreciated luxury. Julius Cæsar wrote his Commentaries by the light of a dull, smoky lamp, made by dipping a loose wick in an open dish of oil. In the Middle Ages houses and streets were lighted with flaring torches made by burning various combustibles in an iron basket. In the height of the whale-fishing industry sperm-oil lamps gave a brilliant light, but were costly and unsafe. Within the memory of men now living the common people had no better illuminant than a pine knot or a "tallow dip" candle. It was not until the latter half of the nineteenth century that the discovery of petroleum gave to everybody a cheap and efficient light. Coal gas has been used in cities for lighting about a century, and now electricity turns night into day.

Power. — The ultimate source of nearly all the power available for doing work on the earth is insolation, or radiant energy from the sun. Sunlight makes plants grow, and vegetation is the source of food which gives animals strength, and of fuel which, when burned, may run a heat engine. The sun heats different parts of the atmosphere unequally and thus makes the wind blow. The sun evaporates water from the sea, which, falling as rain on land, runs off in streams which furnish water power.

Man Power. — Primitive man was dependent upon his own muscles. He traveled and used implements and weapons, but he did not travel fast, build large structures, or transport much freight. He had only two legs and two arms, both weak and short, and with them alone he could not rise above savagery. Human power and labor is still indispensable and always will be.

The greatest amount of human labor is employed in the most advanced industrial communities. It has often been thought that machines would do away with human labor, but they generally increase the number of persons that can find employment and the total amount of muscular energy expended. This is true in manufacturing industries and transportation. Agriculture seems, so far, to be an exception to the rule. The use of agricultural machinery reduces the number of laborers employed, and exclusively rural districts are decreasing in population. This may be a temporary phase, to be followed by the reverse as agriculture becomes more scientific and intensive.

Labor Supply. — The problem of obtaining a sufficient supply of unskilled human labor is one of the most serious which confronts the civilized world to-day. For the most rapid advancement labor should be plentiful, but the supply probably never will equal the demand. Facilities for cheap transportation render possible a circulation of labor, the people of those countries which have a surplus migrating to those which have a deficiency. Indian coolies are transported to South Africa to work in the gold mines, and Jamaica negroes to Panama to dig the canal. Three hundred thousand Italians come to the United States in a single year, one third of whom return to Italy sooner or later. Thousands cross the sea to work in America during the season or as long as the job lasts, and go back home when business is dull. The United States, Canada, Australia, and South Africa, young and growing countries, need the largest supply of unskilled labor. Great Britain, France, and Germany are now self-sufficing, and Spain, Portugal, Italy, Austria, and Hungary have a surplus; but as these countries develop they will not continue in such a condition. Russia, the Balkan countries, India, China, the East and West Indies, and north and central Africa have a large surplus of labor. The African supply increases under civilized control, and the abolition of war and slavery; but the people often lack efficiency, are difficult to control, are unaccustomed to manual labor, and have a high death rate. These defects are characteristic of the natives of tropical countries generally. The people of northern India are industrious and of good physique, but race and religious prejudices, and sensitiveness to climate interfere with their transference to other countries. The people of south and Asiatic Russia, the Balkan states, and the Turkish Empire are semi-European, but rather unintelligent. The Chinaman is docile, peaceable, hardy, easy to feed, and of high efficiency. He does not assimilate with other peoples, and the white man's prejudice against him is so strong that he is excluded by law from the United States and Australia, where a large supply of labor is most needed.

Animal Power. — Domestic animals lifted men out of savagery. America remained barbarous for centuries largely because of the lack of domestic animals. Many of the larger animals are used more or less for power, but the horse is the most generally efficient. The early civilization of Eurasia was largely the result of horse power used for mobility and transportation. The horse survives the introduction of mechanical and chemical power in agriculture, trade, and war, but his importance is relatively declining. The time may come when he will be excluded from cities and used more for pleasure than for business.

Wind Power. — There is no lack of wind power in any part of the world except the calm belts, and it is inexhaustible. Until a century ago all large vessels were propelled by the wind, and sailing vessels still comprise about one eighth of the world's shipping. Wind power is used in Holland and the United States in small units for pumping water and grinding grain. Its use is restricted only by its inconstancy. If means are ever devised by which power can be cheaply stored for use during a calm, the wind may yet drive the machinery and do the work of the world.

Fig. 285. — Windmill, Holland.

Fuel. — The use of power from sun heat stored in vegetable matter was made possible by the invention of the steam engine, which is really a heat engine. It was first made practical by Watt, about 1770, and was successfully applied to vessels by Fulton, in 1807, and to land locomotives by Stephenson between 1815 and 1830. The importance of its effects cannot be calculated. By it man's legs and arms have been multiplied, lengthened, and strengthened enormously. It has made world commerce and world power possible. For all practical, human purposes, it has reduced the size of the earth to about one tenth its former dimensions, and has correspondingly promoted the unity of mankind, making all men neighbors.

Wood has always been the fuel most used for domestic purposes, and the boilers of the first steam engines were heated with wood. While forests are more valuable for construction than for fuel, the world's supply of wood of little value for anything else than to burn is very large.

Peat. — When vegetable matter decays under water it is converted into a brown or black, spongy mass, called peat, muck, or turf. A cool, moist climate is most favorable for its formation, and it has accumulated in the glacial lake beds and bogs of northern Europe and America in large but unmeasured quantities. When dried it forms as good fuel as wood, and in countries where coal and wood are scarce peat is in common use. It is sometimes pressed by machinery into briquettes and used for industrial purposes. Russia, Germany, Sweden, Denmark, Holland, and Ireland are peat-using countries.

Coal. — Coal is fossil fuel, the concentrated residue of a luxuriant vegetation which flourished millions of years ago. It was first converted into peat, then buried under accumulations of sediment, and transformed by heat and pressure into coal. *Lignite*, or brown coal, has been changed so little as to retain the appearance of wood, and has about half the fuel value of the best coal. Very extensive beds of lignite exist in the United States and other countries, but are as yet little used. *Bituminous* or soft coal, containing from 60 to 85 per cent of carbon, is widely distributed, and the world's main reliance for industrial fuel. Large quantities are converted by heating into coke, which resembles anthracite. It is also the source of illuminating gas. *Anthracite* or hard coal contains from 85 to 98 per cent of carbon, and is of the highest value for most purposes. The area of the coal fields of the world is estimated at 650,000 square miles, of which two fifths belong to the United States and one third to China.

Fig. 286. — Coal mine.

The yield of coal per square mile is very variable, the seams in some areas being few and thin, and in others numerous and thick. Coal is mined in England to a depth of over half a mile. The world's output is about 1,300 million tons annually, of which the United States mines nearly one half and Great Britain one fifth. About half of it is used for power purposes. Coal and iron form the basis of modern industrial civilization. In the production and consumption of both these articles per capita, the United States, Great Britain, and Belgium are, in that order, the leading countries, with France and Germany also ranking high.

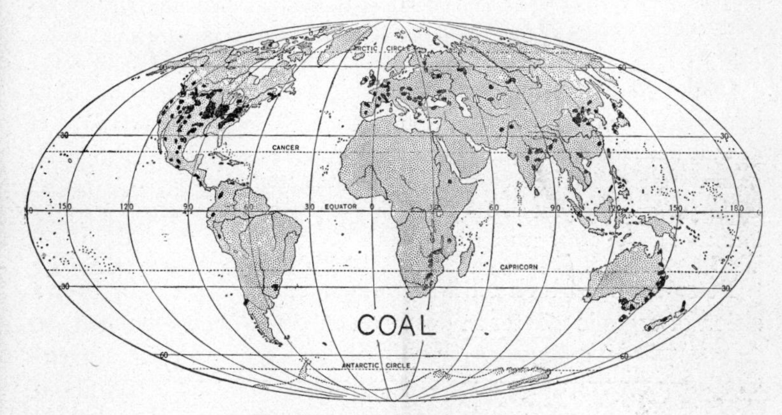

Fig. 287.— Coal-producing regions.

The British coal fields are small in area but very rich, and have been the chief source of British wealth and sea power. In the fourteenth century the use of coal in England was prohibited by law on account of supposed injury to health. Now ten millions of people are living in British coal fields to make use of it. The anthracite or "smokeless coal" of south Wales is used for war vessels, and for smelting ores sent from distant lands for that purpose.

The exhaustion of the British coal supply in the near future is a serious question. The present century may see it so far reduced as to render British competition with manufacturers elsewhere difficult or impossible. On the continent of Europe coal of generally medium or inferior quality exists in strips and patches from Belgium to the Black Sea. The coal fields of China are very large and rich, but as yet wholly undeveloped.

The southern continents are poorly supplied with coal, Australia being most highly favored. While coal occurs in all lands from Greenland to Antarctica, North America perhaps contains as much coal as all the rest of the world. The principal coal fields are (1) the Appalachian, from Nova Scotia to Alabama; (2) the Interior, from Ohio to Kansas and from Texas to Alberta; and (3) the Pacific, from Washington to Alaska. Anthracite is confined to eastern Pennsylvania and a few patches in the Rocky Mountains. On account of easily available coal and iron, great manufacturing industries have grown up around Pittsburgh, Cleveland, and Chicago, and the urban industrial and commercial district of the Atlantic seaboard is near the coal fields. The remarkable development of railroads in the United States and Canada is largely due to the wide distribution of coal. The consumption of coal in the United States nearly doubled in the ten years from 1900 to 1910. No coal is being formed in the earth at the present time, and the supply cannot be anywhere inexhaustible. At the present rate of increase of consumption, the world's store may be used up in 500 or 1,000 years. Its duration will probably be prolonged by the increased use of other sources of power.

Petroleum. — Rock oil is a product of the natural decomposition of organic matter in deep-seated strata of the earth crust,

Fig. 233. — Oil wells and tanks, Russia. (Robin.)

and is obtained from wells. It is not found in the same strata with coal. Of the 460 million barrels consumed annually, the United States produces nearly two thirds, the Caspian field in Russia about one sixth, and Mexico about one eighth.

Oklahoma, California, Illinois, Texas, Kansas, West Virginia, and Louisiana are important oil-producing states. Much oil is pumped through underground pipe lines to refineries at Cleveland, Toledo, and Whiting, Ind., and to the Atlantic coast cities. Petroleum is used in its crude form as fuel for engines, but it is refined by distillation into a large number of products, the most important of which are kerosene, gasoline, lubricating oils, and paraffin. Kerosene is the cheapest and most efficient illuminant the world has ever known. Gasoline has recently attained prime importance for power by the development of the internal-combustion or gas engine, which is especially adapted for small units, and is displacing the steam engine for many purposes. As a liquid fuel easily converted into a gas it has no rival except alcohol.

Natural Gas. — Gas is the most convenient form of fuel, and a cheap and abundant supply of it is of great value. Gas made artificially by heating coal has long been used for lighting and cooking, but its cost precludes its general use. Natural gas, produced by the distillation of organic matter in the earth crust, is of general occurrence in connection with petroleum.

Burning springs have attracted attention in many countries since the earliest times. Those on the shores of the Caspian Sea have been objects of veneration by the Persian fire worshipers since a period before the Christian era. About 1886 gas began to be obtained in large quantities from wells in Pennsylvania, Ohio, and Indiana, and used for lighting, heating, and industrial purposes. It was conducted in pipes to towns within 200 miles of the wells, and the "gas belt" became a busy manufacturing region, especially of those articles requiring high temperatures, such as glass, tin plate, brick, pottery, and steel specialties. West Virginia, Illinois, and Kansas also became prominent gas-producing states. In some cases half the gas was wasted, and the supply for manufacturing and general heating was practically exhausted in about twenty years. West Virginia, Pennsylvania, Ohio, and Oklahoma are now leading gas-producing states.

Explosives. — Gunpowder, giant powder, nitroglycerin, dynamite, cordite, and other high explosives are fuels which burn rapidly and suddenly liberate large volumes of gas, and are used in hunting, war, and blasting rock.

Water Power. — The power of water to drive machinery is proportional to the quantity and the head or height of fall. Natural cataracts in large streams furnish most power, but are not always most available. Dams are constructed to concentrate the fall at one place and to store water, and are most efficient in streams of steep slope and narrow valleys, like those of New England. Good water powers are abundant in mountainous regions, remote from centers of population, but the development of electrical science has made such power more available.

Fig. 289. — Water wheel, Georgia.

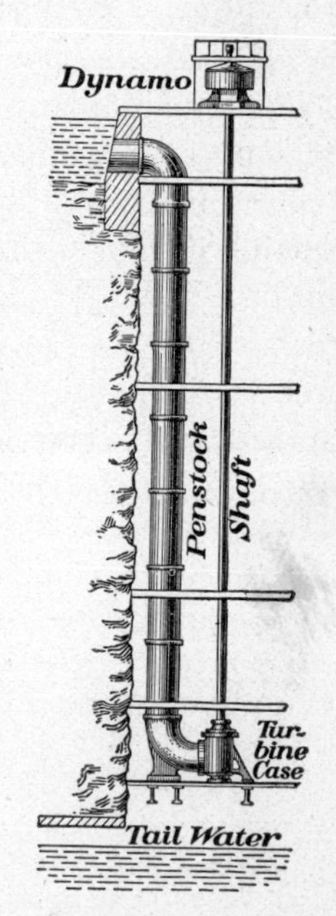

Fig. 290. — Arrangement of hydro-electric machinery at Niagara Falls.

Electricity is not a source of power, but a convenient form in which power can be distributed. The cars of city and interurban lines are run by electricity generated at one or more power stations and transmitted over copper wires. Water power is used to generate electricity, which is used to do work at places sometimes 200 miles distant. The greatest source of hydro-electric power now in use is Niagara Falls (pp. 93, 94, 101). As coal becomes more scarce and costly, mountainous countries, such as Italy,

Switzerland, and Norway, will become, by the use of water power, or "white coal," important centers of industry.

Wave and Tidal Power. — The movement of waves and the rise and fall of tides are possible sources of power, but on account of inconvenience and uncertainty they are little used.

Metals. — Some metals, chiefly zinc, iron, lead, and copper, are used in electric batteries to generate power for special purposes, but are too costly for use on a large scale. Radium and the group of allied metals recently discovered are capable of liberating enormous quantities of power. They are now extremely rare and costly, but suggest interesting possibilities for the future.

Solar and Terrestrial Heat. — To contrive a system of lenses and mirrors by which the direct rays of the sun may be so concentrated as to become commercially available for heat, light, and power has been the dream of engineers, but has never yet been realized. The internal heat of the earth is second in quantity only to that received from the sun. If any means could be devised for utilizing it, it would be sufficient for human needs as long as the earth remains inhabitable. Perhaps the source of the power of the distant future will be in the nature of an artificial geyser or volcano.

CHAPTER XXII

MANUFACTURE, TRADE, AND TRANSPORTATION

Manufacture. — Nearly all natural products must be more or less modified artificially to render them serviceable to man. In low stages of culture all of this, and in all stages much of it, is done literally by hand. With the progress of the industrial arts, a larger and larger portion is done by tools and machines, which are extensions and improvements of the human hand.

In simple societies each family or group does this work for itself and at home. In more advanced and densely populated countries a division of labor arises by which an individual or family makes some special article at home for hire or for sale and exchange. Sometimes a traveling artisan goes from house to house to make shoes or clothes. These phases of *domestic manufacture* prevailed until the introduction of machinery and mechanical power. These made necessary the *capitalistic* or *coöperative factory*, in which an individual or company provides a large building equipped with machines and employs many operatives to work in it for wages. The distribution of hydro-electric power has brought about in some places and industries a partial return to domestic manufacture, in which individuals or small groups operate machines at home.

Conditions of Manufacture. — To make any line of goods on a large scale with profit many conditions are necessary. Buildings, machinery, power, heat, and raw materials must be supplied at the plant. A sufficient supply of skilled labor must exist in the immediate neighborhood. Since factory hands can produce little or no food, a sufficient food supply must be within reach. Lastly, the manufactured goods must be got to market. The location of a successful factory is determined by all of these conditions.

If the raw material is bulky, it costs too much to transport it far, and it is manufactured near the supply. This is the case with sugar cane, from which the sugar is extracted on the plantation, but shipped long distances to be refined. Grain is threshed on the farm, but may be sent any distance to a mill. South American hides are tanned in Massachusetts because capital, skilled labor, tanning materials, and a market for leather exist there more abundantly than in Argentina. The manufacture of cotton, wool, and silk is largely independent of the place of production of the raw fibers, and is carried on where power, skilled labor, capital, and markets combine to make it profitable. Half the cotton grown in the United

Fig. 291.—Factories. Manchester, N. H. On the Merrimac River.

States is sent to England to be made into cloth. The manufacture of iron and steel involves the use of very heavy materials—ore, coke, and limestone. It is carried on where the three can be brought together at least expense and the products find a ready market, as in the districts around Pittsburgh, Cleveland, and Chicago. The higher the value of the finished goods the less dependent is their manufacture upon any conditions except skilled labor. The most general and potent control of the location of manufactures is transportation. Great seaports such as London and New York, and lake ports, river ports, and railroad centers such as Cleveland, Chicago, Cincinnati, and St. Louis, attract all kinds of manufacture, because of the facility with which everything needed may be obtained and the goods sent to market. Great Britain is an example of the same thing on the largest scale. Having power, labor, and capital at home, by the possession of a vast merchant marine and a navy which commands the sea, the British people have grown rich by importing nearly all their food and raw materials from the ends of the earth and sending their products to all the markets of the world.

The United States is by far the greatest manufacturing country in the world, the total value of its products amounting to 20,000 million dollars annually. In respect to area it should be compared with all Europe, and in respect to population with Germany and Great Britain combined. Great Britain is second in value of total product, France third, and Germany fourth, but Belgium and Denmark each exceeds France and Germany in value per capita.

Trade. — The most general fact learned from a study of physical and economic geography is that natural conditions and resources, and human life and culture, differ in different parts of the world. The differences, both in kind and degree, are almost innumerable. Differences in natural conditions — land, water, relief, soil, climate, and the rest — involve differences of resources, and these in turn determine occupations, products, and modes of human economy. It is the business of geography to study and explain the relationships which natural conditions and resources bear to human economies.

Few if any countries can supply anywhere near all the products which its inhabitants want and can use. It would be futile to try to raise corn and cotton in England, sugar cane in Canada, or coffee and spices in the United States. Italy has no coal or gold, and Switzerland, Holland, Denmark, and Ireland have no ores of any kind. Every community can furnish, raise, or manufacture some things to better advantage than others, and the community which undertakes to be independent and supply everything it needs, without help from other communities, will be obliged to limit its wants, which means a relatively low stage of culture and comfort. Out of these conditions arises trade, commerce, or the exchange of commodities between different individuals, families, communities, and countries. Trade is the most complex and important of all the adaptations to his environment which man has accomplished.

Transportation. — All trade depends upon the transportation of goods from one place to another, and has developed with the increase of facilities for transportation. Methods of transportation are either animal or mechanical, or a combination of the two.

Porterage. — The simplest form of transportation is porterage, in which loads are carried by men's hands and arms, or on their backs or heads. Although it is inefficient and expensive, it increases in amount with the increase of trade. The initial and the final movement of goods will always be chiefly by hand, as coal is shoveled into the car in the mine and into the furnace in the house.

Fig. 292. — Porters, China.

Porterage prevails among savage peoples, in tropical forests and savannas, and in mountainous countries. Among the North American Indians the men killed the game, while the squaws brought in the meat, and carried the tents, utensils, and babies on their backs. In central Africa negro porters are the chief reliance. About thirty men are required to carry a ton twenty-five miles a day, and they must be fed. The cost of transportation from the Guinea coast to Lake Chad, about 600 miles, is $360 a ton. The cost on the Uganda railway for nearly the same distance is ten cents a ton. In the high Alps every peasant man, woman, and child carries a loaded basket fastened to the shoulders.

Fig. 293. — Loaded camels, Egypt.

Pack Animals. — Animals are a great improvement on the human porter, and the dog, ass, mule, horse, ox, camel, and elephant are all used as beasts of burden (Figs. 256, 293). Probably the camel is the most efficient, carrying a load up to 1,000 pounds. Caravans of 13,000 camels, carrying goods of a total value of $800,000, cross the Sahara, occupying two years for a round trip.

Vehicles. — Vehicles propelled by man or animal power are the first and simplest of mechanical aids to transportation.

Fig. 294. — **Straw-covered bullock cart, Ceylon.**

The North American Indians used the *travois*, consisting of two poles fastened to a dog's or horse's back with ends dragging on the ground. Cross pieces furnished a bed for carrying a load. The invention of the wheel was a great step in advance, and led to the development of innumerable vehicles, from the Chinese wheelbarrow to the railroad car and the autotruck.

Roads. — The use of wheeled vehicles renders necessary the construction of roads, of which the modern railroad is the

Fig. 295. — **St. Gothard coach road, Switzerland.**

most highly perfected. An ideal road must be smooth, hard, and level. These conditions are more or less fully obtained by grading, or cutting down elevations and filling depressions to reduce the slope as much as possible, and by surfacing the road with wood, gravel, stone, brick, asphalt, cement, or steel. Rivers and straits are crossed by bridges or tunnels. Mountain barriers are overcome by long detours, loops, and zigzags to lengthen the line and reduce the slope, and often by a tunnel at the summit (Figs. 295, 296).

Fig. 296. — Mouth of tunnel, St. Gothard railway.

The Forth bridge in Scotland, the East River bridges at New York, the bridge across the St. Lawrence at Quebec, and several across the Mississippi are among the largest and most costly structures erected by man. Even these are surpassed in magnitude and difficulty of engineering by the Mt.

Fig. 297. — Forth bridge, Scotland.

Cenis, St. Gothard, and Simplon tunnels in the Alps and the Hudson River tunnels at New York. A tunnel under the English Channel is seriously planned, and one under Bering Strait proposed. The Rocky Mountains and the Alps are crossed by many railroads, and the Andes by one.

The railway mileage of the world is over 600,000 miles, of which North America has nearly one half and Europe one third. The network of railroads is much more dense in eastern United States and western Europe than elsewhere. Belgium and the Netherlands have the greatest density, or the largest mileage per square mile of area. The longest and most numerous railroad lines extend east and west. Ten transcontinental lines cross North America and one crosses northern Eurasia. A north-south "pan-American" line from Canada to Argentina, and a "Cape to Cairo" line in Africa are probabilities of the near future. The development of the gas engine and the automobile has given a new impetus to road construction for vehicles of moderate size.

Water Transportation. — Transportation by water is easier and cheaper than by land. Its advantages are that water surfaces are level, or, in the case of navigable rivers, have a gentle slope. There is generally no expense for construction and maintenance, friction and resistance are small, the vehicles may be very large, and the power required for a given load is less than on land.

Fig. 298. — Dugout, with outriggers, Philippines.

Boats of many kinds are in use, from the single log or raft, inflated oxhide, dugout, canoe, and rowboat to the modern steamship of 40,000 tons burden, steaming 600 miles a day and burning a ton of coal per mile. The growth of ocean trade has led to the construction of ship canals, of which the Suez and the Panama are the most important (pp. 158, 159). The Atlantic Ocean, surrounded by important peoples, is most used. The Indian is a connecting link between the Atlantic and the Pacific, and the Pacific is the ocean of the future. Half the ocean commerce of the world is carried on between Europe and North America, one eighth between Europe and the Orient and Australia (Suez route), and one eighth between Europe and Africa.

The St. Lawrence River, with its connecting lakes and canals, furnishes the greatest inland waterway. The great possibilities of the Amazon and the Kongo are as yet little utilized. The Mississippi may regain the trade lost for want of improvement. The civilized world has entered upon an era of water transportation, and the development of waterways is one of the great economic problems of the twentieth century.

Fig. 299. — Ocean steamer: the Olympic.

World Trade. — The larger part of the world's trade is domestic, consisting of an exchange of goods between the different parts of the same country. It is impossible to estimate its total amount. Of foreign commerce, or the exchange of goods between different countries, an account can be made with considerable accuracy. The value of all the goods exchanged between nations is about 50,000 million dollars annually, of which the trade of Europe is more than half. Among nations the United States leads with 17 per cent, and is followed by Great Britain with 14 per cent, France with 12 per cent, and Germany with 9 per cent. The little countries of Switzerland, the Netherlands, and Belgium have the largest foreign commerce in proportion to population.

In trade there are two great movements, one in a north-south direction between the temperate regions and the tropics, and one in an east-west direction between temperate countries in different stages of development. At present the east-west movement is greater, but it may not always remain so.

The present supremacy of the temperate zone, due to coolness and healthfulness, may, by the control of disease and the use of artificial refrigeration, pass to the tropics. Men may devise means of keeping cool in the torrid zone as they have of keeping warm in the frigid. Power and raw materials are plentiful in tropical regions, and centers of industry and population may shift toward the equator.

Summary. — Every natural resource has existed upon the earth since the first appearance of man, and no natural resource has yet been fully utilized. Probably natural resources exist of which mankind is still ignorant. Every human want, art, and economy had its simple beginnings in the lowest stages of savagery and has persisted through all stages of culture. As each want, art, and economy developed, it has influenced more and more every other. The development of civilization and scientific economy has not released men from dependence upon natural resources, but only multiplied the number and increased the complexity of such relations. Modern industrial civilization is as truly based upon grass, trees, coal, iron, and copper as Eskimo life upon snow, seals, and walrus.

The most favored countries possess lands in all climates, from tropical to cold temperate, of varied rainfall, relief, soil, and mineral wealth, and accessible to the sea. In all these respects the United States approaches ideal conditions. France equals or surpasses it on a small scale. Russia lacks only seacoast. China, Australia, and Argentina have a hopeful future. Most of the European states and Japan are less favored, but may extend their territories and supplement their resources by colonization.

The geologist sees no reason to doubt that the earth is destined to remain habitable for a longer period in the future than it has been in the past. The human race is still in its infancy, and is barely beginning to realize the possibilities of its earthly possessions. Man is yet to have his day, and his kingdom, in which he shall control the forces of nature and have dominion over the planet, is yet to come.

Fig. 300. — Airplane.

The art of aviation, greatly stimulated during the World War, has indefinite possibilities of usefulness in time of peace. The airplane and the dirigible balloon are in regular use for the transportation of passengers and mail. They may play a part not less important than the railroad and the steamship. The atmosphere may become as truly a part of the kingdom of man as the land and the sea.

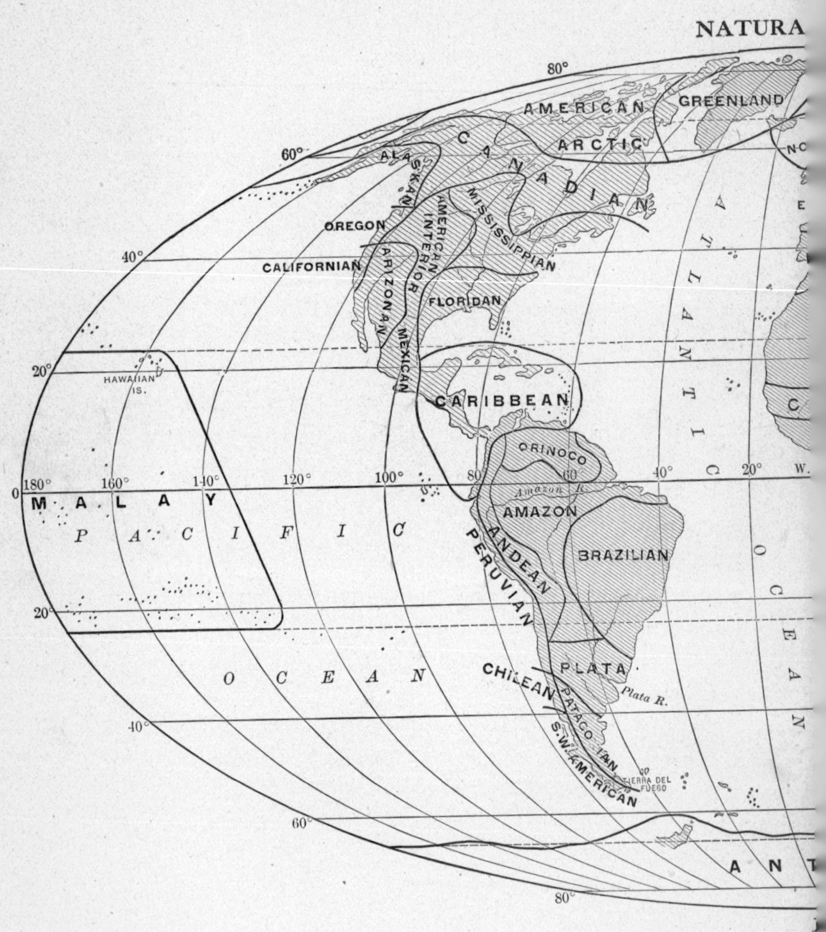
NATURA
AMERICAN
ARCTIC
GREENLAND
CANADIAN
ALASKAN
OREGON
AMERICAN INTERIOR
MISSISSIPPIAN
CALIFORNIAN
ARIZONAN
FLORIDAN
MEXICAN
CARIBBEAN
HAWAIIAN IS.
MALAY
PACIFIC
OCEAN
ORINOCO
Amazon R.
AMAZON
ANDEAN
PERUVIAN
BRAZILIAN
PLATA
Plata R.
CHILEAN
PATAGONIAN
S.W. AMERICAN
TIERRA DEL FUEGO
ATLANTIC
OCEAN
ANT
80°
60°
40°
20°
0
180°
160°
140°
120°
100°
80°
60°
40°
20°
W.

OVINCES

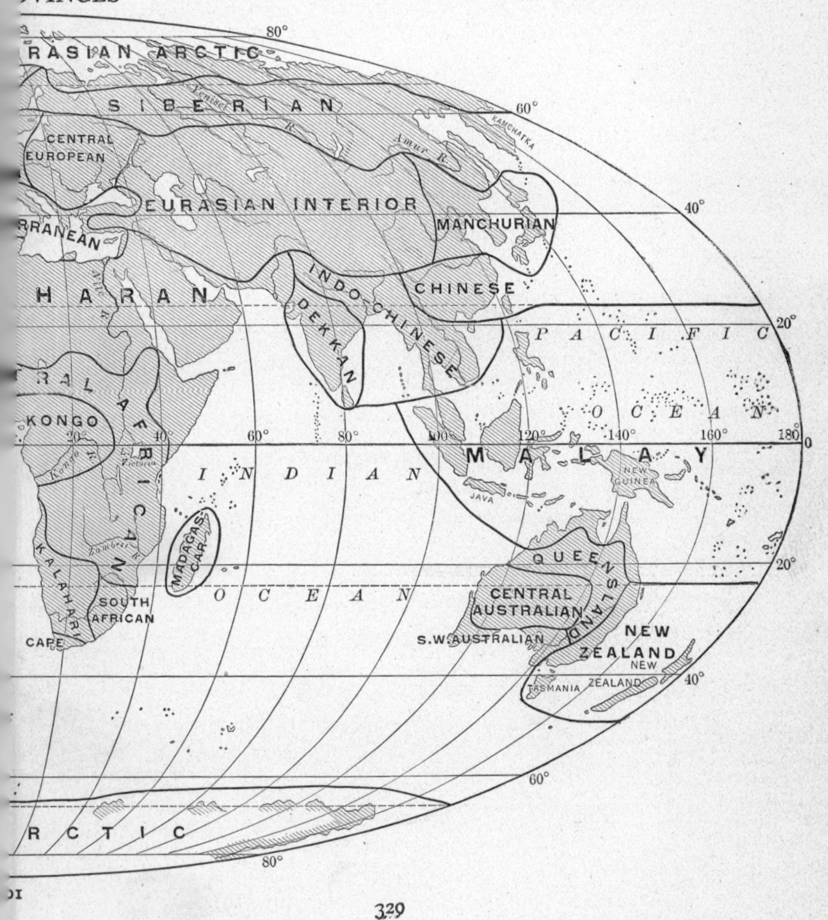

SIBERIAN
CENTRAL EUROPEAN
EURASIAN INTERIOR
MANCHURIAN
CHINESE
INDO-CHINESE
DEKKAN
KAMCHATKA
Amur R.
KONGO
MADAGASCAR
KALAHARI
SOUTH AFRICAN
CAPE
INDIAN OCEAN
PACIFIC OCEAN
MALAY
JAVA
NEW GUINEA
QUEENSLAND
CENTRAL AUSTRALIAN
S.W. AUSTRALIAN
NEW ZEALAND
TASMANIA
80°
60°
40°
20°
0
100°
120°
140°
160°
180

OI

TABLE OF NATURAL PROVINCES

(For reference in connection with the map, Fig. 301, pages 328–329. The page number in parenthesis after the name of each province refers to the description of the province in the text.)

I. Intertropical Provinces.

1. *Amazon type.*—Amazon (499), Kongo (505), Malay (504).
2. *Caribbean type.*—Caribbean (493), Indo-Chinese (503), Madagascar (507).
3. *Mexican type.*—Mexican (489), Andean (498), Orinoco (498), Brazilian (497), Central African (506), Dekkan (501).

II. Subtropical and Warm Temperate Provinces.

4. *Arizonan type.*—Arizonan (391, 400), Saharan (409), Peruvian (411), Kalahari (410), Central Australian (411).
5. *Californian type.*—Californian (412), Mediterranean (467), Chilean (418), Cape (418), Southwest Australian (418).
6. *Plata type.*—Plata (508), South African (509), Queensland (510).
7. *Floridan type.*—Floridan (356), Chinese (481).

III. Temperate and Intemperate Provinces.

8. *Oregon type.*—Oregon (412), West European (425), New Zealand (511).
9. *Mississippian type.*—Mississippian (356), Central European (453), Manchurian (481).
10. *Interior type.*—American Interior (391), Eurasian Interior (398), Patagonian (399).

IV. Cold Temperate Provinces.

11. *Alaskan type.*—Alaskan (513), Norwegian (515), Southwest American (516).
12. *Canadian type.*—Canadian (516), Siberian (519).

V. Polar Provinces.

13. *Arctic type.*—American Arctic (519), Eurasian Arctic (520).
14. *Greenland type.*—Greenland (520), Antarctic (31, 523).

PART III. REGIONAL GEOGRAPHY

CHAPTER XXIII

NATURAL PROVINCES

NEARLY the whole land surface of the earth is now divided into areas having definite boundaries, in each of which government and laws are uniform. These political divisions are called empires, kingdoms, states, provinces, and many other names. The location, extent, and boundaries of political divisions are shown upon a political map, which is generally colored to emphasize their distinctions. They are all conventional and artificial in the sense of being man-made and the products of human society.

The face of the earth may also be divided into areas in each of which all the non-human conditions, such as structure, relief, climate, vegetation, and animal life are uniform. Such areas constitute natural divisions, as distinguished from artificial, and a map of them may be called a natural map. The maps in Part I of this book showing relief, structure, soils, temperature, pressure, winds, rainfall, climate, and plant and animal regions, are natural maps, each of which shows the distribution of one or two natural conditions. A composite map made by printing upon one sheet all the natural maps of this book would be a practically complete and correct natural map, but would be too complex to be useful.

It is more difficult to make a natural map than a political map. The boundaries of political divisions are definite and well known. They are recorded in treaties and laws made by the various governments concerned, and in civilized countries are surveyed and marked by permanent monuments upon the ground. A political boundary is so sharp that by taking one step across it a person may pass abruptly and completely out of the jurisdiction of one government into that of another. On the other hand, natural conditions vary gradually, and in most cases insensibly from one place to another, and natural boundaries are often vague and uncertain. The shore line of the sea, where land and water meet, constitutes a definite boundary on opposite sides of which nearly all natural conditions are strongly contrasted. The largest and most definite of all natural provinces are the continental land masses, and next to them islands and peninsulas. On land the sharpest contrasts occur along lines of abrupt change in elevation, as where plains are bordered by mountains or by plateaus which rise with an abrupt slope.

While the natural divisions of the face of the earth would remain the same if no human being lived upon it, they derive their greatest importance in geography from their relations to human affairs. If these are kept in mind, it is possible to map the earth into large regions, in each of which many, if not all, of the natural conditions are approximately uniform, and determine its general character and possibilities for human habitation and utilization. From this point of view, some natural conditions are more important than others and may be used to divide the face of the earth into great natural provinces. The temperature belts shown in Fig. 164 record the efficiency of solar energy and show in a large way the vigor and quantity of life possible in different parts of the earth. Combined with rainfall regions (Figs. 185, 186, 187), they display more definitely the factors of climate upon which life intimately depends (Fig. 188). The lines of equal temperature and rainfall which bound climatic regions are imperceptible upon the ground and can be located only by a long series of scientific observations. They represent averages and not actual conditions existing on any given day, and serve to locate belts of gradual transition from one climate to another. Nevertheless they are indispensable in mapping natural regions. Differences of climate find concrete expression in vegetation, and the ordinary observer can see clearly the change from forest to grassland and from grassland to desert. Natural vegetation is a visible expression not only of climate, but of soil, relief, and drainage, and in turn determines actual and possible animal life, food supply, and most of the material resources which are not mineral. Position, structure, and relief introduce special modifications which affect accessibility, arability, mineral wealth, and available power. All these conditions determine the large possibilities of human life and civilization, and constitute the basis for the division of the land into natural and economic provinces, that is, into natural environments.

Hardly any part of the face of the earth is unique and wholly unlike every other part. Therefore natural regions fall into groups of two or more which are very much alike. One region in each group may be taken as a type and representative of the whole group, and a thorough study of the type region renders unnecessary a detailed study of the other members of the group. When the type is known, the others may be thought of as substantially similar. Thus natural geography may be made more simple than political geography, because natural divisions do not differ from one another so much as political divisions. The natural conditions in any region determine natural resources and products, and through them influence strongly the food, clothing, implements, dwellings, occupations, trade, and economic affairs of the people who inhabit the region.

Wherever one or more natural conditions prevail in an extreme degree, as in regions which are very hot, very cold, very wet, or very dry, in dense forests, extensive grasslands, or deserts, on lofty mountains or oceanic islands scarcely rising above the waves, human life is rigorously limited and controlled by nature, and men remain in a relatively low stage of culture. Whenever natural conditions are more varied and of medium intensity, as in the mixed forest and grassland of the temperate zones, men have a better chance and are able to control and utilize nature in a great variety of ways and to become civilized. By means of trade all the resources of the earth are made available, and economic life correspondingly complex. But it is no more possible to escape from the influence of natural environment than it is to get off the earth. The occupations of a community, the resources they make use of, the work they do, the kind of living they get, modify the habits, thoughts, and spirit of the people and help to determine their political, educational, and religious institutions. All these things combined constitute the degree of civilization of the community and determine its place in history and its present power, influence, and rank among the peoples of the world. To discover how and to what extent human life is related to natural environment is the main problem of geography. It has been expressed by Le Play in a simple formula which may be stated in various terms:

Place →	Work →	People
Region →	Resources →	Human life
Environment →	Occupations →	Institutions

Natural Provinces. — On the map, Fig. 301, the land areas are divided into natural provinces or environments, each of which may be subdivided into minor regions for detailed study to any degree of thoroughness desired. These provinces are arranged in five classes approximately defined by the temperature belts of Fig. 164. The provinces in each class are grouped according to relief, climate, and vegetation under two or more types. In most cases there is little room for uncertainty as to the type to which the province properly belongs. The exact boundaries and arrangement of the provinces are subject to modification according to individual judgment, and the scheme is not to be regarded as final. Perhaps in the future geographers may agree upon a definite plan for the division of the whole face of the earth, including the sea, into natural environments.

I. Intertropical Provinces. — *Temperature always high and the range small.* In the Intertropical provinces seasonal changes of temperature are less marked than those of rainfall, which, except on plateaus and protected lowlands, is above 60 inches, with excess, if any, in summer. The vegetation, according to rainfall, is either tropical rain and monsoon forests, or tropical dry forest and savanna. Among the economic products are coconut, sago, oil, and other palms, manioc, gums, bananas, cocoa, sugar cane, rice, spices, coffee, opium, cinchona, rubber, cotton, silk, cabinet woods, timber, dyestuffs, ivory, and pearls. Collective economy prevails, with hoe, garden, and plantation culture in favorable localities. Technical arts are poorly developed.

The native peoples are, with few exceptions, savage or semi-civilized, of American, Ethiopian, Mongolian, and Malay races. The prevalence of malaria, dysentery, and other tropical diseases renders these provinces unsuitable as a permanent home for Caucasian peoples. These difficulties may be overcome, and "the tropics" may become the important lands of the future.

Types 1 *and* 2 are oceanic lands, islands, and peninsulas in the equatorial calm belt or exposed to trade and monsoon winds from the ocean. *Rainfall generally above* 60 *inches. Tropical rain and monsoon forests.*

1. *Amazon Type.* Equatorial with no dry season. — Amazon; Kongo; Malay.
2. *Caribbean Type.* Tropical with dry season. — Caribbean; Indo-Chinese; Madagascar.

Type 3 includes continental lands and tropical plateaus, which on account of elevation have a more or less temperate climate. *Rainfall generally* 20 *to* 60 *inches. Tropical dry forest and savanna.*

3. *Mexican Type.* — Mexican; Andean; Orinoco; Brazilian; Central African; Dekkan.

II. Subtropical and Warm Temperate Provinces. — *Hot with a temperate season or temperate with a hot season.* These provinces include the great continental deserts of the world, with adjacent grasslands, and only two provinces in which the rainfall is more than moderate.

Type 4 includes the continental deserts. *Rainfall less than* 10 *inches.* The daily range of temperature far exceeds the annual. *Vegetation absent or scanty and confined to drouth plants.* The economic products are minerals, except in groundwater oases and valleys irrigated by streams which rise in neighboring rainy regions. Desert populations are sparse, generally nomadic and barbarous, and often piratical, parasitic, or tributary to the watered districts.

4. *Arizonan Type.*—Arizonan; Saharan; Peruvian; Kalahari; Central Australian.

Types 5 *and* 6 are oceanic lands with *small range of temperature and a rainfall of* 20 *to* 60 *inches.*

Lands of type 5 have *dry summers, tropical dry forest, and poor grassland.* The economic products are the olive, vine, fig, date, citrus and stone fruits, wheat, corn (maize), and silk. Goats take the place of cattle. Meat and dairy products are scarce. The equable temperature, clear skies, absence of storms, and dry, stimulating air render the climate sanitary and delightful. The Mediterranean province has been the center of a high civilization for many centuries. The other provinces are small and their civilized communities young.

5. *Californian Type.* — Californian; Mediterranean; Chilean; Cape; Southwest Australian.

Lands of type 6 have *dry winters* and are covered with *prairie, steppe, and scrub*, or a combination of them. The economic products are cereal grains, cattle, horses, sheep, wool, hides, and ostrich plumes. The natural resources are poorly developed. The population is sparse, and herding is the chief economy.

6. *Plata Type.* — Plata (pampas); South African (veldt); Queensland (bush).

Type 7 has a *rainfall near or above* 60 *inches and no dry season,* supporting *temperate rain and summer forests.* The economic products are tropical fruits, rice, sugar cane, tea, cotton, and silk.

7. *Floridan Type.* — Floridan; Chinese.

III. Temperate and Intemperate Provinces. — Lands of types 8 and 9 have *mixed summer and coniferous forests and grassland (prairie).* The economic products are corn (maize), wheat, oats, rye, barley, root crops, sugar beet, fruits, berries, tobacco, swine, cattle, horses, sheep, flax, hemp, and timber. These provinces are the special domain of the cereal grains and of animals fed upon them, and are the chief food-producing regions of the world. They are rich in coal and iron, and the technical arts are highly developed. They are densely populated by the most highly civilized Caucasian peoples, except in Asia.

Type 8 includes west coast lands with *small range of temperature.* All seasons are temperate, and the *rainfall is* 20 *to* 100 *inches, with excess in winter.*

8. *Oregon Type.* — Oregon; West European; New Zealand.

Type 9 includes the east coast and interior lowlands with a hot and a cold season and a *large range of temperature.* The *rainfall is generally* 20 *to* 60 *inches, with excess in summer.*

9. *Mississippian Type.* — Mississippian; Central European; Manchurian.

Type 10 comprises interior continental highlands, with *extreme range of temperature and a rainfall less than* 20 *inches.* They are broken by lofty mountain ranges inclosing plateaus and basins near and below sea level. Some of them are the most barren and inhospitable deserts of the world. They are characterized by a vast expanse of *steppe,* in Eurasia the home of Mongolian nomad herdsmen for 3000 years. The North American steppes are occupied by Caucasian ranchmen who are tributary to the more favored regions on either side. In South America the narrowness of the continent mitigates the extreme climatic conditions, but the steppes are as yet occupied only by barbarous native hunters and herdsmen.

10. *Interior Type.* — American Interior; Eurasian Interior; Patagonian.

IV. Cold Temperate Provinces. — *Temperate with a cold season or cold with a temperate season.*

Type 11 includes west coast oceanic highlands with *low temperature, small range, and a perennial rainfall of* 20 *to* 100 *inches.* The numerous snow fields and glaciers are not due to cold winters, but to heavy snowfall and cool summers. The ice-free land is occupied by *coniferous and temperate rain forests.* The economic products are minerals, fish, and timber. The narrow coast lands are largely dependent upon the sea. The scenery is among the most magnificent in the world.

11. *Alaskan Type.* — Alaskan; Norwegian; Southwest American.

Type 12 includes continental lowlands with *very low winter temperatures and large range. The rainfall is* 20 *to* 40 *inches,* including a heavy and persistent snowfall. They comprise the great belts of coniferous forest which stretch across the northern continents from ocean to ocean. The economic products are minerals, furs, and timber. The sparse population of American and Mongolian races is engaged in hunting and trapping. More or less temporary and shifting groups and communities of Caucasians invade these provinces for mining and lumbering purposes.

12. *Canadian Type.* — Canadian; Siberian.

V. Polar Provinces. — *The temperature is always low. Precipitation is less than* 10 *inches,* and mostly in the form of snow. The economic products are the musk ox, reindeer, hare, polar bear, fish, marine mammals, and birds. The population is very sparse and mostly of the Mongolian race.

13. *Arctic Type.* Lowland tundras. — American Arctic; Eurasian Arctic.

14. *Greenland Type.* Highland ice deserts. — Greenland; Antarctic.

VI. Regions belonging to types determined by special conditions of relief, accessibility, arability, and mineral wealth.

Alpine Type. — Mountain lands.
Andean Type. — Tropical plateaus.
Netherlands Type. — Delta lands.
Italian Type. — Peninsular lands.
British Type. — Continental islands.
Hawaiian Type. — Oceanic islands.
Egyptian Type. — Irrigated lands.

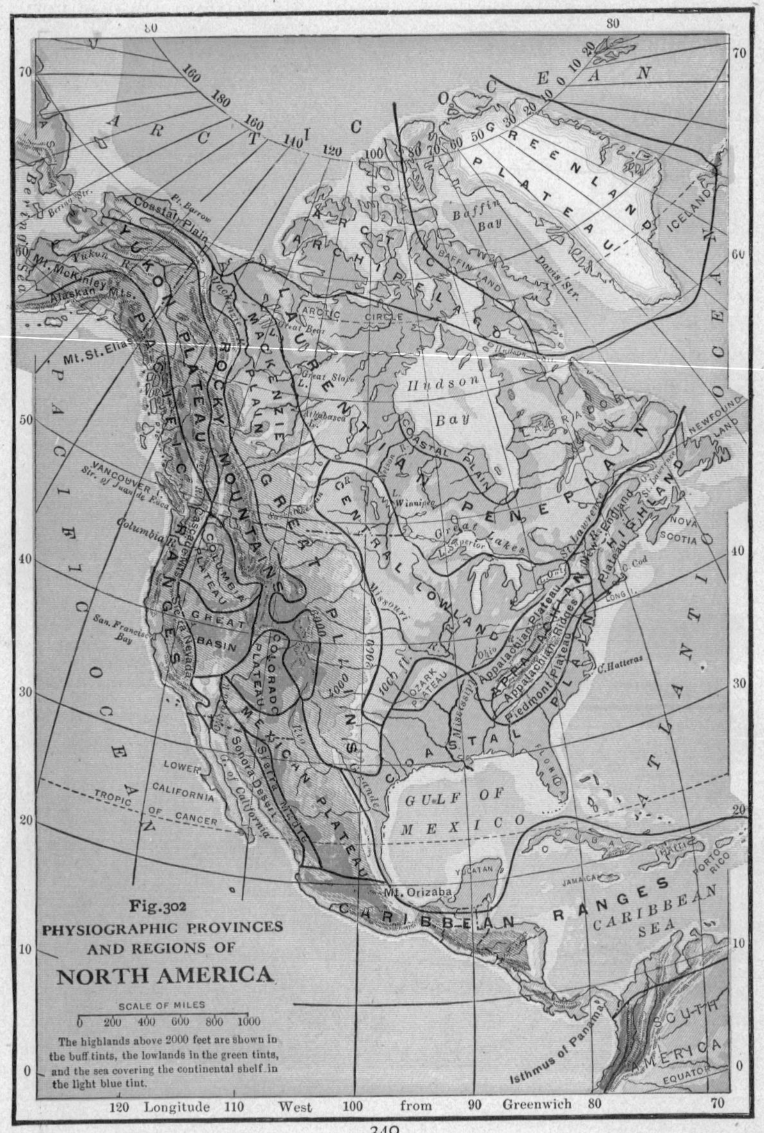

Fig. 302
PHYSIOGRAPHIC PROVINCES AND REGIONS OF
NORTH AMERICA

The highlands above 2000 feet are shown in the buff tints, the lowlands in the green tints, and the sea covering the continental shelf in the light blue tint.

CHAPTER XXIV

NORTH AMERICA — PHYSIOGRAPHIC PROVINCES

THE continent of North America, with its outlying islands, extends through more than seventy degrees of latitude, and is crossed by all the belts of climate. Its shores are washed by all the oceans of the northern hemisphere, and it presents to them a diversified coast line. Its surface is occupied by an assemblage of land forms which include all varieties of structure, relief, soil, and mineral products. Its rivers and lakes are among the largest in the world. It would be difficult to name a plant or animal which could not find a congenial home in some part of it. More than half of it lies in those temperate middle latitudes which are most favorable for the existence of a high degree of civilization. Its position, extent, character, and complexity render it one of the most valuable assets of the human race. It constitutes by itself a world in which nothing essential for human welfare is lacking. All varieties of landscape and scenery exist upon a large scale. Much simpler in plan than Asia, and more complex than any of the other continents, it may be regarded as the typical continent. Its natural provinces belong to nearly every type, and each one is a fair specimen of its class. A detailed study of North America goes far toward an understanding of world geography.

Physiographic Provinces and Regions. — The map (Fig. 302) divides North America into physiographic provinces and regions, based upon the structure and relief of the earth crust.

The Laurentian Peneplain (Figs. 23, 111, 197). — The northeastern part of the continent is occupied by one of the oldest land areas on the globe. It is bordered on the southeast by the St. Lawrence River and Gulf, and on the southwest by a series of great lakes, Ontario, Huron, Superior, Winnipeg,

Athabasca, Great Slave, and Great Bear. On the east it presents a high, fiord coast to the Atlantic. The eastern rim is broken by Hudson Strait, admitting the Atlantic waters to the shallow interior basin of Hudson Bay. Ages of weathering and stream erosion have removed the original cover of sedimentary strata and exposed a complex mass of coarsely crystalline rocks of varied and deformed structure. Severe and prolonged glaciation has swept these rocks nearly bare and rounded and polished their surface, leaving the harder ledges upstanding in hills and ridges of low relief, with irregular hollows between.

The drainage divide between Hudson Bay and the St. Lawrence is a broad plateau between 1000 and 2000 feet in elevation, rising toward the east, where mountains bordering the Labrador coast stand above 5000 feet. The glacial rock basins and drift-dammed valleys of the peneplain are occupied by unnumbered island-studded lakes, of which Mistassini and Abbitibi, draining to Hudson Bay, and Nipigon and St. John to the St. Lawrence, are the largest. The numerous rivers are short, tortuous, disorderly, and frequently interrupted by lakes and rapids.

The Laurentian province is very rich in minerals, which have been developed only along the southern edge, where iron, silver, copper, and nickel are mined.

The Greenland Plateau. — Greenland, the largest island in the world, is a broken-block plateau separated from the continent by a wide stretch of deep water. Most of its area is covered by an ice cap of unknown thickness, the surface of which rises in the south to a height of 9000 feet above the sea. A strip of bare, rocky land, 20 to 100 miles wide, borders the coast, and toward the northern extremity a considerable area is ice-free. The coast is almost everywhere high, precipitous, and broken by profound fiords, through which the inland ice drains to the sea. The rocks exposed are generally crystalline, but beds of good anthracite coal occur in some localities. Baffin Land, one of the largest islands in the world, and the smaller islands to the north resemble Greenland.

The Appalachian Highland. — Another area of old land, separated from the Laurentian peneplain by the valley of the St. Lawrence, extends from Newfoundland nearly to the Gulf of Mexico, a distance of about 2000 miles. As this land rose above the sea, the earth crust was thrown into numerous parallel folds, like those of a heavy rug slid sidewise on the floor. As the folds were compressed and thrust upon one another, the strata were broken and faulted. During the process of folding and faulting, and through the ages since elapsed, erosion has removed layers of rock many miles in thickness. The Mohawk-Hudson gap in New York cuts the highland completely into two contrasted regions.

The New England Plateau. — Northeast of the Hudson gap the New England plateau occupies the space between the St. Lawrence and the Atlantic. Only small areas of sedimentary rock remain, chiefly around the margins, and the plateau resembles the Laurentian peneplain. Many knobs, knots, and ridges of crystalline rock stand above the general surface. The Adirondack Mountains of New York form a roughly circular knot with peaks above 5000 feet. The White Mountains of New Hampshire form the culminating point of the region, where Mt. Washington reaches the highest elevation in northeastern North America, 6279 feet.

Newfoundland is a portion of the highland detached by the drowned valley of the lower St. Lawrence. It is traversed by parallel ridges rising to 2000 feet, and is prolonged far out to sea by the slightly submerged "banks." The peninsulas and bays of Newfoundland and Nova Scotia are expressions of the original crustal folds. The coast line of the New England plateau is broken by numerous fiords and bordered by islands, all on a small scale, but furnishing many good harbors. The surface is covered by a thin mantle of bouldery drift, with sandy outwash plains near the coast. Glacial lakes abound, and the streams generally have narrow valleys and a rapid fall, with drowned mouths. The Connecticut is the longest, and in its southern course traverses a wide valley.

Valuable quarries of granite, slate, and marble are numerous, and rich coal fields underlie Nova Scotia and New Brunswick. Iron is mined in Newfoundland.

The Appalachian Mountains and Plateaus. — South of the Mohawk-Hudson gap, the highland consists of a central mountain belt flanked by a plateau on each side. The folding of the strata in the central belt gave rise to narrow bands of alternately harder and softer rocks, from which the agents of erosion have carved a series of parallel ridges and valleys (Figs. 44, 195).

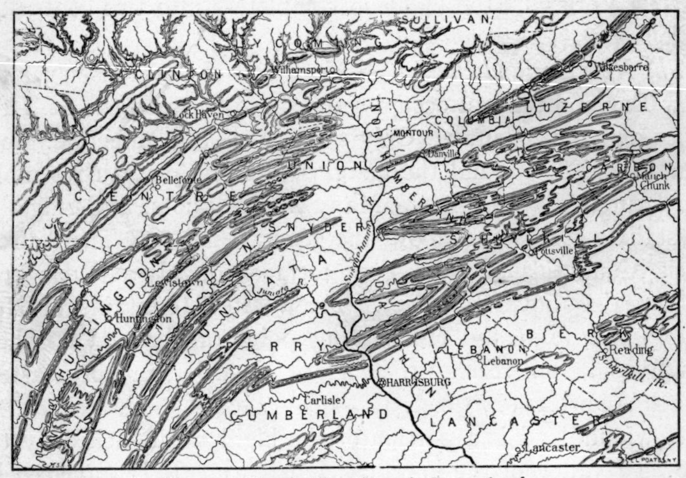

Fig. 303. — Appalachian ridges in Pennsylvania.

The ridges have smooth, symmetrical slopes and even crests, and extend in a straight line ten or twenty miles like a wall. As one dies out another begins at one side, so that the ends overlap. They are sometimes curved or connected in a zigzag pattern. The easternmost ridge south of the Potomac River, called the Blue Ridge, is more massive than the others, and, together with the plateau which borders it, consists of old crystalline rocks. The Blue Ridge is separated from the other ridges to the west of it by an unusually wide interval known as the Great Appalachian Valley. The ridges generally vary in elevation between 1000 and 4000 feet, but near the southern end of the Blue Ridge, a massive knot reaches in Mt. Mitchell a height of 6711 feet, the highest point in eastern North America. The narrow *Piedmont Plateau* which lies between the Blue Ridge and the coastal plain is a southern extension of the New England plateau (Fig. 30). The belt of mountain ridges is bordered on the west by a prominent escarpment, which is the abrupt edge of the *Appalachian Plateau* (Figs. 78, 303). It is dissected by streams, and from the east has the appearance of a mountain range overtopping the others. Hence in New York it is called the Catskill Mountains, in Pennsylvania and Virginia the Allegheny Mountains, and in Kentucky and Tennessee the Cumberland Mountains. The surface of the Appalachian Plateau slopes gently northwestward and merges into the interior plains. The strata which underlie it have been but slightly disturbed from a horizontal position, but near the escarpment have been deeply dissected by the tributaries of the Ohio River.

In the north the Delaware, Susquehanna, and Potomac rivers rise in the western plateau and flow southeastward directly across the grain of the country, cutting narrow water gaps through all the ridges on their way to the Atlantic. The numerous gaps give access to the valleys and enable railroads and canals to cross the highland (Fig. 44). In the south most of the streams rise in the Blue Ridge and flow northwestward. The Kanawha flows directly to the Ohio. The other mountain streams join the Tennessee, which makes its way out by a circuitous course to the Ohio near its mouth.

The soils of the Appalachian mountains and plateaus vary with the kind of rock which underlies them. They are generally poor on the ridges and sandstone areas, and fertile in the valleys and on limestone areas. The mountains and western plateau contain the richest coal fields in North America, also petroleum and gas. Iron ore is extensively mined in Alabama.

The Ozark Plateau. — An outlying portion of the Appalachian highland appears west of the Mississippi River in the Ozark plateau, which stands like an island in the interior plain, as Newfoundland stands in the ocean.

The part north of the Arkansas River is a reproduction on a small scale of the Appalachian Plateau. South of the Arkansas, a belt of parallel ridges and valleys trending east and west, called the Ouachita Mountains, reproduces in miniature the features of the Appalachian Mountains.

The Cordilleras. — The western highland of North America, known as the Cordilleras, extends from southern Mexico to Bering Sea, and on the parallel of 40° N. Lat. is 1000 miles wide. It is divided longitudinally into three great provinces, the Rocky Mountains, the Intermont Plateaus, and the Pacific Ranges.

The Rocky Mountains (Figs. 54, 58, 60, 74, 131, 198). — The Rocky Mountain system forms the eastern member of the Cordilleras and consists of a belt of folded and dissected ranges, with occasional volcanic peaks and knots. The scores of ranges composing the system present a great variety of structure which would require a volume to describe. The general arrangement is of parallel and overlapping ranges separated by high plateaus or valleys. In Canada there are two well-defined series divided by a trench which is continuous for 800 miles, and occupied alternately by the head waters of the Columbia, Fraser, and Mackenzie, which pass out on either side through water gaps. The Rocky Mountain system is broken in Wyoming by a basin about 200 miles in diameter and connected through a gap with the Great Plains on the east. North of this basin the Yellowstone National Park includes a volcanic knot famous for its geysers and hot springs. The width of the system is generally not more than 100 miles, but in northern United States increases to 400 miles. The highest part of the system is in Colorado, where Pikes Peak, Longs Peak, and about one hundred others rise to about 14,000 feet. A height of 10,000 feet or more is maintained as far north as the parallel of 60° N. Lat. The system forms the great continental divide between streams flowing to the Pacific on the west and to the Atlantic and Arctic on the east and north. As a system, the Rocky Mountains do not extend south of Colorado, but are continued by broken block ridges which merge into the escarpment of the Mexican Plateau, known as the eastern Sierra Madre.

The Rocky Mountains are rich in minerals and furnish a large part of the world's supply of gold, silver, copper, and lead. Passes practicable for railroads occur at intervals throughout the length of the system, which is crossed by ten or more trunk lines, with branches to the many mining regions.

The Pacific Ranges (Figs. 40, 43, 51, 84, 104, 106). — The Pacific coast of North America is bordered by a double chain of mountains with a central longitudinal valley. The eastern member rivals the Rocky Mountains in height and continuity. The western Sierra Madre of Mexico is isolated by a wide gap on the north, through which the Colorado River passes. The Sierra Nevada of California is a single massive block uptilted on the east, where a steep escarpment faces the Great Basin with an unbroken wall. The highest point in its even crest line is Mt. Whitney, 15,000 feet. It is continued northward by the Cascade Range, chiefly of volcanic origin, of which Shasta, Hood, and Rainier or Tacoma are conspicuous and symmetrical cones about 14,000 feet high. The range is cut in two by the Columbia valley and ends at the Fraser River gap. North of the Fraser, the Coast Range of British Columbia and Alaska is deeply gashed by fiords and crossed by several small rivers. North of the parallel of 60° N. Lat. the system curves to the west and expands into the Alaskan Mountains, a great volcanic knot which contains some of the highest peaks on the continent, McKinley (20,300 feet), Logan (19,500), St. Elias (18,000), Crillon (15,900), and Fairweather (15,300). Beyond the knot the system is prolonged through the Alaskan peninsula and Aleutian Islands by a chain of volcanoes, many of which are active. The Alaskan mountains are covered by extensive snow fields and their valleys filled with hundreds of glaciers, many of which reach the sea.

They contain deposits of coal, gold, copper, and tin, the extent and value of which are very great, but not yet fully determined.

The western member of the Pacific mountain system is older and far less massive than the eastern, and north of the Strait of Fuca is broken into a chain of islands. The southern extremity forms the backbone of the peninsula of Lower California, between which and the mainland lies the rift valley of the Gulf of California. The Coast Ranges are separated from the Sierra Nevada by the great Valley of California, and from the Cascade Range by the valleys of the Willamette River and Puget Sound. They are broken by San Francisco Bay and the lower Columbia River. Vancouver and other islands contain good coal beds. Mercury is mined south of San Francisco, and Lower California has considerable mineral wealth, as yet little developed.

The Pacific coast of North America, from Panama to the Strait of Fuca, is generally high and smooth, with long lines of cliffs and a few small and shallow bays. There are no important indentations except the Gulf of California, San Francisco Bay, and the mouth of the Columbia. The northern part is still higher but broken by numerous fiords and canals, of which Lynn Canal and Puget Sound are the largest (Figs. 151, 333).

The Intermont Plateaus. — The space between the Rocky Mountains and the Pacific ranges is occupied by a series of plateaus 4000 to 8000 feet in height. Extensive faulting and outflows of lava have occurred. The higher portions are dissected by cañons. The intermont belt is divided at the parallel of 50° N. Lat., where the Rocky Mountains and the Pacific ranges come in contact. The southern portion is drained by the Rio Grande, Colorado, and Columbia, the northern chiefly by the Fraser and the Yukon.

The Yukon Plateau. — In Canada and Alaska a rough and mountainous plateau, widening northwards, descends to the coast lands of Bering Sea. The northern half forms the basin of the Yukon, while the southern is drained by the Fraser and smaller streams which pass directly through the coast mountains to the Pacific. Rich gold fields occur on many of the rivers, among which the Klondike, Tanana, Atlin, Kluane, and

Skeena are most famous. The combined product of all these is nearly equaled by that of the field about Nome, south of Bering Strait. Coal beds occur at many places in the Yukon basin.

The Columbia Plateau (Fig. 141). — An area of 200,000 square miles, mostly in Idaho, Washington, and Oregon, is covered by a series of lava sheets which in some places are more than 4000 feet thick. The smooth surface of the lava meets the slopes of older mountains as the surface of the sea joins a rugged coast. It extends up the valleys and indentations and is itself indented by projecting headlands, while some mountains are completely surrounded and form islands in a frozen sea of lava. In some places it has been extensively eroded by streams, and in others broken by faulting into blocks, as in the block mountains of Oregon. It is traversed by the Snake River, which flows through a cañon in some places 4000 feet deep. Much of the drainage is subterranean, leaving the surface unscarred by stream valleys. The soil is generally scanty, but local accumulations are of great thickness and very productive.

The Great Basin. — Between the Sierra Nevada and Wasatch Mountains an area of 210,000 square miles, extending from $41\frac{1}{2}°$ N. Lat. nearly to the Gulf of California, has, on account of scanty rainfall, no drainage to the sea, and is hence called the Great Basin. Its elevation of 4000 to 6000 feet makes it a typical intermont plateau. It is traversed by numerous north-south mountain ranges separated by flat-floored valleys, and its surface resembles that of a rasp. The ranges are of varied structure, some being the edges of broken blocks and some the remains of ancient folds. Nearly all of them have suffered extensive erosion. Infrequent but violent rains on the summits produce temporary torrents, which score the mountain sides and carry down sediment which accumulates in the valleys. The streams soon disappear by evaporation, and thus the mountains have been half buried in their own waste. There are many " sinks " and salt lakes, all of which are subject to great variations of volume and area and are liable to dry up entirely.

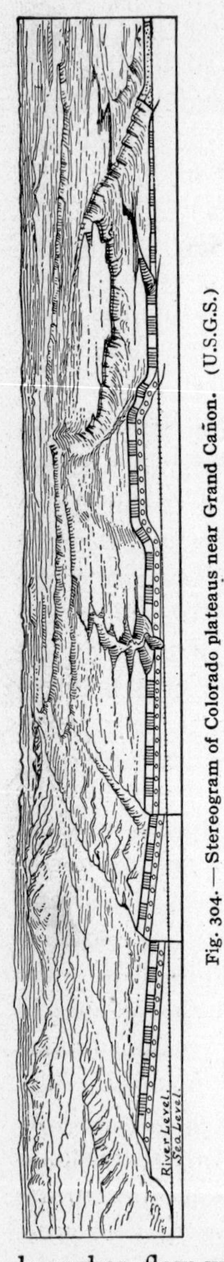

Fig. 304. — Stereogram of Colorado plateaus near Grand Cañon. (U.S.G.S.)

The largest of these is Great Salt Lake in Utah, which is permanent but fluctuating in level and outline. Two depressions, Death Valley and the Salton Sink in California, have floors several hundred feet below sea level. Very rich gold-bearing veins have been discovered in the mountain ranges, and the lake basins contain deposits of salt, borax, and soda. The whole region is desert and its soils are largely eolian, but productive wherever water is available for irrigation, as in the valley of Great Salt Lake and others near the foot of the mountains.

The Colorado Plateau (Figs. 38, 73, 90, 204, 205, 304). — Most of the area drained by the Colorado River, including the Wasatch Mountains, is a plateau above 6000 feet in elevation. It is bounded on the west by the fault scarp of the Wasatch, which overlooks the Great Basin from a height of 6000 to 10,000 feet. Sedimentary beds of great thickness have been denuded, leaving the edges of the harder layers upstanding in long lines of cliffs which trend in a general east-west direction, and divide the plateau into a series of platforms rising by gigantic steps, like a tilted staircase. In the western part north-south faults have broken the strata into parallel blocks, bounded by escarpments at right angles to the other set. The structure and surface are farther complicated by numerous volcanic cones, cisternlike intrusions and outflows of lava. Across this region the Green, Grand, and Colorado rivers, with their branches, flow with little regard to the surface slope, intrenched in profound cañons, of which the Grand Cañon of the Colorado in Arizona is unrivaled in the world. The plateau is well characterized by the Indians as "the land of standing rocks." Important mineral deposits have so far been discovered only in the Wasatch Mountains; yet, on account of its magnificent scenery and the grand scale upon which physiographic forms and processes are displayed, the Colorado Plateau must be reckoned as one of the most valuable regions of the world.

The Mexican Plateau (Figs. 191, 196). — The southernmost portion of the plateau belt rises from the depression of the Gila River to heights of 6000 to 8000 feet south of the tropic. It is an old valley between the ranges of the eastern and western Sierra Madre, which has been filled nearly brimful with an accumulation of waste from the mountains and the discharge from a great number of volcanic openings. In some places peaks and ridges of buried mountains project above the surface of the filling like islands from the sea. There are no large rivers, and the streams are generally torrents during one half the year and dry during the other half. Some of them end in sinks and salt lakes. It is one of the richest mining regions in the world, and contains unestimated stores of silver, gold, copper, lead, mercury, and iron.

The Sonora Desert. — In a belt extending southward from the Great Basin to the Caribbean Ranges in Mexico and bordering the Gulf of California on the east, the rainfall is so scanty and irregular that the relief, drainage, and vegetation are those of a typical desert. (See pp. 136, 213, 218, 409 and Figs. 37, 305.) The peculiarities of this region are so strongly marked that it has been set apart as a distinct physiographic province under the name of the Sonora Desert.

The Caribbean Ranges. — Southern Mexico, Central America, and the large islands of the West Indies (the Greater Antilles) are formed by partly submerged volcanic mountain ranges trending east and west, which with the northern Andes nearly inclose the deep basin of the Caribbean Sea. Volcanic cones, many of which are active, are numbered by scores, of which Orizaba (18,250), Popocatepetl (17,520), Ixtaccihuatl (17,000), and Toluca (15,000) in Mexico are the loftiest. The continental ranges are lowest at the Isthmus of Tehuantepec, now crossed by a railroad with a summit level of 700 feet, and at the narrow Isthmus of Panama, where there is a ship canal.

The Interior Plains. — The interior of North America is occupied by a continuous plain from the Gulf of Mexico to the Arctic Ocean. Its length is more than 3000 miles, and its greatest width about 1200 miles. The northern part is broken into a group of ragged islands forming the Arctic Archipelago. The Arctic shore is bordered by a narrow strip of coastal plain, the Gulf shore by a wider one. The remainder, which is truly interior, may be divided into three principal regions. On the north the long, narrow trough of the *Mackenzie Plain* slopes from an elevation above 2000 feet at the foot of the Rocky Mountains, eastward and northward to sea level. The trunk stream is one of the great rivers of the continent, with a volume of water sufficient to make it navigable for more than 1000 miles, but except for a few months in the year it is choked with ice. The wider and utilizable part of the interior plains, south of 55° N. Lat., is divided by differences of rainfall and vegetation, as well as of relief, into two contrasted portions.

The Great Plains (Figs. 36, 94, 133, 134, 202, 253) slope from an elevation of 4000 or 5000 feet at the foot of the Rocky Mountains eastward about 300 miles to the 2000-foot contour line, and hence are technically a plateau. In places the eastern edge is marked by an escarpment, but generally the surface merges imperceptibly into the lower plains. A large part of the Great Plains appears to be as smooth and level as the sea, and distant objects are hidden, like ships, only by the curve of the earth. The monotony, however, is broken in the northern states by uplifts and protrusions of igneous rock, which in the case of the Black Hills attain the magnitude of mountains. The higher portions are deeply cut by stream valleys, and in some localities carved into the fantastic and intricate forms of the "bad lands." Local areas of drifting sand dunes occur in western Kansas and Nebraska. The large rivers rise in the Rocky Mountains and, fed by melting snows, meander through wide valleys toward the Nelson and the Mississippi. Losing in volume of water by evaporation as they go, they are, except in times of flood, heavily loaded with sediment, and navigation, always difficult, is generally impossible for anything but small boats.

The Central Lowland (Figs. 34, 35, 45, 47, 48, 112, 113, 114, 115). — That part of the Interior plains extending from the lower Saskatchewan River approximately to the Missouri and Ohio, and including the basins of lakes Winnipeg, Michigan, Huron, Erie, and Ontario, is covered by a heavy mantle of glacial drift which has filled the depressions and obliterated most of the surface irregularities of the bed rock beneath. Only the large streams have been able to keep their original valleys open, and even the Missouri, Mississippi, and Ohio were diverted and displaced by the ice sheets which deposited the drift. The smaller streams are all young, and since the retreat of the ice have been unable to drain the innumerable lakes and marshes which occupy the hollows of the drift surface. The divides are low, flat, and difficult to locate. The only prominent features of relief are the bluffs which border the flood plains of the larger streams, and the belts of morainic hills which sweep in great loops and festoons with convex curves to the south and sharp reëntrant angles to the north (Fig. 113).

The glacial drift and bordering deposits of loess constitute soils of great fertility and endurance.

The whole area of the Interior plains, with some local exceptions, is underlain by sedimentary strata of great thickness which have been but little disturbed from their original horizontal position. They contain beds of coal and lignite second in value only to those of the Appalachian highland. Lead and zinc are mined in Missouri and Wisconsin, and the Black Hills contain rich veins of gold, silver, and lead.

The Coastal Plains (Figs. 28, 69, 136, 194). — The coast of the Gulf of Mexico and the Atlantic as far north as New York is bordered by a coastal plain of varying width. Long Island, Marthas Vineyard, Nantucket, and the Cape Cod peninsula are fragments of a former northward extension. South of the Rio Grande the plain is very narrow, but northward it extends up the Mississippi 600 miles to the mouth of the Ohio. On the Atlantic

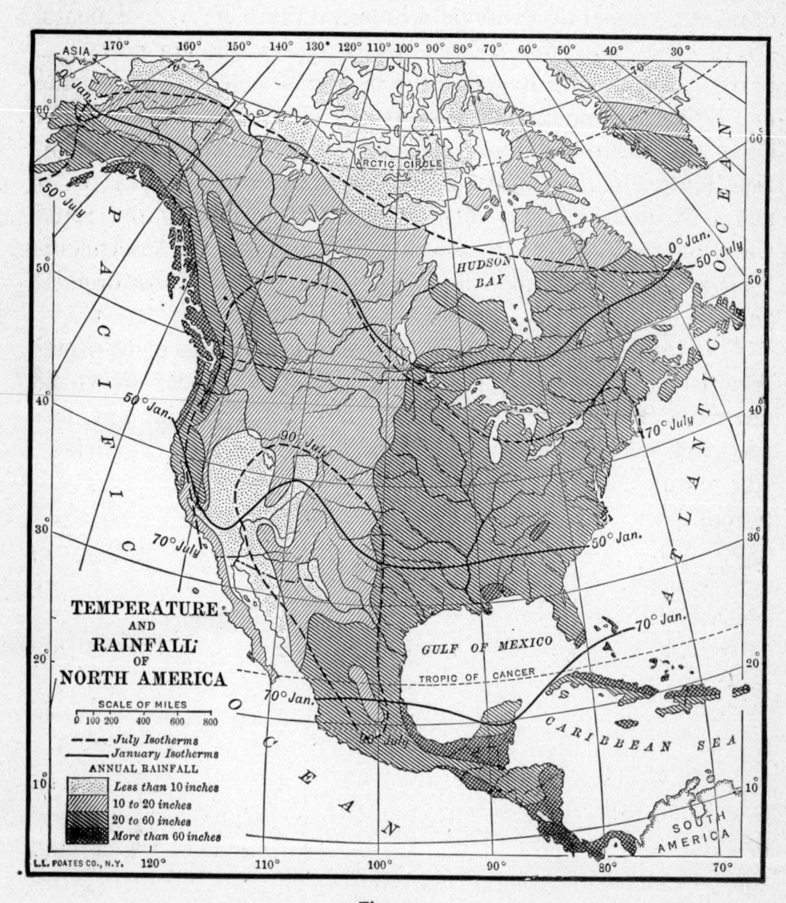

Fig. 305.

side the inner margin is the edge of the Piedmont Plateau, which forms a low escarpment, or Fall Line, where rapids or falls occur in all the streams crossing it. The larger rivers are invaded by the tide up to the Fall Line. The low, limestone peninsulas of Florida and Yucatan differ in structure from the rest of the plain. The drainage is chiefly subterranean, and in Florida numerous small sink-hole lakes occur. On the outer side the coast is bordered by the wide submerged plain of the continental shelf. The coast line is indented by many shallow bays and barred from the sea by extensive barrier beaches. The beaches of Florida are peculiar in being partly of coral formation. The delta and mouth of the Mississippi constitute the most important feature of the Gulf coast. Mineral deposits of value are generally absent. Beds of phosphate rock in Florida and South Carolina, and of salt and sulphur in Louisiana, and petroleum "pools" in Texas and Oklahoma form notable exceptions to this rule.

The temperature, rainfall, climate, and vegetation of North America are described in Chapters XIII–XVI and shown on the maps, Figs. 158, 159, 160, 161, 162, 164, 165, 166, 185, 186, 187, 188, 192, 305.

CHAPTER XXV

THE MISSISSIPPIAN AND FLORIDAN PROVINCES

THE natural provinces which occupy the middle latitudes of North America fall into three well-marked divisions of two each. The Atlantic division comprises the Mississippian and Floridan provinces, the Middle division the Interior and Arizonan provinces, and the Pacific division the Oregon and Californian provinces.

The Atlantic Division. — The Mississippian and Floridan provinces constitute a well-defined natural and economic unit, the only important distinction between them being climatic. The Mississippian province belongs to the intemperate belt of hot summers and cold winters and has a rainfall between 20 and 50 inches, while the Floridan is in the subtropical belt of hot summers and temperate winters and has a rainfall a little below or above 60 inches. There is no sharp line of demarcation between them. They are bounded on two sides by Atlantic waters, on the west by the line of 20 inches of rainfall and the borders of the steppe (Figs. 185, 192), and on the north approximately by the July isotherm of 70 degrees and the margin of the Laurentian peneplain. They include the Appalachian Highland, except Newfoundland, the whole of the Central Lowland, nearly all of the Atlantic and Gulf coastal plain and a small portion of the Great Plains. The area is nearly 2,000,000 square miles, or one fifth of North America. It is half as large as Europe and nearly two thirds as large as the United States. The population is about 90,000,000, or 70 per cent of the total population of North America. The density of population is about 45 per square mile.

Importance. — This region is the most densely populated large area in the western hemisphere and the most important

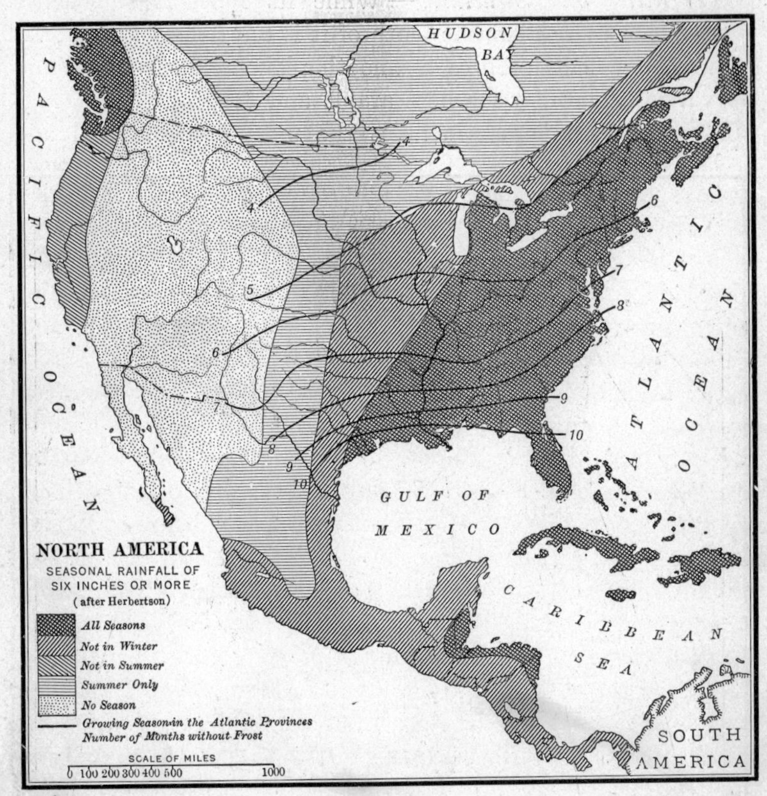

Fig. 306.

center of civilization outside of Europe. The bordering Canadian and Interior provinces are closely related and tributary to it. This preëminence is due to many causes, natural and historical.

(1) *Position.* — It lies on the west side of the north Atlantic Ocean and north of the American Mediterranean. The long, low coast line, with many drowned valleys, and the number of

navigable waterways which penetrate the interior, render it easily accessible by water from the better half of the world.

(2) *Relief and Structure.* — While its relief is sufficiently varied, not more than one tenth of it is too rugged for cultivation. Four fifths of it is a smooth plain below 2000 feet in elevation, almost everywhere arable and traversable by roads and canals. Its crust includes the most valuable coal and

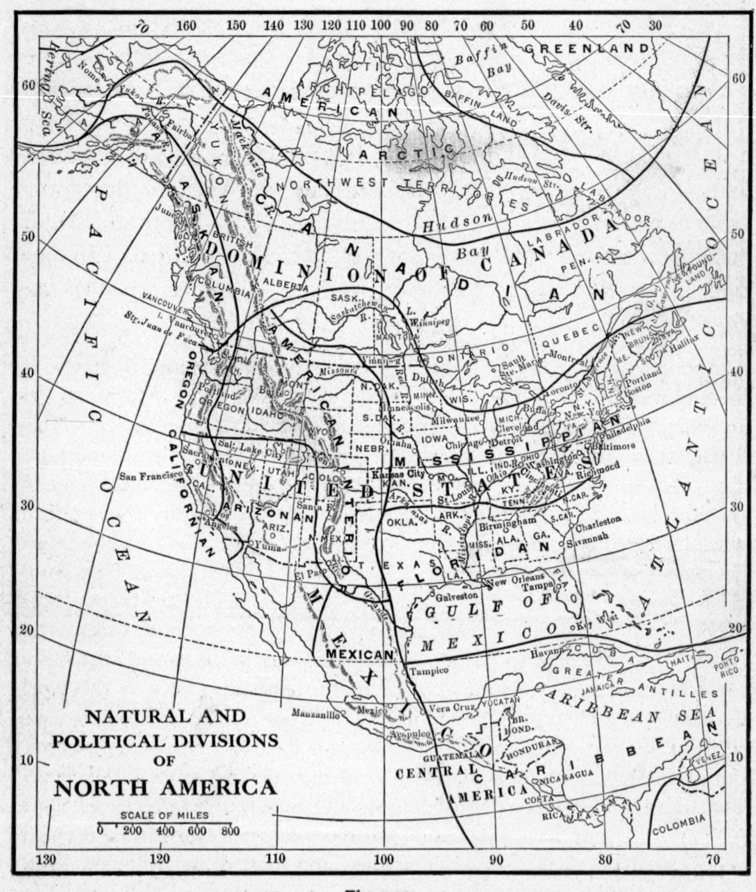

Fig. 307.

petroleum fields yet developed in the world, with important deposits of iron, lead, zinc, and other minerals. Two fifths of its area is covered with the best of glacial soils. In the rougher parts water power is abundant.

(3) *Climate.* — It lies in that part of the so-called temperate zone where the summers are long and warm enough to ripen the cereal grains and the rainfall in the growing season is everywhere sufficient for agriculture.

(4) *Vegetation.* — The natural vegetation includes large areas of coniferous and summer forests and prairie. The summer forests are easily converted by clearing into grass and agricultural lands.

(5) *People.* — The bulk of the population is of Baltic Caucasian stock (p. 260), which the presence of negroes, descended from former slaves, and the recent influx of Alpine and Mediterranean immigrants have not yet notably modified. In race and civilization the region is an oversea colony of western and central Europe.

Aboriginal Inhabitants. — Aside from destroying patches of forest by fire and restricting to some extent the natural increase of wild animals, the Indians of this region played an insignificant part in its history. They had scarcely disturbed the balance of nature and were of less importance than trees and deer. It was substantially a virgin environment of continental dimensions of the most favorable character, literally a new world, which civilized men discovered in the sixteenth century and finally gained possession of in the eighteenth and nineteenth centuries. The immigrants brought with them every kind of domestic animal now kept in this region except the turkey (and some dogs), all the cereal grains except corn (maize), and all the other plants of great economic value except cotton and tobacco. Even the species of cotton now extensively grown in the Floridan province probably originated in India. The changed environment was stimulating and caused plants, animals, and men to develop new adaptations, which, in most cases, resulted in an increase of vigor and efficiency. The native species often proved inferior and gave way before the invaders. As the white man has swept aside the red man, so English timothy grass and clover have displaced native grasses, and most of our common weeds are of European origin. Corn, tobacco, the potato, and the turkey are the only important American aborigines which have held their ground and increased and multiplied under foreign dominion.

Agriculture

Agriculture, combined with stock raising, extends over the whole area of the Atlantic provinces (Mississippian and Floridan) except the mountainous and dissected parts of the Appalachian highlands, and even there is of considerable importance in the valleys. It reaches its highest development on the Central Lowland.

Fig. 306 shows the approximate length of the growing season, or period between frosts, which reaches ten months on the Gulf coast and is about four months in the extreme northwest. Fig. 186 shows that the seasonal distribution of rainfall is everywhere favorable for agriculture. Where the annual rainfall is least, the maximum occurs in summer, and is sufficient for crops because evaporation is relatively small. The isotherms in summer bend far northward (Fig. 159) in Alberta and Saskatchewan, and while the winter temperatures are considerably below zero, this is not a controlling factor in agriculture. All the natural conditions are nicely adjusted for the existence of a wide range of vegetation from the subtropical to the cold temperate.

Corn. — Corn (maize) is grown throughout the Atlantic provinces, but is not an important crop in the region where the growing season is less than 4.5 months. The most productive corn belt lies in the southern part of the Central Lowland, from Ohio westward. The states included in this belt produce about 70 per cent of the total crop. This belt leads also in the production of all grains.

Corn is planted in rows, usually in May, cultivated to kill weeds and keep the soil moist until half grown, and harvested in September and October. The stalks of ripe corn are taller and heavier than those of any other grain, and correspondingly difficult to handle. They are often cut with the stroke of a long knife and set up in shocks to cure (Figs. 242, 244). Many farmers pick the ripe ears from the stalks, which are left standing, and cattle are turned into the field to eat as much as they will of the fodder; but such methods are wasteful. Machines are now in use which cut and bind the corn. After a month or more of curing in the shock, the ears are husked, largely by hand, the work being carried on through the late autumn in the field, and sometimes in barns during the winter. Machines are now in use, which, driven by a steam or gasoline engine, separate the ears

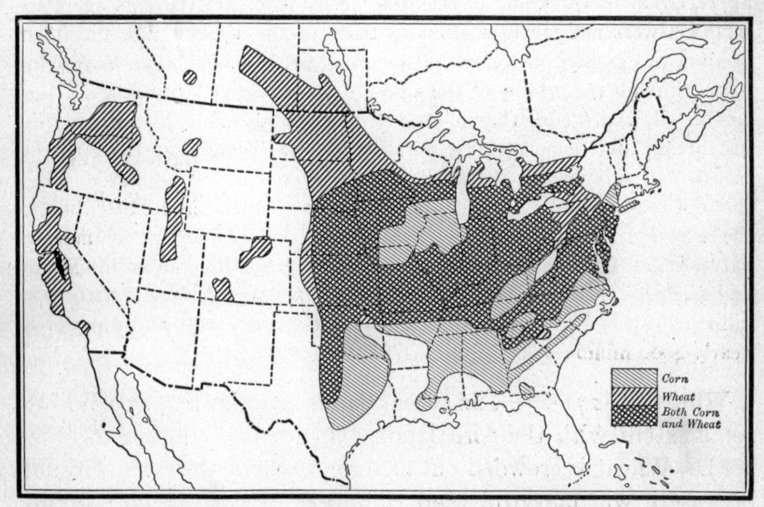

Fig. 308.—Chief corn and wheat producing regions of the United States and Canada.

and tear the stalks into shreds, rendering them more easily handled and consumed by stock. The ears are stored in cribs, or roofed pens open for circulation of air, and fed out to swine, cattle, and horses. Some portion of the grain is shelled and ground into meal or made into hominy, breakfast food, and other articles for human consumption. Corn cobs make excellent fuel for a quick, hot fire.

The unripe grain of some varieties, while still soft and milky, known as green corn, is roasted or boiled for immediate use, or preserved in sealed cans. Unripe corn stalks and ears are cut and packed in large bins, or silos, so tightly as to exclude the air. In this condition the material does not spoil or decay, and furnishes green fodder much relished by cattle in winter. The corn-swine-cattle system furnishes one of the most complete and economical combinations of agriculture and stock raising known. A large yield of both bulky and concentrated food is utilized and converted into pork and beef or milk, while sufficient fertilizer is returned to the land to prevent serious loss of fertility. Such a farm is a very efficient food factory. Perhaps one half of the corn crop is sold from the farms and manufactured elsewhere into starch, sugar, sirup, alcohol, and many other commercial products.

The cultivation of corn has reacted upon the farmers to give them a high appreciation of the value of scientific agriculture. Fifty years ago their methods were not much superior to those of the squaws, although their product was greater on account of the use of better tools and animal power. Now, through the agency of the agricultural colleges, "corn schools" are conducted, and "corn trains" travel over the railroads, giving practical instruction and demonstration to all who will assemble at the stopping places. In rural public schools prizes are offered to the pupil who raises the best crop of corn. Every enterprising farmer pays careful attention to the selection of seed, fertilizers, cultivation, and economical methods of harvesting. The results are that corn growing has become an intelligent and scientific business, and the crop of 1917 amounted to more than 3000 million bushels, or about 80 per cent of the world's crop, and was worth nearly 4000 million dollars.

Wheat (p. 271). — The wheat lands overlap and coincide to some extent with the corn lands, but are less continuous (Fig. 308). Wheat is crowded out of some parts of the corn belt, not because it will not grow there, but because corn is more profitable. Wheat does not require so long or so warm a season to ripen as corn, and hence extends much farther north, even to the Mackenzie plain and the Rocky Mountains. The wheat fields of the Saskatchewan and Red River basins are possible because of the many hours of sunshine and frequent showers in summer.

In the southern part of the wheat belt the grain is sown in the autumn and harvested the following summer, and is hence called winter wheat. The seed is sown in finely pulverized soil by means of horse drills which plant it in rows at a uniform depth. No cultivation is necessary. A snow covering in winter, and a cool, damp spring are most favorable. The grain is harvested in June or July by means of reapers which cut and bind it into bundles. It is left to cure in shocks and is drawn thence to threshers in the field, or is first placed in stacks or barns for protection from rain. Threshing machines are run by steam engines, and travel about from farm to farm. The straw is stacked for bedding and fodder for stock, or baled and drawn to paper mills.

In the northwest, where the winters are severe and the growing season less than five months, spring wheat is the leading crop. It is sown in April or May, and as the ground thaws, water rises to the roots. Thousands of acres may be comprised in a single field, and the work of harvesting in August and September is done by machinery upon a correspondingly large scale (Fig. 243). Little or no effort is made to utilize the straw, which is burned upon the ground, and thus a part of the plant food is returned to the soil in the form of ashes.

Fig. 309. — Village and grain elevators, North Dakota.

Wheat is generally marketed at an elevator, which is a tall building erected beside a railroad, and equipped for the handling and storage of grain. Thence it is sent to mills, the largest of which are situated at Minneapolis, where the falls of St. Anthony furnish water power. At the mills the grain is cleaned, crushed between steel rollers, sifted, and reground until about 75 per cent of its weight is converted into flour. The remainder, consisting of middlings and bran, is fed to stock.

The wheat crop of the Atlantic provinces in 1918 was about 980 million bushels, worth about 2000 million dollars. This is 90 per cent of the total crop of North America, which is the only part of the world where "the struggle for bread" has been entirely successful, and where "white bread" is so cheap and abundant that it is sometimes furnished at restaurants and hotels without extra charge.

Oats (p. 273). — Oats are grown in the same manner as spring wheat throughout the wheat belt, and in regions too cool and wet for wheat. The grain and straw are largely fed to horses and mules, which furnish nearly all the animal power for cultivating the land and for local travel and transportation. The use of oatmeal for human food, formerly common in Scotland where wheat cannot be raised, has spread to all parts of temperate North America. The crop of 1918 in the Atlantic provinces was about 1800 million bushels, or 90 per cent of the total for North America.

Rye and Barley (p. 273). — Rye and barley are hardy grains which are profitable under conditions of climate and cultivation too severe for wheat. Rye is usually sown in the late autumn, and barley in the spring. They are used for stock food, and for making beer and whisky. A limited amount of rye is made into bread. Rye straw is valuable for making coarse wrapping paper. In 1918 the barley crop of the Atlantic provinces was 276 million bushels, or 80 per cent of that of North America, and the rye crop 97 million bushels, or 98 per cent of that of North America.

Potatoes (p. 274). — The potato plant is a native of South America, where it formed the food basis of the native Inca civilization of Peru. Potatoes flourish in a wide range of climate through the temperate and cold temperate zones even as far north as the Arctic circle. From their use as the chief food supply of Ireland, they have received the name of Irish potatoes. The best quality is produced upon light, sandy soils, especially those of glacial moraines and kames (p. 121 and Figs. 47, 112). Besides being one of the most common and cheapest of foods, they are a source of laundry starch and in some countries of alcohol. The crop of 1918 in the Atlantic provinces was 457 million bushels, or 90 per cent of that of North America.

Mississippian Fruits. — Among the fruits of the Mississippian province, the apple is foremost and is raised from Ontario to Tennessee. The great apple belt extends from New York to Missouri, the total product being about 200 million bushels. Large quantities are dried in local kilns for shipment abroad. Pears, peaches, plums, and cherries are often grown in the apple districts. Lake Erie and some of the Finger Lakes of New York (p. 126) are nearly surrounded by belts of vineyards, which are protected by the water from too early warm spells in spring and too early frosts in autumn (Fig. 251). The Erie belt occupies a strip of land once covered by a glacial predecessor of the present lake (p. 125). New York is second only to California, among the states, in number of vines and in quantity of grapes produced.

Tobacco (p. 286). — Tobacco can be raised wherever corn can, but its actual distribution is determined by many factors other than climate, and is very patchy. Kentucky, North Carolina, Virginia, Ohio, Wisconsin, Pennsylvania, Tennessee, and South Carolina produce nine tenths of the United States crop, but it is grown from Vermont to Florida. The Atlantic provinces raise two thirds of the crop of North America, and one half of the world's crop.

Floridan Crops. — The characteristic crops of the Floridan province are cotton, sugar cane, rice, and tropical fruits. The corn crop is increasing rapidly in acreage and value.

Cotton (p. 289). — Formerly cotton was grown by slave labor on the plantation system, which, although immediately profitable, was destructive to soil fertility. Land was exhausted by successive crops and then abandoned. The present system is peculiar in its adjustments to labor and capital. The colored laborer, with little or no capital, rents from the white owner 10 to 20 acres, as much as he can cultivate without hiring help. Seed is planted in rows in early spring and the crop is cultivated largely by hand. The long period of harvest, from September to December, makes it possible for the work to be done by few hands. The change from plantation to garden culture is now being followed by another change toward field culture. The baled fiber from the gins is shipped to local mills, or to seaports, chiefly Galveston, New Orleans, and Savannah, where the bale is compressed to smaller bulk and sent to Europe or the northern states. In most years the Floridan province furnishes about 11 million bales, or two thirds of the world's crop, more than half of which is sent abroad.

The cotton seed, formerly wasted, is now worth about one tenth as much as the fiber. The expressed oil is used as food in place of olive oil and in making soap. The cake left after extraction of the oil is used at home and abroad as stock food and as a fertilizer. Paper is made from the hulls and stalks. Cotton fiber has largely displaced linen, wool, and silk, both in pure fabrics and in mixtures, and has greatly enlarged and cheapened the world's supply of clothing. The present cotton production of the Floridan province could be easily doubled.

Sugar Cane (p. 275). — The area available for sugar cane is limited to the coastal plain and mostly to the alluvial valley of the Mississippi River. The business requires large capital invested in land and machinery. Light railroads are used on large plantations to haul the cane to the mill. The total product is less than 7 per cent of the 10 billion pounds consumed annually in the United States.

Floridan Fruits. — Peaches, melons, and small fruits are grown in all the Gulf states. Florida is second only to California in the production of tropical fruits, chiefly oranges. Lemons, grapefruit, and pineapples are also grown. A large area in southern Florida is occupied by the Everglades, a body of shallow, fresh water partly overgrown with marsh plants. It is now being drained by the state and reclaimed for agriculture and fruit growing.

Rice (p. 273). — Rice has never been a very important crop in America, but has been grown in the Floridan province for two centuries. Since about 1890, rice culture has received a new impetus from the introduction of improved machinery and methods into the coastal plain of Texas and Louisiana. Large fields are leveled and surrounded by a dike, and, after seeding, water is supplied from a stream, sometimes by pumping, to flood the ground to the depth of a few inches. The water is drawn off before harvest, which is accomplished by binders and threshers similar to those used for wheat. The milling of rice, which consists in removing the husk and polishing the grain, is difficult and costly. Rice is poor in food constituents except starch, but its use in America is increasing. The crop in 1918 was about 40 million bushels.

Minerals, Manufactures, and Commerce

Coal. — The Mississippian province has more coal than any other province or country in the world, possibly excepting China (pp. 312–314). The annual output is nearly 600,000,000 tons. There are four principal coal fields, — the Canadian in Nova

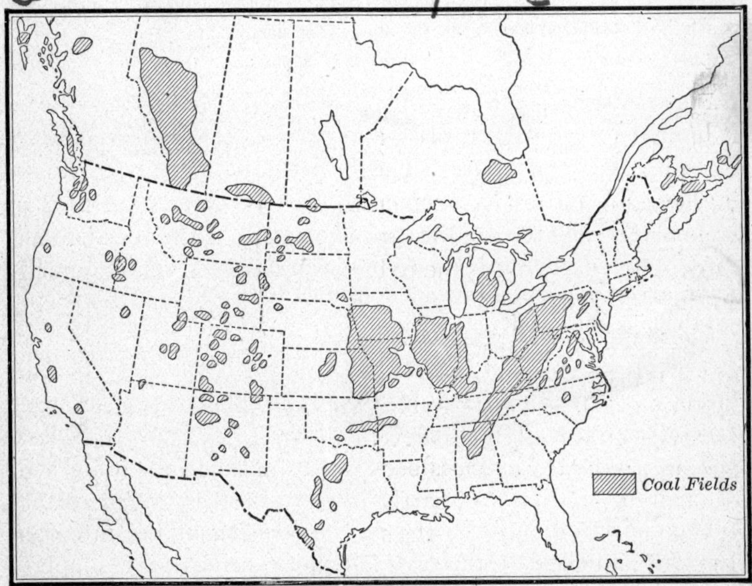

Fig. 310. — Coal fields of the United States and Canada.

Scotia and New Brunswick, the Appalachian, extending from Pennsylvania to Alabama, the eastern Interior in Illinois, Indiana, and Kentucky, and the western Interior west of the Mississippi River. The Gulf states and Alberta have immense deposits of lignite as yet little used. Pennsylvania, West Virginia, Illinois, Ohio, Kentucky, Indiana, and Alabama, in order, head the list of coal-producing states, Pennsylvania alone furnishing about one half.

The anthracite coal, found only in a region of much disturbed and folded rocks in northeastern Pennsylvania, amounts to about one fifth of the total product by weight. Its value per ton is about twice that of bituminous coal. It is drilled, blasted, and hoisted to the surface, where it is assorted in part by hand labor, and shipped to all the surrounding country within 500 miles or more, according to the cost of transportation. It reaches the Missouri River, the head of the Great Lakes, and in the bunkers of ocean steamships many foreign ports.

The Appalachian field furnishes 60 per cent of the bituminous coal, which is distributed as far as the lower Mississippi and through Atlantic seaports to Central and South America. About one tenth of the bituminous coal is converted into coke by heating in ovens, the volatile parts going to waste. This does not include the gas-house coke made as a by-product in the manufacture of illuminating gas. The coke is used chiefly for smelting and melting iron, and is sent as far as Chicago.

The coal of the Interior fields, about one third of the whole, supplies local markets and finds its way westward nearly to the Rocky Mountains.

About half of all the coal mined is used in metallurgy, for power in manufacturing and transportation, and for lighting.

In mining coal, shafts are sunk to the seam and then drifts or tunnels are run in every direction. A seam less than 4 feet thick is difficult to work. If the overlying rock or roof is not strong, timbers must be used to support it. Pillars of coal are also left for this purpose, and in this way from one fourth to a half of the coal is left in the ground. This waste is sometimes avoided by filling the space with earth and broken rock.

The consumption of coal is now increasing at the rate of 10 per cent a year. If this rate should continue, the supply is likely to be exhausted within two centuries. More efficient use of coal, more complete methods of mining, the utilization of dust and waste, and the increasing use of water power are likely to prolong the fuel supply indefinitely.

Petroleum and Natural Gas (pp. 314–315). — The Atlantic provinces produce about 70 per cent of the petroleum of North America, and 46 per cent of the world's supply. Oklahoma, Texas, Illinois, Louisiana, Kansas and West Virginia are now the leading states. These provinces also produce about 96 per cent of the natural gas used in North America, West Virginia, Pennsylvania, Oklahoma, and Ohio having the largest supply. This is one of the most uncertain of natural resources. Productive fields are liable to be soon exhausted and new fields are frequently discovered.

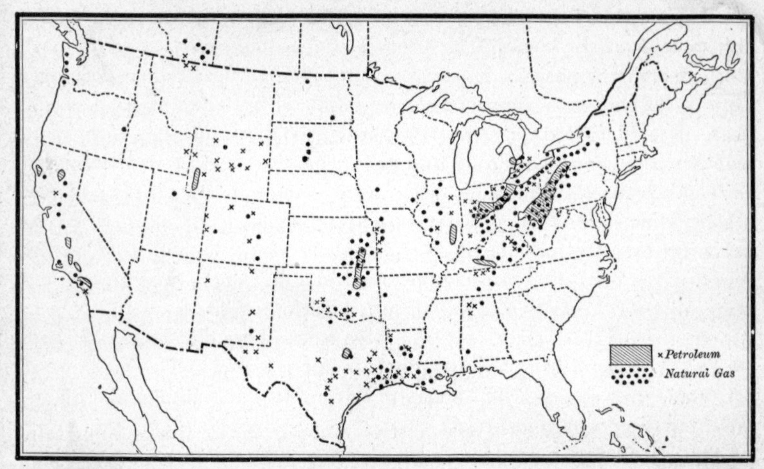

Fig. 311. — Petroleum and natural gas fields of the United States and Canada.

Iron (p. 299). — There are two great iron-mining districts in eastern North America,— the Lake Superior and the Alabama,— with minor centers in Newfoundland, New York, Pennsylvania, Tennessee, Virginia, and New Jersey. Of these the Superior district produces about 85 per cent of the total, and the Alabama district one tenth.

The Superior district is a part of the Laurentian peneplain and belongs to the Canadian province, but is commercially a part of the Mississippian province. Iron occurs in nine "ranges" or ore belts near the shores of Lake Superior in Michigan, Wisconsin, Minnesota, and Ontario. The ore is generally rich in metal and free from troublesome impurities. In the Mesabi range in Minnesota it is excavated from open pits by steam shovels, and the cost is thus reduced to a minimum (Fig. 278). To these mines are due the leading position of the United States in iron and steel production, and the extraordinary development of all American industries. They would, however, be comparatively

Fig. 312. — Superior iron and copper district.

worthless without the waterway of the Great Lakes by which the ore is transported to the coal fields. The Michigan ore goes largely to South Chicago, Joliet, and Gary, at the head of Lake Michigan, while the larger portion shipped from Duluth, Superior, Ashland, and Two Harbors is discharged at Cleveland and specially constructed ports on the south shore of Lake Erie, from Toledo to Buffalo. Thence it is distributed by rail throughout the Pittsburgh district, which includes western Pennsylvania, eastern Ohio, and northern West Virginia. Mechanical appliances are so perfected that the material is scarcely touched by a human hand on the way from the ore bed to its exit from the steel mill. Ore may be transported 1000 miles for 50 cents a ton. Since navigation on the lakes is closed in winter, the furnaces must lay in a large stock of ore during the summer.

The Alabama district has Birmingham for a center. The ores are of low grade, but coal and limestone are so near that the mining and manufacturing districts are identical.

The Pittsburgh district produces about 60 per cent of all the iron and steel. The Chicago district stands second, and the Birmingham third. The supply of high-grade and cheaply mined ores will scarcely equal the demand for more than thirty years, but iron is very abundant and widely distributed in the earth crust, and the discovery of new deposits, and the use of poorer and less available ores, are likely to postpone the danger of an iron famine to the remote future.

Lead and Zinc. — The Ozark region in Missouri produces 34 per cent of the lead and 23 per cent of the zinc of North America.

Manufacturing Districts and Centers. — The Atlantic provinces produce about nine tenths of all the goods manufactured in North America. Some form of manufacture is carried on in nearly every community. Industries in which the cost of labor, especially skilled labor, is greater than that of raw materials are relatively independent of natural conditions and may be carried on almost anywhere. An industry once established often persists after the special advantages which brought it into existence have disappeared, by what may be called economic inertia. Under the control of raw materials, power, and transportation, there are several districts of concentration, each of which has some special characteristics.

New England has priority in time and product per capita

because the natural conditions are almost ideal (page 318). Among them are position near to European markets and labor supply, good harbors and ocean transportation, water power, and communication with the food resources and markets of the Central Lowland. Water power derived from streams of rapid fall and narrow valleys is easily supplemented by coal from Pennsylvania. Labor now comes largely from French Canadian immigrants. The textile industries predominate, especially cotton and wool spinning and weaving in New Hampshire, Massachusetts, Connecticut, and Rhode Island. Fall River is the greatest cotton-manufacturing city in America. Massachusetts leads in the output of boots and shoes, but there is a strong tendency to westward migration of the industry. The metal work is chiefly in small wares, such as bicycles, firearms, brass and plated ware, clocks, watches, and jewelry. Steel ships are built at Bath, Me., Quincy, Mass., and New London, Conn. New England produces about one seventh of the manufactured goods of the United States.

The Northern Appalachian district, from New York to Maryland, enjoys all the advantages of New England, with the addition of abundant coal and larger food-producing capacity. The iron industries have been previously described. Philadelphia is noted for carpets and woolen goods. The cities of New Jersey near New York form a center of silk manufacture. The Mohawk-Hudson valley is preëminent in knit goods, gloves, collars, and cuffs. Ready-made clothing gives rise to a very large industry in all the great cities, especially New York. Bayonne, N. J., is the refining center for petroleum brought by pipe lines from the Pennsylvania fields. The Delaware River is the center of American steel ship building. Cars are built at Albany, N. Y., Wilmington, Del., and Altoona, Pa., and locomotives at Chester, Pa., and Schenectady, N. Y. The clays of the Hudson and Lehigh valleys and the coastal plain are of great importance in the manufacture of brick, tile, pottery, and Portland cement. Beds of rock salt and gypsum in central

New York furnish material for soda, fertilizer, and plaster. The canning of fruit and vegetables is a widespread industry. Roasting and grinding of coffee and spices and refining of sugar are carried on at the great seaports, especially New York and Philadelphia. The industries of the Northern Appalachian district include almost every line of manufacture, and transportation facilities are such that most of them are independent of narrowly local conditions. The manufacture of 60 per cent of the gloves of the United States at Gloversville, N. Y., and of 80 per cent of the collars and cuffs at Troy, N. Y., are accidents rather than the results of local conditions. The district is credited with about three eighths of all the manufactures of the United States.

In the *Central district* (Ohio to Missouri and Minnesota), coinciding substantially with the Central Lowland, the industries are more varied and diffused than those of any other district. This is due to the wide distribution of coal and the abundance of raw material for foodstuffs. There is marked concentration along the waterways, especially the Great Lakes, which play a part similar to that of the sea in the East. Aside from the iron industry already noticed, processes connected with the preparation of foodstuffs, such as meat packing, flour milling, fruit and vegetable canning, and the preparation of breakfast foods, naturally hold first place. Chicago does a larger business in the slaughtering of animals, and the utilization of animal products, than any other city in the world. No part of the animal is wasted, even the hair, horns, hoofs, blood, and bones being turned to account. Kansas City, St. Joseph, Omaha, St. Louis, and Indianapolis do a large business in the same line. Minneapolis has grown up at the falls of St. Anthony, which have made it the first city in the world in the grinding of wheat. This is a leading industry also in Kansas City and Toledo. Starch, glucose, and sirup made at Chicago, and breakfast foods from wheat, oats, and corn at Cedar Rapids, Iowa, and Battle Creek, Mich., are not confined to those cities. The lumber and wood-working industries, once foremost, are declining with the disappearance of the forests, but survive in many localities. Cities on the lakes and the upper Mississippi still saw pine lumber and make sash and doors. Wood pulp for paper is ground by water power near Green Bay, Wis., and Duluth, and at Sault Ste. Marie. Grand Rapids, Mich., Rockford, Ill., Sheboygan, Wis., and Cincinnati are centers for furniture made from hard wood. Agricultural implements, tools, and vehicles are made in this district more extensively than elsewhere because they are more used there. Chicago is the principal center, with Moline, Ill., Springfield, O., St. Louis, South Bend, Ind., Jackson, Mich., and Racine, Wis., as competitors. The making of leather and leather goods has extended from New England to the district where hides are plentiful and footwear in demand. St. Louis is second to the Massachusetts cities in the manufacture of boots and shoes.

The center of manufacture of the United States has moved westward with the center of population, but not so rapidly,

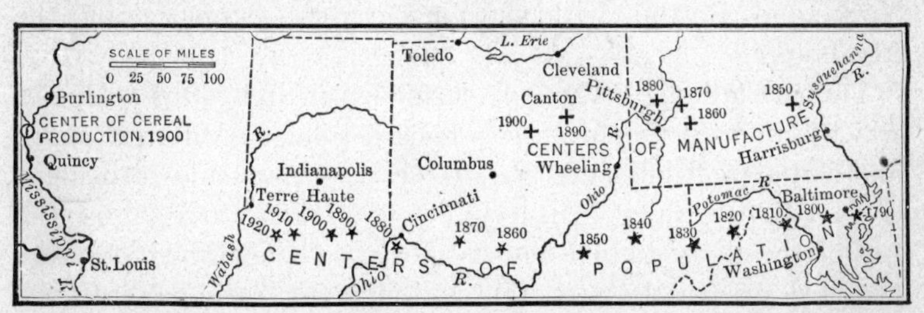

Fig. 313.—Centers of population, manufacture, and cereal production.

and is now in Ohio. The states in order of manufacturing importance are New York, Pennsylvania, Illinois, Massachusetts, and Ohio. The Central district is credited with three tenths of the total manufactures of the United States.

The Southern district, comprising the states south of the Potomac and Ohio rivers, is in the main agricultural. As long as the plantation system and slave labor existed little but agriculture was possible. The manufactures of the southern district are chiefly from domestic materials, of which cotton is the most valuable. Since 1905 cotton mills have been built chiefly along the Fall Line (p. 105), where water power is plentiful, and now about one fifth of the cotton grown is manufactured at home, the southern mills equaling in capacity those of the northern states. Tobacco from Cuba is made into cigars at Key West and Tampa, and the domestic crop is handled at Louisville, Richmond, Petersburg, and Durham, N. C. Sugar is refined at New Orleans. The forest products consist of tar, pitch, turpentine, and lumber. The cypress of the swamps, the yellow pine of the sandy coastal plain, and the hard woods of the uplands make the South the chief seat of the lumber industry in the eastern United States. The Southern district produces one tenth of the total manufactured goods of the United States.

With the probable future extension of waterways, the industrial districts will have a tendency to coalesce. One practically continuous urban and manufacturing district may be looked for, extending from St. Louis and Chicago to Philadelphia, New York, and Boston, with outlying centers strung along the Mississippi.

Transportation. — The Appalachian highland forms a barrier which separates the Atlantic seaboard from the Interior plain, and had a great influence upon the early history and settlement of North America. It is completely broken through by the gap of the Laurentian lakes and river. The drowned valley of the St. Lawrence lets the tide and shipping 900 miles into the land, to Montreal, and small boats penetrate to the head of Lake Superior, 2000 miles by water and 1000 miles in a direct line from the sea. Modern improvements have made this the greatest commercial waterway of the world, next to the north Atlantic Ocean (p. 103).

Canals. — The St. Marys Falls Canal, commonly known as "the Soo," first opened in 1855, and subsequently enlarged, enables vessels drawing 21 feet to pass the rapids between lakes Superior and Huron. A second canal, of equal depth, has been built on the Canadian side. The total tonnage passing through these canals in one season of less than eight months is about 60,000,000 tons, or more than four times that of the Suez Canal, and equal to the combined tonnage of New York, London, and Liverpool. This freight, however, consists principally of iron ore, lumber, and coal, bulky articles of much less value than those passing Suez. The total traffic of the upper lakes through the Detroit River amounts to 70,000,000 tons. The drop of 326 feet in 30 miles from Lake Erie to Lake Ontario is a barrier which can be passed only by the Welland Canal, 14 feet deep and having 26 locks. In Lake Erie the stream of goods breaks up into many branches, a small part passing to Lake Ontario and down the St. Lawrence. Most of it is transshipped at Erie ports and forwarded by rail. The Canadians are deepening their canals to give a 24-foot waterway to Montreal and plan to construct a ship canal from Lake Huron through the Nipissing outlet (Fig. 113) to the Ottawa.

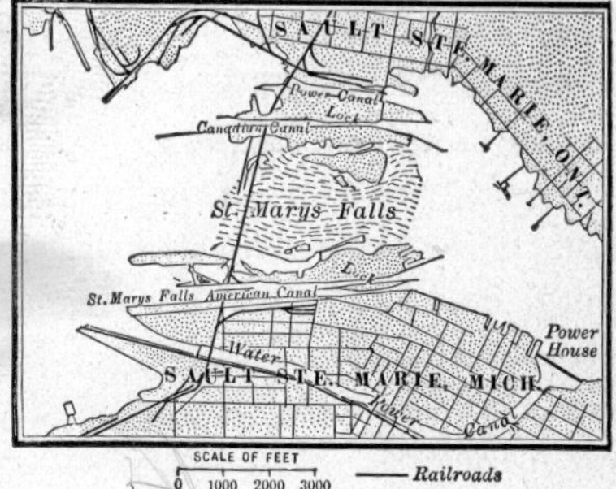

Fig. 314. — Soo Canals.

Another gateway through the Appalachian barrier, now even more important than the St. Lawrence, is the Mohawk-Hudson valley, traversed by the Erie Canal and the New York Central Railroad with six or more lines of track. The Mohawk outlet (Fig. 113) is a water gap which cuts the highland down to 445 feet above sea level and joins the tide-water Hudson at Troy.

The Erie Canal, completed in 1825, from Lake Erie to the Hudson, was then an internal improvement of greater value than the subsequent construction of the railroad. Since that time the increase in the efficiency of the railroads has rendered a canal 7 feet deep almost useless. It has been deepened to 12 feet and enlarged to transmit barges of 1000 tons. This is probably a halfway measure, to be followed in the future by a ship canal 24 feet deep, which will enable large vessels to pass from Duluth and Chicago to New York.

Several canals of the old-fashioned type at one time connected the St. Lawrence and Mississippi systems, but all are now abandoned. Various plans for a deep waterway from the lakes to the Gulf are proposed, and one or more of them will probably be sometime carried out. The most useful and promising routes are from Lake Erie to Pittsburgh, and from Chicago to St. Louis. The opening of the Panama Canal will be a powerful

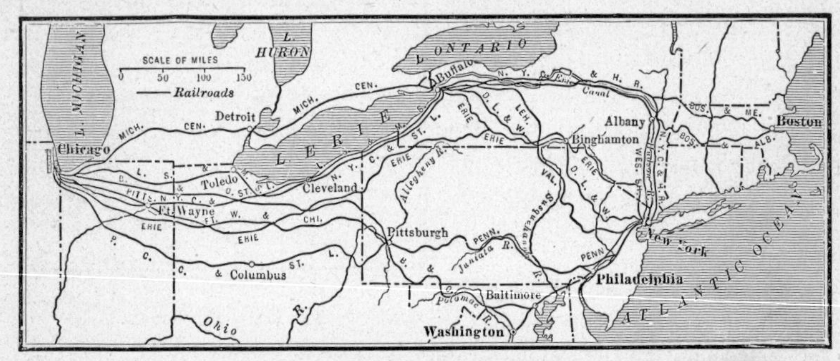

Fig. 315. — Routes of transportation between Chicago and Atlantic ports.

incentive to the improvement of the Mississippi, which has been previously discussed (pp. 105–111). The complete control and utilization of that river may be accomplished in the future, but it is a greater undertaking than man has yet anywhere attempted.

Railroads. — The vast plains of the Atlantic provinces, the absence of serious barriers, and the variety of products have encouraged railroad building to an extent unparalleled elsewhere in the world. The network is very close in the north Atlantic seaboard and the Central Lowland (Fig. 316), where few places are more than ten miles from a station. The main lines extend east and west, some powerful influence seeming to orient the rails.

In Canada the Grand Trunk and Canadian Pacific railways connect Halifax and Portland, Me., with all the territory as far west as Chicago, Winnipeg, and the Rocky Mountains. The New York Central lines through the Mohawk-Hudson gap have no steep grade, long tunnel, high trestle, or long bridge between New York and the Mississippi. The Pennsylvania system follows the Susquehanna-Juniata to a summit 2160 feet above the sea and descends to the Allegheny and Ohio at Pittsburgh. The Baltimore & Ohio utilizes the Potomac valley, and crosses the divide at an elevation of 2620 feet. These systems connect New York, Philadelphia, Baltimore, and

Washington with Chicago and St. Louis. The Chesapeake & Ohio follows the valleys of the James and Kanawha to the Ohio, and extends to Chicago. One railroad crosses the southern Appalachians at the Swannanoa pass (N. C.). The Southern Railway system penetrates the whole South from the Atlantic to the Mississippi, and from the Chesapeake to the Gulf of Mexico. Of the north-south lines, the Illinois Central from Chicago to New Orleans parallels the Mississippi and has been a large factor in the

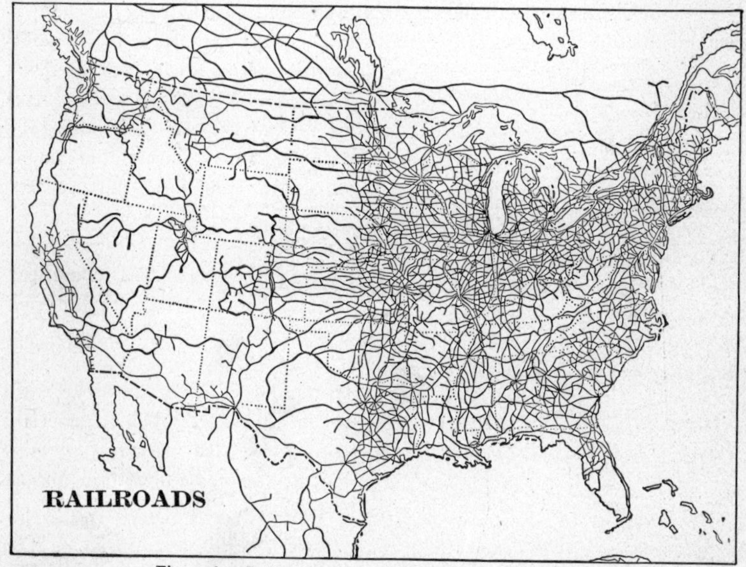

Fig. 316. — Railroads of the United States and Canada.

decline of river traffic. An interesting enterprise is the Florida East Coast Railway, which traverses the line of "keys" or small islands from the mainland to Key West, about half of it being supported by concrete arches erected in the shallow sea.

Such is the excellence of the roadbed, track, bridges, and general equipment of the principal trunk lines that one engine may draw a train containing 3500 tons of freight, and express trains maintain a speed of 60 miles an hour. In spite of this and in spite of about 240,000 miles of road in operation, the production and movement of goods have become so great that the roads are inadequate, and would require something like a doubling of present trackage and facilities to handle the business promptly. This condition is a compelling argument for the improvement of waterways.

Electric Railways. — The present century has brought a rapid extension of "interurban trolley lines," or railways for local passenger and light freight business, usually following highways and costing little for right of way or grading. Single cars at frequent intervals stopping at many points bring rapid transit near to every man's door. These roads have multiplied, especially in Ohio and Indiana, where lines radiate in all directions from important centers, such as Cleveland, Columbus, and Indianapolis. They destroy rural isolation, relieve urban overcrowding, and promote a desirable blending of city and country life.

Fig. 317. — Electric railways of Indiana.

Highways. — Common wagon roads have been until recently much neglected, being generally little more than a track between fences, and in bad weather almost impassable. The use of the bicycle and automobile has led to the construction of well-graded highways, surfaced with gravel, broken stone, cement, or asphalt. Public interest is manifested in "good roads" associations, conventions, and demonstrations, and a general awakening to the enormous loss entailed by the use of bad roads. As a result of multiplied means of transportation, there has never been in any period or country so much movement among the people and so little isolation, a condition which tends to increase knowledge, sympathy, and a civilization generally diffused among the whole body of citizens.

Foreign Commerce. — The Atlantic provinces are so large and varied in resources that if cut off from foreign trade they would be comfortably self-sufficing. At the same time the support of their rapidly increasing population and the development of new lands have made a large home market. For these reasons domestic trade is much larger than foreign, and is likely to continue so. The southern states were the first to produce goods to send abroad, and subsisted largely by exporting tobacco and cotton. The northern states and provinces did not have much to sell until the settlement of the Central Lowland opened wheat and corn lands and the Superior mines furnished iron ore for industrial development. The demands of the World War increased the export of iron and steel, explosives, vehicles, and mineral oils to enormous proportions which cannot remain permanent. The United States and Canada had to feed a large part of Europe, and breadstuffs, meat, dairy products, and live animals were sent abroad in vast quantities. Cotton and cotton goods, leather, boots and shoes, copper, coal, chemicals, and tobacco were also important items. The total exports of the Atlantic provinces amounted to about $6,000,000,000 annually. Among a great variety of imports amounting to about $3,000,000,000, sugar, coffee, cocoa, fruits, hides, rubber, cotton, wool, silk, and other fibers and textiles, vegetable oils, and fine chemicals held prominent places. The total foreign trade of the two provinces is more than four fifths that of all North America. About one fourth of it belongs to Canada. These conditions of foreign commerce will not continue in times of peace.

Seaports. — The rich harvest of the sea is clearly shown on the Atlantic coast of North America, where five ports of very large population, one of them the second city in the world, handle most of the maritime commerce of the continent.

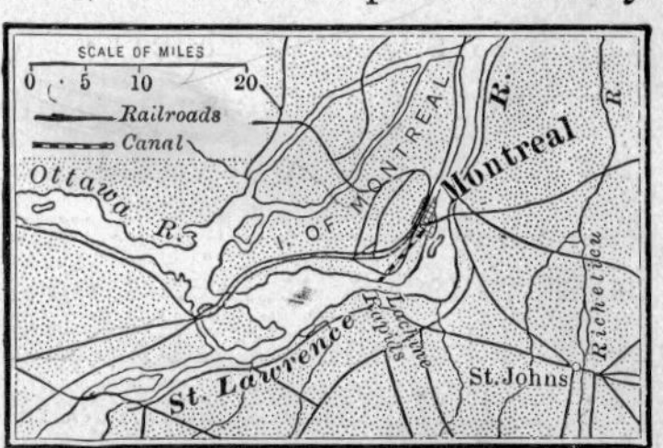

Fig. 318.— Vicinity of Montreal.

Montreal (population 471,000) has the unique advantage of being an inland seaport, nearly 1000 miles from the coast, yet accessible by all but the largest vessels. Thus inexpensive water carriage is made as long as possible and foreign markets are brought to the heart of the country. The city is built upon a large island at the mouth of the Ottawa, where two great inland waterways reach tide water. The Champlain gap opens a gateway south to the Hudson. Its commercial position would be unexcelled on the continent, if the St. Lawrence were not closed by ice about four months in the year, during which goods go by rail to Quebec, Halifax, and Portland.

Boston. — At the head of Massachusetts Bay, on a harbor made by the drowning of several small valleys, Boston presents all the conditions required for a great port. The city, originally built upon a hilly peninsula of irregular outline, has extended to neighboring peninsulas and islands. The original site has been graded and enlarged by the filling of shallow bays, and is now largely occupied by public and business buildings. On the highest point near the center stands the State House, from which streets radiate in many directions, after the spider-web plan. The site presents that intimate relation between land and water which secures a long dock line and brings ships and warehouses close together. There is space for the residence portion to spread out, and it now occupies the mainland to a distance of ten miles. The city is accessible by railroads from nearly every direction, but, on account of the rough and difficult country of western Massachusetts, it is cut off from a large share in the trade of the lakes and the Mohawk gap. It is the commercial center of the great manufacturing district around it, and the metropolis of New England.

Fig. 319. — Boston and vicinity.

In a broadly geographic sense, a city is a large body of people living close together and having common industrial and social interests. Such a unit may be called an urban district and is seldom limited by municipal boundaries. The official city of Boston has a population of 748,000, and the urban district (called metropolitan district in the census reports), 1,772,000.

New York. — The harbor of New York has been described (p. 170 and Fig. 155). The city was originally located at the south end of Manhattan Island and now covers that island, the west end of Long Island, Staten Island, and a part of the mainland on the north.

Manhattan, about 13 miles long and 2 miles wide, is a ridge of gneiss and other crystalline rocks, descending from a height of 200 feet at the north to sea level at the south. The slopes, especially the western, are in some places steep. The ridge is broken about midway by a transverse rift valley, which forms a convenient gap. To prepare such a surface for occupation by a crowded, modern city has involved great labor and expense. The streets are laid out with mathematical regularity, the longitudinal avenues being spaced to give six blocks, and the cross streets to give twenty blocks, to the mile. The triangular area at the south end, about 2 miles on a side, the oldest part of the city, is less regular and forms the heart of the shipping and commercial district. On the west the island is separated from the mainland by the Hudson River, too wide and deep to be bridged. The west bank of the river is formed by the Palisades, a high cliff of igneous rock, beyond which is a belt of shallow water and tidal marsh 4 miles wide. If defense from attack by land were of importance, New York would be a strong natural fortress. The East River, about half as wide as the Hudson, separates Manhattan from Long Island, and the narrow Harlem River (the "rivers" around New York are all straits) from the mainland. Natural barriers render Manhattan almost inaccessible by railroads, and until recently only two lines reached it. Such a site makes the problems of housing, overcrowding, and transit especially difficult. The business concentration in lower Manhattan gives that space a value too high for residences, and has crowded people on the east side into tenement houses, where the density of 500,000 to the square mile is the highest accurately known in the world. A million or more of people doing business there are compelled to sleep elsewhere, and have their homes in upper Manhattan or in the surrounding region within fifty miles. For the passage of these streams of humanity, the surface of the streets has long been inadequate. Railroads elevated upon steel trestles form an upper story on many streets, and lines of subway, blasted out of the rock beneath the streets, traverse the length of the island. The rivers are crossed by ferryboats, and four bridges connect Manhattan with Long Island. Many tunnels under the Hudson and East rivers are completed or under construction to facilitate the movement of people. The Pennsylvania Railroad has spent $50,000,000 in constructing a double tunnel from the Jersey shore, under Manhattan and both rivers, to Long Island, with an immense station in the heart of the city. Brooklyn is built upon the undulating surface of a terminal moraine, and is a great boarding house and residence district for the metropolis. On the Jersey side of the Hudson, Jersey City, Hoboken, Newark, Elizabeth, Paterson, and many other towns are a part of the New York urban district.

The high value of land on Manhattan has led to an unprecedented utilization of space by the erection of steel-framed "skyscrapers," or office buildings of many stories, rising in some cases to 700 feet above the streets, which are thus made to resemble cañons. The official city of Greater New York has 5,620,000 inhabitants, but the Jersey cities and the suburbs elsewhere swell the population of the urban district to nearly 8,000,000. The present rate of increase is so large that New York will probably soon overtake London and become the largest city in the world, if it has not already done so.

New York is not only the financial and commercial center of North America, but is also the greatest manufacturing city and seaport. Among a vast variety of industries, it perhaps exceeds all other cities in clothing, printing and publishing, sugar, copper and petroleum refining, tobacco, and malt liquors. Its manufactures constitute one tenth of those of the whole United States. The tonnage of the port exceeds that of any other port in the world and includes about three eighths of all the foreign commerce of the Atlantic provinces.

A city like New York is one of the most complex and momentous features of modern geography, and is the result of many causes.

1. The prime factor is the commodious harbor, long dock line, and un-

Fig. 320.—Street scene, Broadway, New York.

paralleled interlocking of bays, straits, and islands, where land and sea lie literally in each other's arms.

2. The most valuable part of its immediate hinterland, or tributary area, is the anthracite coal field, about 100 miles to the west.

3. Its more remote hinterland is extended to and beyond the Mississippi by the Mohawk-Hudson gap leading to the Great Lakes (p. 375). The facilities of this route from the interior to the seaboard are so superior to all others that the opening of the Erie Canal in 1825 soon gave New York a lead which its own momentum, if nothing else, will maintain. In spite of the formidable barriers which wall in the city on the land side, one gateway is sufficient to give it a command of resources which no other can hope to rival.

4. As the landing place of most of the foreign immigrants, it has a large and continuous supply of cheap labor, and has become a city of many nationalities and languages. Eighty per cent of its inhabitants are foreign-born or of foreign parentage.

Philadelphia (1,824,000), in contrast with Boston and New York, is a river port 100 miles from the sea, built upon a level tract between the Delaware and the Schuylkill. Including Camden on the Jersey side of the Delaware, it has a dock line about ten miles long. It is accessible by the largest vessels, but its greater distance from Europe, as compared with New York, is a disadvantage. Its land gateways are by the valleys of the Susquehanna and its tributaries to Lake Erie and the Ohio. Its distance by rail from Cleveland is about the same as that from Buffalo to New York, but the grades and curves are more difficult. The excellent engineering of the Pennsylvania Railroad, which crosses the Appalachian ridges by a series of water gaps (Fig. 44),

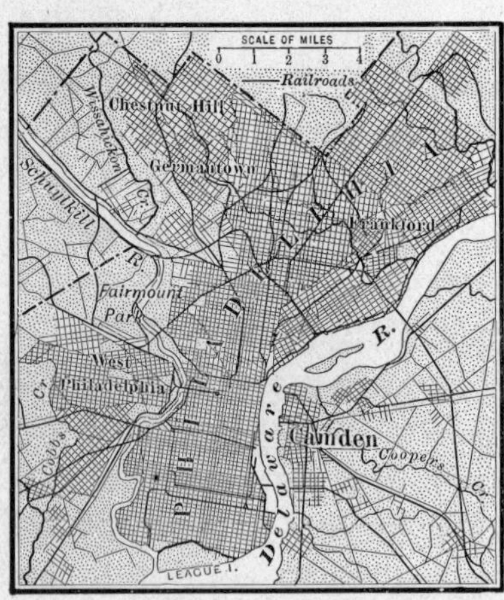

Fig. 321. — Philadelphia.

has done much to overcome this handicap. Philadelphia is closely connected with the Pennsylvania coal field and the Pittsburgh iron district. Its foreign commerce is about one eighth that of New York. There are no barriers to prevent the extension of the city, and it has fewer tenement dwellers and more detached residences than any other great Atlantic city.

Baltimore (734,000), near the head of Chesapeake Bay, 160 miles from the sea, has a good harbor on the drowned valley of the small Patapsco River. Its immediate hinterland includes the fruit belt of the coastal plain and the oyster fisheries of Chesapeake Bay. Its western gateway is the valley of the Potomac, traversed by the Baltimore & Ohio railroad. This route across the highlands is more difficult than that of the Pennsylvania and is too far south to profit much by connection with the Great Lakes. The foreign commerce of Baltimore is about one twelfth that of New York.

Washington (438,000), at the head of navigation on the Potomac, is a seaport by nature, but not a commercial or industrial city. It was arbitrarily located and built as the seat of the Federal government and is devoted entirely to national administration. The site is hilly and admirably adapted for picturesque effects. To the usual gridiron pattern is added a system of diagonal streets, radiating chiefly from the Capitol and White House, which have commanding situations. Street intersections furnish many opportunities for small parks, and the extent of public

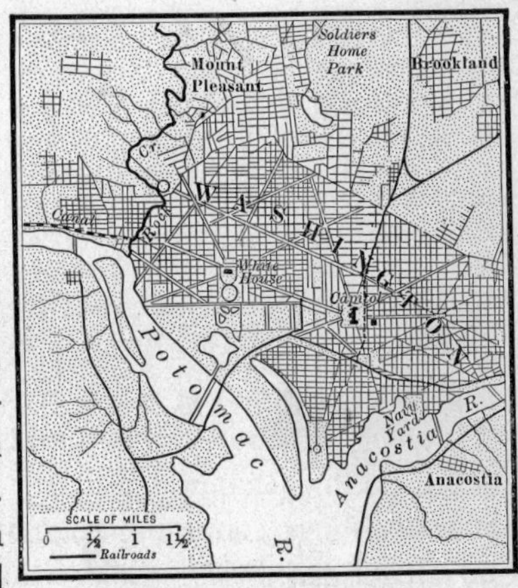

Fig. 322. — Washington.

grounds and the number of imposing buildings make Washington a "city of magnificent distances," unique in America if not in the world. Its population is made up largely of government officials and employees. The city is governed directly by Congress and its citizens have no vote or voice in its management.

New Orleans (387,000), the delta city 80 miles above the mouth of the Mississippi, was founded upon a site which was seldom overflowed, but its general level is now about 18 feet below the top of the levee (Figs. 69, 100). It is a river and seaport and a shipping point for cotton and sugar. Its foreign commerce, chiefly in exports of cotton, is greater than that of Boston or Philadelphia. The opening of the Panama Canal and the improvement of the terminals at New Orleans have greatly increased its importance.

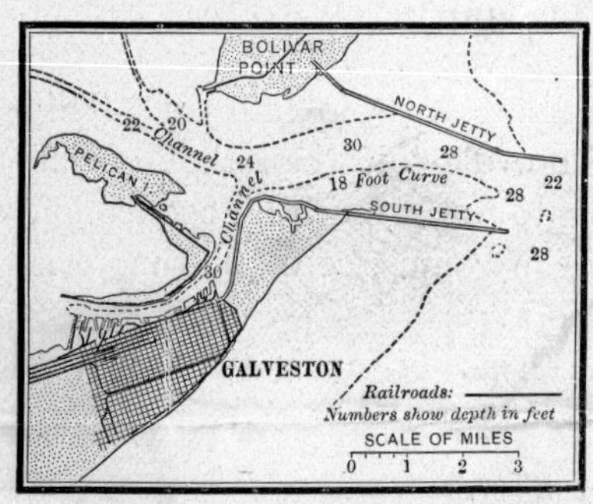

Fig. 323. — Galveston.

Galveston (44,000) is not a large city, but is interesting for several reasons. The economic pressure from its hinterland, which includes the western part of the Floridan province and southern part of the Interior, compelled first the establishment of a port without a harbor, then the creation of an artificial harbor, and finally the rebuilding of the city after its destruction by a hurricane (Fig. 181). Its exports of cotton make it the fifth seaport of the United States in amount of foreign commerce.

Lake Ports. — A chain of cities second in importance only to the seaports occupy strategic points along the shores of the Great Lakes.

Toronto (500,000), the second city of Canada, and the capital of Ontario, has that rich agricultural province for an immediate hinterland, and communication westward through the Welland Canal to Lake Erie and by short railways to Georgian Bay. A ship canal connecting that bay with Lake Ontario is a promising project.

Buffalo (507,000). — No interior city except Chicago has a more favorable position than Buffalo. At the east end of the lake route in the United States and at the west end of the Mohawk-Hudson highway, and the terminus of several railroads from the Pennsylvania coal fields, it commands all the great resources of the northern states. The water power of Niagara Falls (p. 94) is at its door and the development of a great industrial and commercial district seems assured.

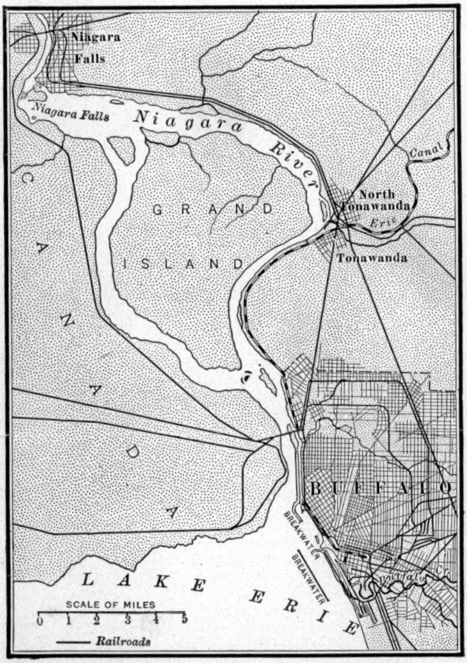

Fig. 324. — Buffalo and Niagara Falls.

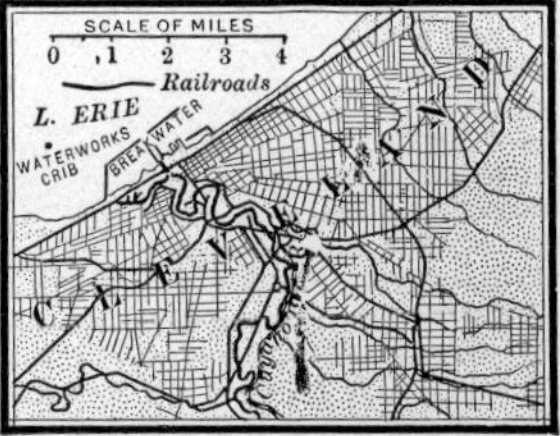

Fig. 325. — Cleveland.

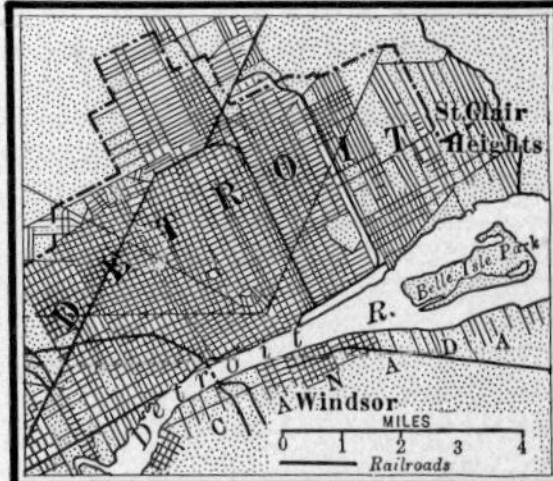

Fig. 326. — Detroit.

Cleveland (797,000), on a good harbor at the mouth of the Cuyahoga River, shares with Pittsburgh the advantages of the leading coal and iron districts of America. It nearly monopolizes the building of steel ships for the lake trade.

Detroit (994,000) is an inland strait city by which all the traffic of the upper lakes, 25,000 vessels a year, must pass. It is also the point of crossing for east-west trunk lines, for which a tunnel under the Detroit River has recently been constructed.

Chicago (2,702,000). — Among modern cities Chicago surpasses all records in rapidity of growth. From a small frontier village and trading post, it has become the second city in America, and the fourth in the world, within the memory of persons still living. The head of Lake Michigan is necessarily a strategic point of prime importance, and the exact location of its city was determined by the mouth of a small river, which led by an easy portage to the Illinois and Mississippi. The site is low, marshy, and distinctly unfavorable, and the business part of the city is built upon a mud flat. In 1870 it was found necessary to raise the grade of streets and buildings several feet. Neither this, nor the great fire of 1871, which destroyed a large part of the city, was sufficient to check its progress. Such a result is due to an extraordinary combination of conditions. Chicago is at the head of the lake route in the north central states. All the east-west land traffic must pass around the head of Lake Michigan, producing a concentration of railways unequaled elsewhere. It is the trade center of the Central Lowland, including the corn, wheat, cattle, and swine belts, and its hinterland extends to the Rocky Mountains. It is nearer than the Lake Erie ports to the Superior iron and copper mines, and has the eastern Interior coal field at its doors. It commands the timber of the coniferous forest in the North and the hardwood forests in the South. All the elements which create and sustain commercial and industrial greatness are present on a large scale. It is preëminently a market for grain

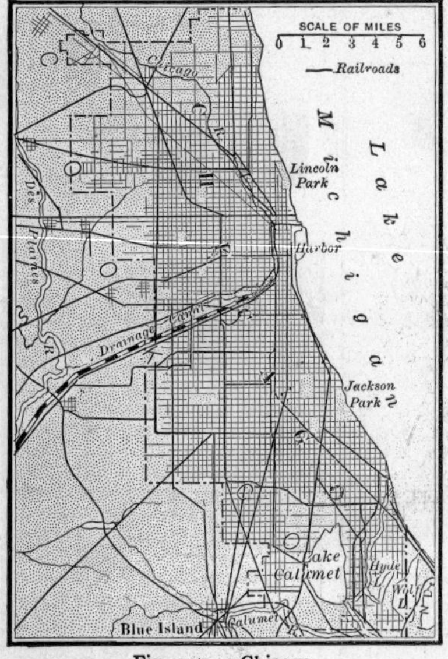

Fig. 327. — Chicago.

and wheat. The Chicago River harbor is artificial and inadequate and is supplemented by that of the Calumet and others farther south. The city has spread out over an area of glacial plain about 10 by 25 miles. Although there are crowded districts, as in all large cities, the general density of population is low. The highest points in the city are only 30 feet above the lake, and the drainage problem has been solved by a canal to the Illinois River. Thus an old glacial lake outlet (Fig. 113) has been reopened and part of the drainage of the upper lakes is diverted from the St. Lawrence channel. The population includes people of every European nationality, the foreign-born amounting to 30 per cent.

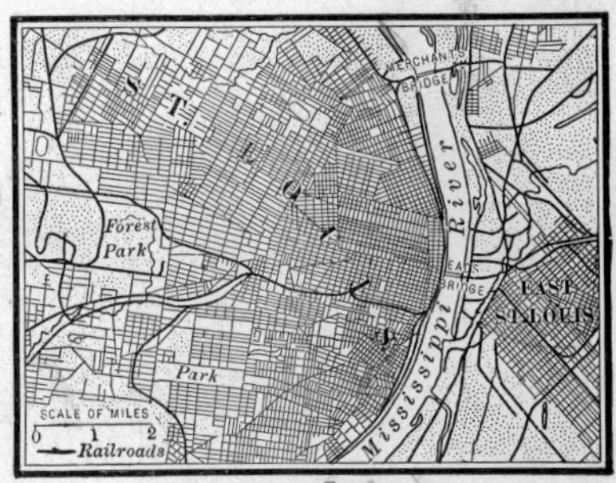

Fig. 328. — St. Louis.

Other Cities. — *St. Louis* (773,000), once the rival of Chicago, has been retarded by the decline of Mississippi River traffic, but vies with it as a railway center. On the Mississippi, between the mouths of the Missouri and Ohio, it stands at the center of the whole river system. Its future is largely bound up with that of river navigation, but in any event must be great. The levee forms a dock line, and the river is crossed by two bridges.

Fig. 329. — Pittsburgh.

Minneapolis and St. Paul (615,000), twin cities, at the head of navigation on the Mississippi, are centers of the grain and lumber trade of the Northwest.

Pittsburgh (588,000; urban district, 1,207,000), at the head of the Ohio, has been made primarily by a single seam of coal 16 feet thick. Its leading position in the iron industry has been discussed.

Cincinnati (401,000) and *Kansas City* (426,000), each located at an important bend of a great river, rely more upon railroads than upon water connections. Improvements in either river might reverse this.

Winnipeg (186,000), Manitoba, midway between the international boundary and Lake Winnipeg, stands in a gateway or narrows through which all east-west Canadian traffic must pass, in that respect resembling Chicago. It is and must remain the trade center of the grain and grazing territory of the Canadian Northwest. If that develops according to present indications, Winnipeg is destined to be the largest strictly inland city of America, and may be connected with Hudson Bay by rail, and with Lake Superior by a canal.

Summary of Productions, etc., of the Mississippian and Floridan Provinces

	North America, per cent	World, per cent
Corn (maize)	99	70
Wheat	90	22
Oats	90	
Barley	80	
Rye	98	
Potatoes	90	
Cotton	98	62
Tobacco	70	50
Rice	80	
Coal	90	50
Iron ore (including Superior district)	98	40
Petroleum	70	46
Natural gas	96	
Foreign commerce	80	18
Population	70	5.5

The Other Provinces of the Mississippian and Floridan Types are of so great industrial importance that they will be treated in later chapters (Chaps. XXX and XXXII).

CHAPTER XXVI

THE INTERIOR AND ARIZONAN PROVINCES

THE Interior and Arizonan provinces of North America have many common and strongly marked characteristics. (1) They are nearly all plateaus and mountains, most of the surface lying above 2000 feet, and above all but the higher peaks of the Atlantic division. (2) They are continental and interior, for, although the Arizonan province touches the sea, neither province is much affected by its influence. (3) The ranges and contrasts of temperature are extreme, the annual absolute range in the north amounting to 160 degrees. Minima of $-60°$ and maxima of 127° occur, but not at the same place. (4) They are arid or semiarid, the rainfall being, everywhere except on the mountains, less than 20 inches, and in some places less than 5 inches. (5) Except at elevations above 6000 or 8000 feet, they are treeless and exhibit every gradation from rich steppe to absolute desert. (6) They are rich in gold, silver, copper, lead, and other metalliferous ores. They are bounded on the southeast by that most important natural limit, near the 100th meridian, where the 2000-foot contour and the 20-inch rainfall line nearly coincide; and on the west by the Cascade Mountains, Sierra Nevada, and the Pacific. Their area is about 1,500,000 square miles and their population about 5,000,000, or $3\frac{1}{3}$ to the square mile.

The American Interior Province

The American Interior province includes the Great Plains, the southern Rocky Mountains, the Columbia Plateau, and a part of the Mexican Plateau. It is distinguished from the Arizonan province by having a rainfall above 10 inches, and constitutes the great North American steppe.

Vegetation. — The economic basis of the plateaus lies in three species of grass which grow in bunches, leaving bare spaces between (Figs. 201, 202). Bunch grass cures upon the ground without cutting, and furnishes nutritious pasturage all the year round. It is luxuriant in the valleys, thinner upon the uplands, and in drier areas sparse or absent. In the north grass is sometimes replaced by various species of artemisia, or sagebrush, from a few inches to 3 or 4 feet high, and of some value for pasturage. The greasewood, an ill-smelling shrub, is used for fuel. In the south various species of cactus and the yucca, or Spanish bayonet, abound. Along the streams thickets of willow and aspen and groves of cottonwood furnish shelter, fuel, and timber better than none. The cottonwood is the only important tree, growing occasionally to 5 feet in diameter and 70 feet in height, but generally much smaller. The wood is soft, easily worked, and fairly durable in a dry climate. On the mountains, pine, spruce, fir, and cedar form a forest belt between the contours of 6000 and 10,000 feet.

Animals. — East of the mountains animal life was originally abundant. The buffalo was the monarch of the plains. These "humpbacked cattle," as the early Spaniards called them, were one of the largest species of the bison family, the males sometimes weighing a ton and standing nearly 6 feet high at the shoulders. They originally roamed in incredible numbers over nearly the whole interior plain of North America. No accurate count was ever made, but their numbers were millions. A single herd sometimes formed a nearly solid column 25 miles wide. There are no records except of their slaughter. During the fifteen years required to exterminate them, from 250,000 to more than 1,000,000 hides were marketed annually. The bones of more than 30,000,000 animals were shipped east to bone-black and fertilizer factories. The wild horse, descended from stock imported by the Spaniards, was plentiful from about 1700 to the middle of the last century.

Indian Tribes. — The aboriginal inhabitants of the Interior province were red Indians of many tribes and stocks, but all, as was natural in a "big game" country, nomadic hunters. Other game was not scarce, but the buffalo alone could furnish everything needed for food, clothing, and housing. Food supply from this source was often so plentiful that the tongues alone were eaten. The tepee, or tent, was covered with skins, which were also tanned and made pliable for jackets, leggings, and moccasins. The red men were in the stone age of culture, and used no metal except native copper for ornament. Their chief weapons were the bow, made of wood strengthened with buffalo sinew, and arrows pointed with flint. The bow was powerful enough to drive an arrow completely through a buffalo's body. Knives, scrapers, and axes were made also of flint. The advent of the wild horse, which the Indian learned to capture and ride without saddle, gave the tribes of the plains a great advantage, not only over their brute neighbors, but over human enemies. Their total number probably never exceeded 50,000, and they spent their power and resources in petty warfare. For 200 years they made their country a terror to the white man. During the whole period of white occupation and settlement they were a formidable obstacle, but the destruction of the buffalo cut off their food supply, and the close of the Civil War and the advent of the railroad made it possible to send against them an adequate military force.

Cattle Ranges and Ranches. — The first invaders to dispute with the buffalo and the Indian possession of the plains were cattle and cowboys. European cattle were brought to Mexico by the Spaniards in the sixteenth century, and at the opening of the nineteenth century had spread in herds of little commercial value over southern Texas. By the middle of that century it had been discovered that the grass of the north, upon which the buffalo thrived, would rear cattle of one-third greater size than that of the south, and herds of wild, long-horned Texas cattle began to be driven northward. The "long trail" began to stretch its main lines, with many branches, and in ten years covered the land from Texas to Montana, and from the Missouri to the Rocky Mountains. The Spanish cattle were displaced and absorbed by better breeds, and the swarthy Mexican cowboy gave way to blue-eyed young Americans of a much higher type. The strife was ever for more and better grass, and for an outlet to market. The drive was at first northward and back southward, but with the extension of the Union Pacific Railroad across the plains between 1865 and 1869 the main tide was toward the railroad, along which cattle towns sprang up as if by magic and became shipping points where hundreds of thousands of cattle were transferred from hoof to car.

The cattlemen had hardly taken possession of the available area when the long trail was abandoned and the free range was broken up into ranches, often of immense size, but inclosed with barbed-wire fence. Ranch houses were built, of adobe in the south, of logs in the north, wells were bored, and windmills to pump water became conspicuous features of the landscape. In the north the loss of cattle by starvation and cold was often serious, but hay is now made and shelter provided for the time of heavy snow or sleet, when the cattle cannot get to the ground. Herding has ceased to be a nomadic occupation except in a restricted sense.

Sheep Herding. — In all the steppe, mountain, and desert regions, sheep herding has acquired large proportions, and is profitable where herbage is too scanty for cattle. The pasturage has been in many localities seriously injured or permanently destroyed by overgrazing. A prolonged and sometimes bloody war between the sheepmen and cattlemen has occurred. About 58 per cent of all the sheep in the United States are raised west of the 100th meridian.

Transportation and Migration. — Routes of travel and transportation through the Interior province extend in many cases through the Arizonan province also. They have developed under peculiar conditions. On account of the absence, or the shallow and shifting character, of the streams, many of which disappear in summer, waterways play a subordinate part. The vast stretches of smooth, gently sloping surface facilitated land travel, but the limited food supply and the mountain ranges were formidable obstacles. Between the Pacific slope and the Mississippi valley was interposed a barrier of steppe, desert, and mountain comparable with that of the Sahara between central Africa and the Mediterranean coast. It was popularly known and commonly mapped as the "Great American Desert."

In 1847 the Mormons, driven out of Illinois, began to migrate to the Salt Lake valley, using ox wagons and handcarts to transport women, children, provisions, bedding, and utensils. Each party was accompanied by beef cattle and milch cows. In 1846–48, the opening of the Oregon country tempted thousands of settlers to "cross the plains" by a wagon journey of 2000 miles, occupying four or five months. Thus the Salt Lake and Oregon trails were made, following the valleys of the Platte and Sweetwater, and through the South Pass to Green River, near which the trail forked. The south branch crossed the Wasatch Mountains to Salt Lake; the northern branch followed approximately the Snake River to the Columbia. At the close of the Mexican War in 1848, an extensive area was added to the United States on the southwest, with which a large trade immediately sprang up, making use of the Santa Fe trail from

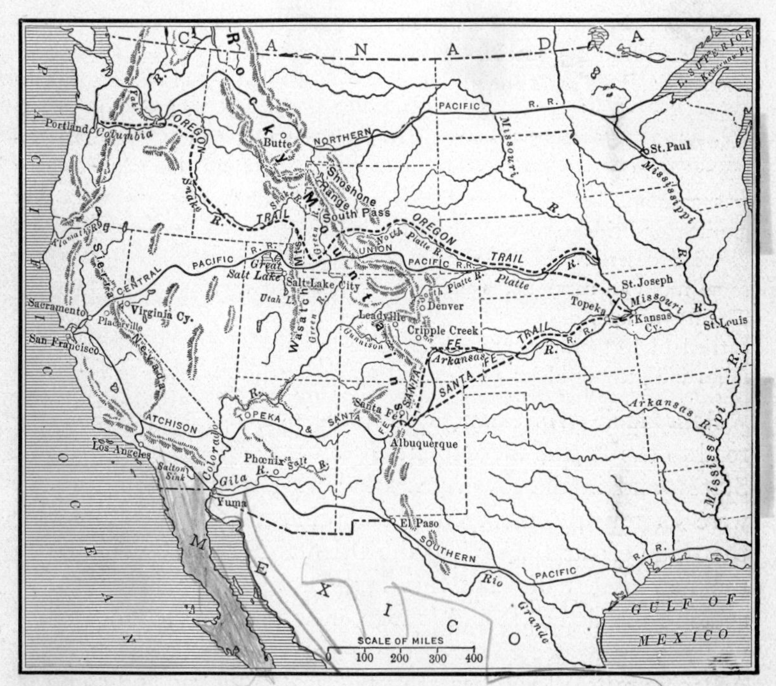

Fig. 330. — Salt Lake, Oregon, and Santa Fe trails, and Pacific railroads.

the Missouri to the Arkansas, up that valley to the foothills, and thence southward to Santa Fe. The discovery of gold in California in 1849 brought a rush of adventurous fortune seekers over the Salt Lake trail, which was extended through the Great Basin and over the Sierra Nevada to Sacramento. Thus began the era of the "prairie schooner," a large, well-built wagon with a canvas cover, drawn by multiple teams of mules or oxen. In 1858 the discovery of gold on the South Platte, near the present city of Denver, swelled still further the flood of emigrants, in this case destined to settle in the province instead of merely passing through. It has been estimated that during the height of this movement the transient population amounted to 250,000.

Freight caravans of twenty-five or more wagons, each of about eight tons capacity, drawn by twelve yoke of oxen or as many mules, and manned by thirty drivers and guards, made the journey from the Missouri to Denver in about a month. A line of stagecoaches ran to Santa Fe, carrying the mails and eleven passengers each. This developed into the Southern Overland Mail, the coaches of which ran from St. Louis by way of Albuquerque, El Paso, Yuma, and Los Angeles to San Francisco, a distance of 2759 miles, in about 23 days. During the Civil War the route was shifted northward by way of Denver and Salt Lake City. The distance was thus reduced to 2000 miles, and the time to 17 days. This was accomplished over natural, unimproved roads, mostly destitute of grading or bridges, and involved fording rivers, climbing mountains, and crossing deserts. In 1860 the pony express was established over the same route to carry mails between St. Joseph, Mo., and San Francisco. Twenty pounds of letters written on the thinnest possible paper were carried in leather pouches. The horse was ridden at full speed for 10 miles and exchanged for another. The whole trip was made in 10 days.

Railroads. — As early as 1853 the proposal to build a railroad to the Pacific was submitted to the Congress of the United States, and in the seven years following many possible routes were thoroughly surveyed. The prime object was to secure the trade of the Pacific and the Orient. During the Civil War the new states of California and Oregon were in danger of attack from domestic and foreign enemies, and the government was paying $7,000,000 a year for the transportation of mails. A Pacific railroad had become a political, military, and commercial necessity. It was not until 1864 that capitalists were induced by a liberal grant of land and money to undertake the construction of a railroad 2000 miles long, with only two considerable centers of population near the line, one around Denver and the other in the Salt Lake basin. Little local traffic was expected, and the line had to be built and defended in the face of hostile Indians. In 1865 the Union Pacific was begun from Omaha westward, following closely the old emigrant trail to

Salt Lake. At the same time the Central Pacific began to be extended eastward from Sacramento along the overland mail-coach route, and in 1869 the rails of the two roads met on the north shore of Great Salt Lake.

The opening of the first railroad was the beginning of the end of a state of society such as never existed before or since. A conglomeration of hunters, cowboys, gold seekers, miners, " bullwhackers," " mule skinners," coach drivers, express riders, soldiers, civil engineers, graders, track layers, emigrant families, adventurers, gamblers, thieves, and desperadoes of all sorts rendered organized society impossible. There was no established civil government, no courts, no law, and no policing except by small detachments of troops, stationed at scattered army posts. Over and against all were the ever-active Indian tribes, raiding, burning, stealing, and killing in desperate defense of their homes and fatherland. Local organizations of *vigilantes* administered summary justice under "lynch law," and maintained such semblance of order as was possible. Human life was one of the cheapest and most precarious of possessions. No estimate can be made of the thousands of men, women, and children who were sacrificed in the struggle and filled nameless graves. The environment called for men of reckless courage, iron hardihood, and incredible physical endurance. Only the fittest survived. This chapter in the development of the North American steppe covers barely twenty-five years, but stands unique in human economics. The "Great American Desert" was conquered for civilization, and white men won the plateaus and mountains for a permanent possession. The buffalo was speedily exterminated, and the Indian reign of terror was soon put to an end. Wild beasts, wild Indians, and bad white men do not thrive near a railroad. It is a great promoter of peaceful and prosperous civilization.

Progress of Agriculture. — The sale of railroad lands in small tracts and the invasion of the Interior province by the farmers were among the factors which led to the breaking up of the free cattle ranges and the reduction of the size of ranches. Since the opening of the present century, the encroachments of agriculture upon the pastoral region have been rapid. This has been due to two causes, — irrigation and dry-farming. Irrigation has extended along the valleys of the large and permanent streams

(Figs. 36, 60, 90, 94) from the mountains eastward. It is probable that, by the construction of dams at the mouths of the cañons and the storage of flood waters, a continuous belt of land along the eastern foot of the Rocky Mountains will be reclaimed for agriculture, as has been so successfully done along the western foot of the Wasatch. The Great Plains are underlain by water-bearing strata (Fig. 133) which can be reached by artesian wells, and many of these furnish sufficient water to irrigate a good-sized farm.

Perhaps still more important is the process of dry-farming. The method consists in conserving the rainfall of two or three years to raise one crop. This is done by frequent cultivation, which keeps the surface soil pulverized and prevents evaporation (p. 147). The introduction of new varieties of plants, such as durum wheat, Kafir corn, millet, spelt, sorghum, and alfalfa, which yield a crop with less moisture than the old varieties, is an essential factor. The most valuable of these drouth-resisting plants is alfalfa, a species of clover which, by means of very deep roots, utilizes ground water and yields several crops a year. Alfalfa fodder is very nutritious and fattens all kinds of domestic animals, while its root tubercles maintain the fertility of the soil (Fig. 282).

The remarkable success of dry-farming may be due to a period of unusual rainfall and may be checked by a period of scant rainfall to follow. The arid regions are now in an unstable state of economic development, and what their condition will be ten or twenty years hence is uncertain. Much the larger part of the area will always remain a typical steppe devoted to herding, but with considerable local modification by agriculture.

Mining. — The importance of mining, especially of the precious metals, in the development of the Interior province, has already been noticed. A detailed discussion of mining will be given in connection with the Arizonan province (pp. 405–408).

The Eurasian Interior Province. — The great Interior province of Eurasia presents features and conditions similar to that of North America but on a much larger scale. It comprises the loftiest plateaus and mountains in the world, and the largest depression below sea level. Its climate is subject to great extremes of temperature, and it is a land of strong contrasts.

The depressions are arid wastes of drifting sand, dotted with shifting lakes, and marshes incrusted with salt. The mid-slopes, watered by light rains and intermittent streams from the highlands, are covered with luxuriant grass in summer, and constitute the most extensive steppe and pastoral region in the world. The summits are rugged, barren, and covered with snow and ice. Trees are generally absent, and flowers in their season very abundant. It is the original home of our domestic horses, cattle, and camels, as well as many of the cereal grains. Insects and migrating birds are numerous, reptiles and wild mammals few.

The Khirghiz of Turkestan are typical pastoral nomads, migrating with their herds of sheep and cattle to the high pastures in summer, and retreating to the valleys in winter. Agriculture is confined to the raising of hardy grains and the cutting of hay, and is carried on only by the poorer people. Wealth consists wholly of live stock. Fat-tailed sheep are most common, and their flesh, milk, wool, and skin form the basis of human economy. Cattle, yaks, and camels are kept for milk, hair, and hides, and are used as beasts of burden. Horses are held in such high estimation that they are never used as pack animals. The dwellings are round tents of poles covered with woolen felts, and can be taken down, packed on oxen and camels, and set up in a few hours. Furniture and utensils are all easily movable, consisting of felts, rugs, quilts, leather buckets, and wooden bowls and spoons (Fig. 252). Cooking is done in iron pots over a fire of dried dung. The principal garments are quilted gowns of cotton, sheepskin coats, rawhide boots, and felt caps. The usual meal consists of a first course of tea and *kumiss*, or fermented mare's milk, followed by roasted or boiled mutton. The people are extremely courteous and hospitable to travelers, especially to foreigners, providing tent, food, and fresh horses without charge. The province is now mostly under Chinese and Russian control. Railroads have penetrated a short distance from the west and bring to the natives such luxuries as tea, sugar, china bowls, and silk cloth.

The Patagonian Province. — Southern South America, east of the Andes, is a bleak, wind-swept steppe, occupied by a tribe of gigantic Indians who originally subsisted wholly by hunting the guanaco and rhea. Their characteristic weapons are *bolas*, consisting of two or three balls of stone or metal, connected by rawhide lines, which are thrown in such a manner as to wind around and entangle the legs or neck of an animal. They have become expert and inveterate horse riders, and use horse flesh for food, and hides for clothing, tents, and saddles.

The Arizonan Province

The Arizonan * province comprises the Great Basin, the Colorado plateau and Wasatch Mountains, and the northern portion of the Mexican plateau. The plateaus stand at an elevation of 2000 to 8000 feet, but are interrupted by the depression of the Gila and lower Colorado rivers.

Climate and Vegetation. — The Arizonan province is distinguished by the highest temperatures and smallest rainfall in North America. The July temperature rises locally to 110° and the maximum to 127°. The mean annual rainfall is in some places less than two inches. The general absence of ground water renders oases few and of little importance. This is partly compensated by two rainy seasons a year, which enable many plants to survive the period of drouth. Hence during the season of light rains vegetation is surprisingly abundant. On the other hand, the rainfall is so variable and in dry years so small that a locality with an average of 20 inches may be as unproductive as one with much less. The rainfall is roughly proportional to altitude, and much of it occurs in the form of thunderstorms and "cloud-bursts" upon the mountains. Hence the province presents a considerable variety of vegetation, — coniferous forests on the high plateaus, steppe grasses and thorn scrub of many degrees of density at lower levels, and extreme desert conditions in the depressions. "The life of the desert lives only by adapting itself to the conditions of the desert." The economic basis lies in more or less scanty herbage, shrubbery, and small trees, all after their peculiar kind, adapted to drouth conditions (pp. 228, 233, 239).

The Animals of the Arizonan province are characterized by ability to live with little water, the use of which is apparently unknown to some species. The hard conditions of life have developed protective coloration, keenness of sight and hearing, swiftness of movement on all sorts of ground, appetite

* Spanish, *arida zona* (dry belt).

without squeamishness, and tolerance of hunger and thirst to a high degree. Desert animals have need of more cunning, energy, endurance, ferocity, and efficiency than their relatives in fatter lands. Yet plants and animals unconsciously coöperate to maintain the total quantity of life nearly at a possible maximum. The desert becomes dotted with colonies or communities of plants and animals which live together in harmony and mutual helpfulness, while the wide spaces between remain lifeless. Without such coöperation, few plants and no animals could live at all.

People. — The indigenous human inhabitants are various tribes of Indians, among which the Papagos, or "bean people," are typical desert dwellers. They occupy a territory about the size of Iowa in southern Arizona and northwestern Mexico, and number about 5000. Whenever the rains come they plant corn and beans and harvest two crops a year, but not always from the same land. They keep horses for riding and herds of half-wild cattle, which are driven about wherever water and pasturage are procurable. The better houses are built of adobe, with flat roofs. The common dwelling is a dome-shaped hut of mesquite poles thatched with grass. The center of family life is the grinding stone, a slab about one foot wide and two feet high, set up slanting. On this by means of another stone the women grind corn, kneeling and working like a laundress over a washboard. By this slow and laborious process meal is made, to be mixed into dough and baked on an iron plate into flat cakes called "*tortillas*," which are the staff of life.

The Papago can ride two or three days without drinking, and subsist through a season on very little solid food. Both men and women are very strong, fleet of foot, and long-lived. In playing football they will run from 30 to 40 miles in an afternoon. These desert Indian tribes hold the highest records for fleetness and endurance. One courier carried a letter on foot nearly 800 miles in five days.

Pueblo Indians. — The high plateaus and mesas north of the Gila River and west of the Rio Grande have been the home of the Pueblo, or village Indians, from a time centuries before the coming of the white man. In northern New Mexico and Arizona, about twenty pueblos, among which Zuni and Moqui are the most important, are now inhabited by about 10,000 people. A pueblo generally stands upon a high and isolated mesa, reached by a single difficult path or rough stairway, and is designed primarily for defense. It consists of a single communal dwelling of many rooms, built in several terraced stories. There are few openings except holes in the flat roof, and the apartments are reached by climbing up and down ladders. The material is stone and adobe, with wooden beams to support the roof. These people have always been agricultural. Corn is the main crop, to which beans and melons, and in recent times wheat, have been added. Clothing is made of skin and fabrics woven from native cotton and yucca fiber. Perhaps nowhere else have the arts of primitive pottery, and of making stone axes, arrowheads, pestles, and ornamental articles, been carried to greater perfection. Irrigation has been practiced more extensively in

Fig 331.—Pueblo, New Mexico.

the past than at present, and the abandoned canal systems testify to a former large population. An irrigation system can be constructed and maintained only by the coöperation of many people, and has always been a strong agency in promoting community life. The Pueblo Indians show a distinct advance in culture over the Papagos, because by means of irrigation they became sedentary agriculturists instead of half-nomad herdsmen.

Stock Raising. — Under white occupation, the Arizonan province is being developed by cattle and sheep ranching, mining, and irrigation. The open range prevails and the capacity of the country to support stock has been greatly reduced by overgrazing. That capacity, here as everywhere, depends upon rainfall. The heated air of the plateaus is displaced upwards by inflow from the Pacific; the mountains, acting as condensers, receive most of the rainfall, and when covered with natural vegetation act as storage reservoirs, from which water is given out gradually. Before the white men took possession, the country was well grassed and supported vast herds of antelopes and deer. With the introduction of cattle, horses, and sheep from Texas, grass disappeared, shrubbery and forests were destroyed by browsing and fire, and the land was laid bare by torrential rains and eroding streams. The drying up of springs and the reduction of plant and animal life have been so marked as to suggest a change of climate to greater aridity.

Agriculture. — The agricultural possibilities of the province are limited as much by the extreme irregularity of rainfall as by its general scantiness. Periods of drought may continue for from three to five years, during which practically no rain falls, and all except the hardiest vegetation dies. The dry period is followed by a period of heavy rainfall. These conditions can be overcome only by storage reservoirs on a large scale and by dams in the few great rivers. The Mexicans made some feeble attempts to restore the extensive prehistoric canal systems of the Indians, but accomplished little. The first use of irrigation on a large scale by white men was made by the Mormons in the Salt Lake basin. They availed themselves of a nearly perfect system which nature had provided. The streams flowing from the Wasatch Mountains reach the lake through the Jordan River. An ancient lava flow had dammed the river about midway of its length, forming Utah Lake, a body of fresh water 30 miles long. An inexpensive dam in the cañon which the river had cut through the lava, and ditches to distribute the water, secured an immediate food supply for the impoverished immigrants, and the community soon became prosperous.

Salt River Project. — Irrigation began in the Salt River valley, near Phœnix, Ariz., soon after the Civil War, and in twenty years more land had been reclaimed than could be watered in dry years. This led to the construction, under the United States Reclamation Service, of the Roosevelt dam, completed in 1911. This dam, 284 feet high and 1080 long at the top, impounds 1,284,000 acre feet* of water. This, with other smaller reservoirs in the district, stores water to irrigate 270,000 acres in the valley below. The watershed is mountainous, largely forested, and under government control. Evaporation is so great that the run-off of the Salt River basin equals only 2.26 inches of the 16.8 inches of rain that falls upon it. Hydroelectric power developed in the canal will be used for pumping ground water and sold for industrial purposes. The total cost of the project is about $8,000,000, which will be repaid by the land owners using the water.

Yuma Project. — The only large river in the province is the Colorado, which obtains its volume from the melting snows of the Rocky and Wasatch mountains. These produce an annual flood lasting from April to July, and a low stage from September to April. The upper two thirds of the river traverses high plateaus in profound cañons. In the lower 600 miles it has a gentle slope and is bordered by a flood plain terminating in a great delta which fills the head of the Gulf of California. In this part of its course it repeats upon a smaller scale the features of the Nile in Egypt. The Indians, like the ancient Egyptians, raise quick-growing crops upon the wet soil left by the receding floods. The available water amounts to about 9,000,000 acre feet, or sufficient to irrigate 1,375,000 acres in Arizona, California, and northwest Mexico, but its complete utilization requires extensive storage reservoirs. The United States Reclamation Service has completed a dam at Laguna, above Yuma, 19 feet high and 4780 feet long, canals, levees, and pumping stations, to irrigate 130,000 acres.

The Imperial Valley, on the boundary between Mexico and California, lies many feet below the level of the Colorado, and is bordered by the Salton sink, the bottom of which is 276 feet below sea level. A canal was cut to distribute water from the Colorado over this valley. In 1904 the whole river at high water turned aside through this canal and discharged into the sink, forming a large lake. It required two years' time and $3,500,000 to stop the opening and turn the river back to the Gulf.

Crops. — The lowlands of the Arizonan province produce, under irrigation, a great variety of crops. While the summer temperatures are very high, the winters are hardly anywhere free from frost. During the cool season cereal grains and hardy

* An acre foot means enough water to cover one acre to a depth of one foot.

vegetables are grown, and during the hot season corn, sugar beets, tobacco, cotton, and many other kinds of crops. Alfalfa grows all the year round and yields five to eight cuttings of hay. Date palms, olives, figs, pomegranates, and citrus fruits flourish in some localities, and every month in the year brings its harvest. The state of Arizona has water to irrigate 1,000,000 acres (less than 2 per cent of its area) and to support 500,000 people.

United States Reclamation Service. — The United States Reclamation Service has undertaken or completed many irrigation projects in the Interior and Arizonan provinces, of which the following are among the most important: Snake River, Idaho, 400,000 acres; Rio Grande, New Mexico and Texas, 180,000 acres; Yakima, Washington, 340,000 acres; Truckee-Carson, Nevada, 350,000 acres; Uncompahgre, Colorado, where 150,000 acres are irrigated by water brought through a six-mile tunnel from the Gunnison River; Klamath, Oregon and California, 236,000 acres; Shoshone, Wyoming, 175,000 acres. About 7,500,000 acres are now under irrigation by private enterprise. The total area of irrigable land in the United States is estimated by different authorities to be from 60,000,000 to 100,000,000 acres, or one tenth the area of the Interior and Arizonan provinces, of which perhaps 30,000,000 acres will be reclaimed by the government and sold to settlers in tracts of 20 to 40 acres at prices sufficient to repay the cost of the works. It is probable that in the near future from 5,000,000 to 10,000,000 people will be living upon irrigated lands.

Mining in the Arizonan and Interior Provinces. — The mountains abound in metalliferous veins, and gold and silver mines occur in all the states and territories from Alaska to Mexico. The history of their development in different localities is substantially the same. Placer mining (Fig. 280) is always the first to be carried on, because it requires little machinery or capital, and is possible in regions however rough and remote from centers of population. The Washoe district in western Nevada, and the Leadville and Cripple Creek districts in Colorado, are typical mining camps.

Washoe District. — The Washoe Mountains are one of the ranges of the Great Basin on the western border of the Arizonan province, separated from the Sierra Nevada by only a narrow valley. Placer mines had been worked there for some years, and were showing signs of exhaustion when, in 1859, a vein yielding ore worth several thousand dollars a ton, which came to be known as the Comstock lode, was struck. A stampede of miners to the new "diggings" occurred at once, and Virginia City sprang into existence. Shafts were sunk and "drifts," or tunnels, run in many directions through solid rock to reach the ore. The very wide and rich ore bodies, called "bonanzas," were the most difficult to work on account of the danger of collapse of the walls. To prevent this, the space from which ore was removed had to be filled with timber and waste rock. The mines were often flooded with water which, at great depths, was hot. Tunnels were constructed to drain the lower levels, and gigantic pumps had to be used to lift eight or ten million gallons a day. The extraction of the metal from the ore involved the use of costly mechanical and chemical processes. The ore was usually reduced in stamp mills, where it was crushed under falling weights to a fine powder. The metal was then extracted by the use of mercury, potassium cyanide, or chlorine.

Well-graded wagon roads were built over the mountains from Placerville to Virginia City. Over these roads enormous wagons loaded with supplies or ore were drawn by mules in an almost continuous double procession. Before the Central Pacific Railroad was built 3000 men and 15,000 animals were employed in transporting 750,000 tons of freight a year. Probably at no other time or place has animal-wagon transportation reached such magnitude and efficiency. Stagecoaches, carrying mails and passengers, made the trip between Sacramento and Virginia City, 162 miles, in 18 hours. The mining district produced nothing but ore and had to be fed with everything from outside. It therefore made a market for hay, grain, fruit, hogs, cattle, poultry, and other products of California, and stimulated every industry in the accessible territory.

In 1872 the Comstock lode seemed to be nearly exhausted, but a bonanza of unparalleled size and richness was opened at a depth of 1500 feet, and yielded, in five years, $105,000,000. During this period the whole group of mines was valued at nearly $400,000,000. Such conditions led to endless speculation, in which fabulous fortunes were won and lost. The high temperature in the lower levels made it necessary to blow in air and to use ice in large quantities. A tunnel four miles long was run in to drain the mine, but proved inadequate. On account of failure of the vein and floods of hot water, work on a large scale ceased about 1880. The Comstock lode yielded, in twenty years, gold and silver to the value of $358,000,000. The cost of obtaining it cannot be calculated.

The industrial, financial, and political effects were far-reaching. The population of the region increased from a few hundreds to about 20,000 in 1864, when the interests of the community seemed so important that the state of Nevada was admitted to the Union and began to send a representative and two senators to the Congress of the United States. In 1880 the population of the state had risen to over 60,000 and of the Washoe district to about 20,000. In 1900 these numbers had fallen to about 42,000 and 5000 respectively. Few mining districts have a history so dramatic as that of the Washoe.

Leadville, on the headwaters of the Arkansas River in Colorado, was a rich placer mining camp as early as 1850, but lost its importance with the exhaustion of the placers. In 1875 immense veins of lead ore, very rich in silver, were discovered, and for some years the output of silver was greater than that of any foreign country except Mexico. Silver is now of secondary importance, being exceeded in value by lead, copper, zinc, and iron. Leadville, at an elevation of 10,000 feet, is a well-built city of about 7000 people, provided with all urban conveniences.

The Cripple Creek District, on the southwest shoulder of Pikes Peak, 9500 feet above the sea, produced in the first ten years after the discovery of gold there more than $120,000,000, and now has a population of about 10,000. The ground has been so thoroughly explored by "prospect holes" in search of ore that the surface resembles a prairie-dog village. The earth crust has been literally ransacked and pilfered. Over 200 mines are in active operation, and are connected with one another by electric car lines. Leadville and Cripple Creek have had the advantage of railroad connections almost from the first, and the period of difficulty and disorder usual at such places was brief.

In 1916 the production of the most important gold and silver districts was as follows:

	Gold.	Silver.
Colorado, Cripple Creek district	$12,110,000	....
Colorado, total for state	19,154,000	$4,976,000
Nevada	8,886,000	8,994,000
South Dakota, Black Hills district	7,460,000	....
British Columbia	5,166,000	2,060,000
Montana	4,550,000	10,727,000
Arizona	3,985,000	4,687,000
Utah	3,574,000	8,614,000
Idaho	1,116,000	7,995,000

There are several small coal fields, of which one near Newcastle, Colorado, yields anthracite. A very extensive coal field in southern Alberta and deposits of lignite in Montana and North Dakota are as yet slightly developed. The Arizonan and Interior provinces are rich in water power.

Copper Mining. — The district near Butte, Montana, produces more copper than any other in the world, the Anaconda mine alone yielding one-tenth of the world's supply. Placer gold began to be mined there in 1864, and silver ore in 1875. In 1881 the discovery of copper ore made the district famous. The sulphurous fumes produced by the roasting of ores are destructive to all vegetation in the vicinity, so that, while Butte is one of the wealthiest cities in proportion to population in the United States, it is a city without grass or trees.

Several rich districts in Arizona now give that state first rank in the production of copper. Older and even more famous copper mines on Keweenaw Point, Michigan, were opened in 1846, and have now reached a depth of about a mile. The copper occurs in scales and lumps of nearly pure metal. One nugget was found weighing 500 tons and worth $150,000.

Mining Economy. — While mining and mineral industries are absolutely essential for the existence of an industrial civilization, and afford opportunity for the rapid accumulation of wealth, they are, in contrast with agriculture and herding, wholly destructive. They are inroads upon what may be called the capital stock of the human family, laid up in the bank of the earth crust, and no amount of accumulated wealth can ever replace them. Gold and silver appeal strongly to the imagination and ambition of men, on account of their high value per ounce and their use as money, but in the arts they are less useful than copper, lead, iron, or coal. The actual market value of the precious metals mined in the United States hardly equals that of eggs, and the total value of all mineral products is less than that of the corn crop. In mountainous and arid regions, like the Interior and Arizonan provinces, mining is a pioneer industry, which first attracts population, labor, and capital. Railroads, manufactures, and agriculture follow, and all the natural resources come to be more fully utilized.

Transportation. — The development of transportation in the Arizonan province is closely connected with that of the Interior province already described (pages 394–397). Transportation and travel in the desert by animal power are difficult and dangerous on account of scarcity of water. The automobile, on account of its speed and broad tread, is found to be peculiarly adapted for desert travel. Man has invented a vehicle superior to the camel.

The Saharan Province. — The largest desert tract in the world extends from the Atlantic coast of Africa eastward to India. Its area is half as large again as that of the United States. In relief, it is less varied than the Arizonan province. It consists mostly of low, stony plateaus and plains of drifting sand dunes. In the central Sahara, the mountainous plateaus of Asgar and Tibesti rise above 3000 feet, with peaks up to 8000 feet above the sea. Arabia is a tilted table-land with a high margin on the south and west. There are no permanent streams except the Nile, Euphrates, Tigris, and Indus, which flow through the province from exterior rainy regions. The temperature sometimes rises to 150°, and falls below freezing. Light summer rains produce a little grass upon the highlands, but vegetation is mostly confined to ground-water oases (Fig. 206) and tracts irrigated from the through-flowing rivers or artesian wells. The date palm and the camel form the economic basis of human life. A little grain is grown, and goats, asses, and horses are used. The people are Caucasians of the Mediterranean type (p. 260), among which the Moors, Berbers, and Arabs are the most numerous. They are nearly all under the political control of France, Great Britain, or Italy, but many of the tribes are practically independent.

Egypt, one of the oldest centers of civilization in the world, has supported a dense population for 6000 years. This is made possible only by the overflow of the Nile, which flows across the desert, through a cleft in the plateau five to thirty miles wide, for 1000 miles without a tributary. The flood plain nowhere exceeds nine miles in breadth. The flood begins to rise in June, reaches its highest stage of about 25 feet in September, and falls rapidly until January. Under British rule the irrigated area has been greatly extended and improved. A dam at Assuan, 6400 feet long and 91 feet high, was completed in 1902 at a cost of $10,000,000. The water above is set back 200 miles, forming a reservoir which contains 215,000,000 acre feet of water. The irrigated area of Egypt is about 6,000,000 acres, and two or three crops a year are grown. The principal crops are, in summer, cotton, sugar, rice, and fruits; in winter, wheat, barley, and flax; and in autumn, corn (maize) and millet. The camel, donkey, and buffalo are the most common domestic animals. The present population of Egypt is about 12,000,000.

The Sudan. — The Sahara is bordered on the south by the Sudan, a transition belt of steppe and scrub land where grass and acacia flourish in proportion to rainfall. The principal occupation is cattle raising. The people are of mixed negro and Arab stock.

Arabia. — The high western and southern margins of this plateau receive sufficient rain to produce cereals, coffee, and dates. The rest of the country is desert, inhabited only by wandering Bedouin herdsmen and robbers. Their wealth consists of sheep, goats, camels, and horses.

Mesopotamia bears the same relation to the Tigris and Euphrates rivers that Egypt does to the Nile. It is an alluvial plain of extreme fertility but almost rainless. It needs only the restoration and improvement of the ancient irrigation systems to bring back the conditions of the Garden of Eden, which once existed there. It is now a land of date palms, but might produce tropical fruits, cereals, and cotton. It is sparsely inhabited by a mongrel population living in wretchedness.

Syria and Palestine form a strip of habitable land between the desert and the Mediterranean. Its productiveness is limited by scanty rainfall. There are some rich oases like that of Damascus (250,000). The population is one of the most mixed on earth.

The World War has relieved these countries in the Asiatic portion of the Saharan Province from the blight of Turkish oppression. The best part of Arabia now forms the Kingdom of Hedjaz under a native ruler. Mesopotamia, Syria, and Palestine, under the control of Great Britain and France, may soon realize their natural possibilities.

The Kalahari Province, in South Africa, is a worn-down eolian plain (p. 49), broken by *kopjes*, or knobs of resistant rock. It is almost devoid of permanent streams, but in the rainy seasons contains shallow lakes, marshes, and salt-incrusted mud flats. There are patches of bunch grass and bushes which support a rather numerous fauna, including the antelope, zebra, giraffe, rhinoceros, elephant, hyena, jackal, lion, ostrich, and flamingo. A conspicuous part in the economy of the province is played by several species of melon, which in moist years cover large tracts. Animals of all kinds, including man, depend upon them for water supply. Their seeds are oily and fattening. The only permanent human inhabitants are the Bushmen, yellow dwarfs wholly distinct from the negro. They are nomad fishermen, hunters, and thieves, using the simplest weapons, clothing, and shelter, and possessing no wealth whatever. Although among the lowest of men in civilization, they display considerable art in decorating their bodies, hair, and clothing, are fond of singing and dancing, and draw and paint pictures of animals with astonishing skill.

The Central Australian Province. — The Central Australian desert is made especially repellent by masses of spinifex, a coarse grass growing in hummocks full of needlelike prickles. The life of the native inhabitants has been noticed on p. 263. Some artesian well areas are utilized by white men for grazing, but the only considerable economic resource lies in the marvelously rich gold "reefs" around Coolgardie in the southwest. Railroads have been built to reach the mining districts, and water is pumped through an aqueduct 378 miles long.

The Peruvian Province extends along the Pacific coast of South America nearly 2000 miles. It is almost rainless, but slightly moistened by fogs. Agriculture is carried on in a small way along the little streams which descend from the Andes but do not reach the sea. The province is very rich in deposits of sodium nitrate (p. 304), which is mined and shipped to Europe as a fertilizer. Well-equipped, modern cities have been built near the nitrate beds, and many short lines of railroad connect them with the sea. Fresh water was formerly distributed by coasting vessels, but is now piped from the mountains.

CHAPTER XXVII

THE CALIFORNIAN AND OREGON PROVINCES

THE Californian and Oregon provinces occupy the Pacific ranges and valleys from the Gulf of California to the Strait of Fuca. They comprise the Pacific slope of California, Oregon, and Washington, an area of about 177,000 square miles, and have a population of about 3,500,000. The Coast Ranges border the sea throughout, except in southern California, where a plain about 50 miles wide intervenes. From the parallel of 35° N. Lat., where the Sierra Nevada joins the Coast Range, the great California Valley, 50 miles wide, extends northward 400 miles. In northern California and southern Oregon the valley is interrupted by the knot of the Klamath Mountains, beyond which the valleys of the Willamette River and Puget Sound extend to the northern end of the Oregon province.

Climate and Vegetation. — The two provinces are distinguished from each other by climatic conditions which change gradually between extremes of difference at the northern and southern ends. The westerly winds bring to the whole Pacific coast a mild, oceanic climate, modified in the north by frequent cyclonic disturbances. The range of temperature is generally less than 20 degrees. The rainfall increases from less than 10 inches in the south to more than 100 inches in the north. It is heaviest on the western slopes of the mountains and lightest in the valleys. The summers of the Californian province are almost rainless. In the Oregon province the rainfall is more evenly distributed through the year, with a large excess in winter.

The southern lowlands present a characteristic semi-desert

vegetation, in which the mesquite, greasewood, cactus, yucca, and date palm are conspicuous. The foothills and lower mountain slopes are generally covered with chapparal (p. 234), or groves of oak and other deciduous trees. In the south the coniferous forest does not reach below 5000 feet, but extends down to sea level in the north. It includes species of great variety and large size, of which the Oregon pine, Douglas fir, spruce, incense cedar, and redwood are most valuable (Figs. 199, 271). The high mountain summits have an Alpine climate with a few small glaciers.

Agriculture. — The agricultural products of the provinces are as varied as the climate. The lowlands of the southern half of California, irrigated from the mountain streams, are unsurpassed for the production of tropical fruits, such as oranges, lemons, figs, olives, and raisin grapes. In the valleys throughout both provinces, apricots, peaches, prunes, cherries, pears, apples, berries, and wine grapes are prolific and of fine quality. The wheat crop of the three states amounts to about 50,000,000 bushels, but about half of it is raised in the Interior province east of the mountains.

Stock raising has been an important industry since the days of Spanish occupation. The settling up and reservation of public lands has restricted the open range. Cattle and sheep are driven up to the high pastures in summer and back to the lowlands in winter.

Fisheries. — Salmon fishing and canning on the Columbia and other rivers, once marvelously productive, is still an important industry, although many canneries have been removed to Alaska.

Lumbering. — Of all the forest resources at present available in North America, those of the Pacific provinces are probably the most valuable. They now furnish about 14 per cent of the total annual cut of the United States. Wasteful methods have prevailed, and the forests have suffered from sheep and from fires. National forest reserves guarded by fire fighters, and the education of the people in forest conservation, may be expected to lessen destruction in the future.

Minerals and Mining. — The discovery of gold in a mill race near Sacramento in 1848 was the immediate cause of a rapid occupation of the country by people from the eastern states. About 100,000 immigrants arrived in one year and $40,000,000 were taken out. The surface placers were first exhausted. On the Sierra slope, many old stream channels, filled with auriferous gravel and buried under lava flows, were discovered. This led to *hydraulic* mining. Water brought from the mountains under great pressure, and discharged through a movable iron pipe, called a "monitor," was used to wash gravel on a very large scale. After a time, the agricultural lands below became so encumbered with waste that hydraulic mining was discontinued. In the meantime the "Mother Lode," one of the most important series of gold-bearing quartz veins in the world, was developed along the middle portion of the Sierra for 150 miles, and still yields about $12,000,000 a year. About $8,000,000 a year are obtained by excavating and sifting alluvial deposits by means of dredges, which make a place for themselves as they go, and bring up gold from depths down to 70 feet. For many years California led the world in the production of gold, and now slightly surpasses Colorado among the states.

The Coast Ranges of California are one of the principal sources of the world's supply of mercury. Since 1850 they have produced 150,000,000 pounds. California also produces copper, nearly all from the Klamath Mountains, which is smelted with coke brought from Australia. On account of the high cost of imported coal, hydroelectric power is used at most of the mines of all kinds.

In southern California there are several small but very rich petroleum fields, one in the city of Los Angeles, and one on the coast, which give the state a rank second only to Oklahoma. Along the foothills of the Cascade Mountains, within 50 miles of the shores of Puget Sound, fields of bituminous coal yield about

3,000,000 tons annually. More valuable coal fields exist on Vancouver Island in British Columbia.

Scenery. — The Pacific mountains, valleys, and coasts furnish some of the finest scenery in the world. The high Sierra of California, "with spreading ridge and foothill, rises like some huge, sprawling monster, its granite back unbroken for a thousand miles." The crest has been carved by frost and glaciers into a mass of peaks, domes, and cirques, dotted with unnumbered lakes (Figs. 40, 84, 104). The streams flowing down the western slope have cut profound cañons, of which the Yosemite Valley is the most famous. The Hetch-Hetchy, Tehipite, and Kings River cañons are scarcely inferior to the Yosemite. Many volcanic peaks of the Cascade Range, including Lassen, Shasta (Fig. 51), Hood, St. Helens, Rainier or Tacoma, and Baker, loom up from sea level to near 14,000 feet, in full view from the lowlands. Wide views of mountain, forest, and sea, with large and clear outlines, are to be had almost everywhere.

In the Californian province, the weather is predictable for a long period in advance. The seasons have been described as "half a year of clouds and flowers — half a year of dust and sky." The summer is an unbroken succession of sunshiny days, warm but never sultry. Even in winter fires are seldom needed. Houses are not used primarily as shelters from the weather. If it is chilly indoors, people go out to get warm. The air is mild but not enervating, and conduces to the enjoyment of outdoor life. Nature seems kindly, not hostile. By irrigation man virtually controls crop production. The great wheat and cattle ranches are being broken up into small holdings, from which a thrifty family can win a competence without excessive labor or anxiety. The natural conditions tend to foster a vigorous and long-lived people, conspicuous for individuality and independence of thought and action. Southern California is especially popular as a health resort.

Cities and Ports. — Foreign and domestic commerce by sea must always play a large part in the economy of the Pacific provinces. Their productive area, though rich, is not large. It is a narrow belt isolated on the continental side by a mountain wall and a wide tract of rugged desert and steppe. Whatever men may do to overcome these barriers, the land faces seaward, and natural conditions conspire to compel close relations with Pacific and Asiatic lands. Foreign intercourse westward to the Orient is likely to increase indefinitely in the future. On the coast large inlets are few and far apart, but three of them offer harbor and port facilities which are unsurpassed.

San Francisco (507,000). — Midway of the Californian coast, a local subsidence of the land has drowned the lower Sacramento River and let the sea into a longitudinal valley of the Coast ranges. The result is San Francisco Bay, 50 miles long and 10 miles wide, landlocked, and open to the sea only through the Golden Gate, a strait about one mile wide. It is a miniature Mediterranean. The conditions for a great seaport are almost ideal. Fogs over the strait and shallow water along the eastern shore are the only serious disadvantages. The city of San Francisco, the metropolis of Pacific America, almost surrounded by water, faces the bay and strait, while Oakland on the mainland opposite forms an essential part of the port. In spite of an earthquake and fire which nearly destroyed the city in 1906, it has been rebuilt and has increased in population at the rate of 21 per cent in ten years. The natural advantages of site and geographic position compel the existence there of a great commercial city. It is reached by four transcontinental railway lines, three from the south and one across the Sierra from the east. Its foreign trade exceeds that of any other city on the western coast of America.

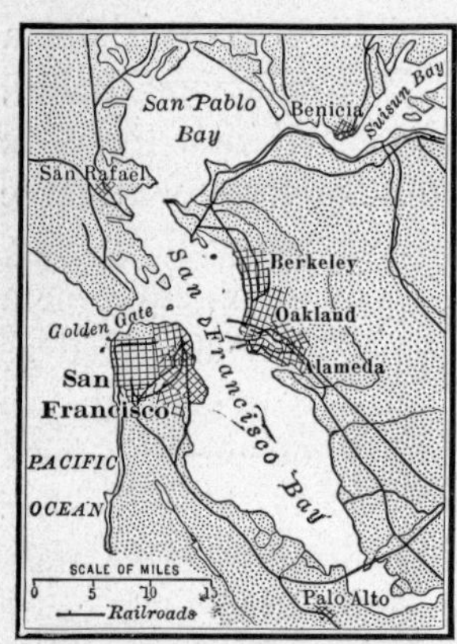

Fig. 332. — San Francisco Bay.

Portland (258,000), on the Willamette River, 12 miles from the Columbia and 80 miles from the sea, enjoys the advantage of a position virtually on the only river of the Pacific coast which is navigable beyond the mountains. It increased 25 per cent in population in the last decade and steadily holds a large share in the commerce of the Pacific. Its chief exports are wheat and lumber.

Puget Sound, a southern extension of the canal coast (Fig. 151) of the Alaskan province, is remarkable for the complexity of its branches, and depth of water. It extends southward 75 miles from the Strait of Fuca and has a coast line of 2000 miles. Sites for seaports are numerous, but *Seattle* (315,000) and *Tacoma* (97,000) are the only large cities. Seattle controls the Alaskan trade and has increased its population 33 per cent in the last decade (194 per cent in the preceding decade). The Puget Sound ports are reached by four transcontinental lines from the east, and are nearer to Japan and China than San Francisco. They have a large foreign trade.

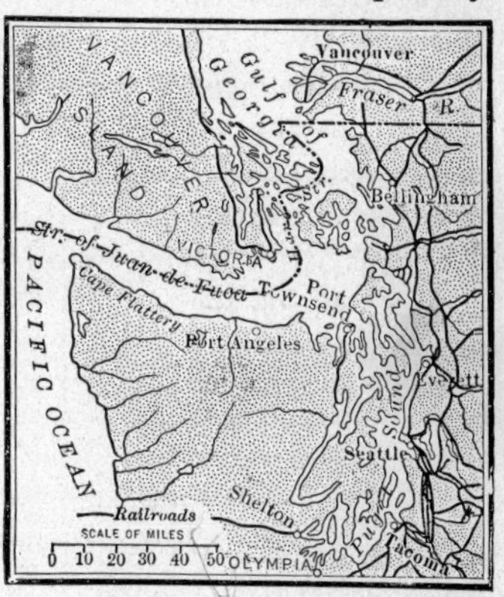

Fig. 333.—Puget Sound.

Los Angeles (577,000) is the metropolis of the tropical fruit region of southern California. While the main part of the city is inland, it has a narrow extension that reaches to the coast on San Pedro Bay, where a natural harbor has been recently improved. Directly east of it the low San Gorgonio pass admits the Southern Pacific Railway. It is one of the most prosperous and enterprising cities in the United States (Fig. 87) and its population increased 80 per cent in ten years (1910–1920).

The opening of the Panama Canal has stimulated to a degree difficult of estimation the already rapid economic development of the Pacific provinces.

The Chilean Province. — The narrow strip in South America west of the Andes and between 30° and 40° S. Lat. is in many ways a counterpart of the Californian province. Most of the rain falls in winter and varies from 60 inches in the south to 10 inches in the north. A low coast range and a narrow valley between it and the Andes complete the resemblance to California. This province is agricultural and contains the bulk of the population of Chile. The products are grain, fruit, and cattle. Santiago (408,000), the capital and largest city, is situated in the central valley, about 100 miles from its seaport, Valparaiso.

The Cape Province. — The southeast extremity of Africa in Cape Colony enjoys a climate in which the range of temperature is scarcely more than ten degrees and most of the 30 inches of rain falls in winter. The province has a peculiar flora rich in showy flowering plants, many of which have been transplanted to European gardens. The agricultural products are wheat, corn, wine, and tobacco. Cape Town (78,000), on Table Bay, is the metropolis of South Africa and an important port and naval station on the sea route to Australia and the Orient.

The Southwest Australian Province. — The southwest coast lands of Australia are exposed in winter to cyclonic winds which bring a rainfall of from 20 to 30 inches, while the summers are dry. The vegetation varies from forests of gigantic eucalyptus trees to steppe and thorn scrub. Nearly all grains, root crops and fruits are grown, but sheep raising and cattle raising are the most important industries. Perth is the seaport for the rich gold fields of the interior (p. 411), and Adelaide (192,000) is the commercial and political center of a large agricultural and grazing district.

The Mediterranean Province is discussed in Chapter XXXI.

CHAPTER XXVIII

THE PEOPLE OF THE UNITED STATES AND CANADA

WITH the exception of the French on the lower St. Lawrence, the people of the United States and Canada were originally of almost pure British stock. The period of active immigration and permanent settlement extended from 1607 to about 1750. They then increased by natural excess of births over deaths to about 14,000,000 in 1830. Shortly after 1830 immigration began on a large scale, and with some fluctuations has increased until the present, when in some years a million aliens land upon American shores. The total number amounts to about 30,000,000, of which 90 per cent have come from Europe.

Previous to 1890, 75 per cent of the immigrants were Baltic and Teutonic people from the British Isles, Germany, and Scandinavia. Since 1890, 60 per cent have been Alpine and Mediterranean people from Italy, Austria-Hungary, and Russia, including many Slavs and Jews. This change in character of the immigrants, and the influx of people who differ widely from the original stock in temperament, habits, language, and religion, make the problem of assimilation and blending into a homogeneous people a serious one. The matter is made more difficult by the tendency of the later immigrants to segregate in great cities like New York and Chicago, and to maintain there their own peculiar habits of life. The most efficient agent of Americanization is the public school, where the children learn the English language, absorb American ideas, and undergo a change even in the form of their heads. Many of the Slavs and Hungarians go inland to work in the coal mines and steel mills, while the Italians build railroads, streets, sewers, and aqueducts, and perform all sorts of unskilled labor. The Alpine peoples are noted for their domestic virtues and devotion to family, divorce being almost unknown among them. The Italians have a native talent and passion for art and music. These are qualities in which the typical American is often lacking, and are desirable contributions to the society of the future.

The colored people, descendants of former slaves, have occupied the field of labor in the southern states almost to the exclusion of foreigners. They are most numerous in the "black belt" from South Carolina to Louisiana, where in many communities they outnumber the whites. Their number in proportion to the total population is decreasing.

Of the 106,000,000 people in the United States, 10.3 per cent are colored and 13 per cent foreign-born. The native whites of native parents form only 55.3 per cent of the whole. The Americans are certainly destined to be a composite and cosmopolitan people. The proportion of urban population living in towns of 2500 or more has increased from 45.8 per cent in 1910 to 51.4 per cent in 1920. Many rural districts lost population in the decade 1910 to 1920. This is true of the whole states of Vermont and Mississippi. It is an indication and result of the improvement of farm machinery and the development of manufactures and transportation. At the same time the movement from the country to the city retards the progress of agriculture, upon which all industry depends, diminishes the food supply in relation to demand, and increases the cost of living.

Distribution of Population. — The chief natural conditions which control density are: (1) rainfall, no state wholly west of the 20-inch line having a density above 15 except Washington; (2) arability, states of the next higher ranks having productive glacial or other soils; (3) coal, iron, and the Great Lakes, which give the states enjoying them a rank next to the highest; (4) the Atlantic seaboard, which in combination with (3) renders possible a density approaching that of the leading countries of the Old World. The density of population decreases in every direction from the vicinity of the metropolis, but not uniformly.

The decrease is slowest westward parallel with the path which the center of population has traveled from near Baltimore in 1790 to central Indiana in 1920 (Fig. 313).

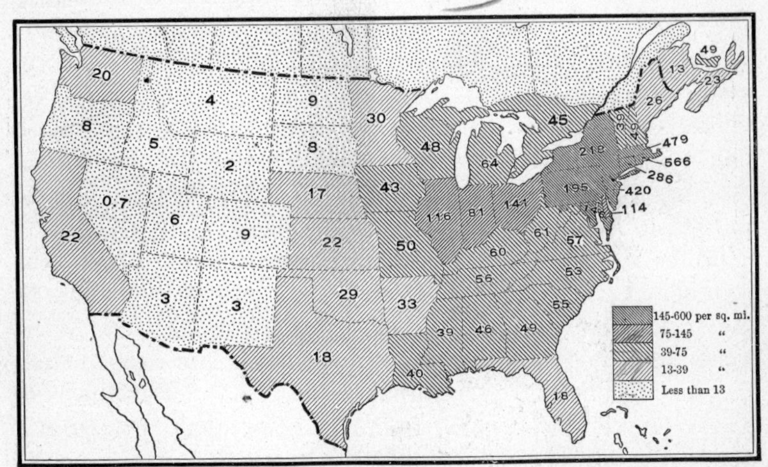

Fig. 334.—Density of population in the United States and Canada.

Future Population. — In spite of increased immigration, the rate of increase of population has decreased from 3.64 per cent per annum in 1810 to 1.5 per cent in 1920. Allowing for a similar decrease in the future, the probable population of the United States in the year 2000 has been estimated at 250 to 350 millions. The possible capacity of the United States to support population is affected by many factors, among which utilizable water and the standard of living are the chief. As the latter may vary, the country may sometime contain from 500 to 1000 million people.

The population of Canada has grown by natural increase and British immigration to more than 7,000,000, of which 23 per cent retain the language and customs of their French ancestors. One fifth of the native-born Canadians are living in the United States. On account of the unknown possibilities of a large part of the country, its future growth and development are difficult to calculate, but that they will be large is certain. The climate will exclude south Europeans, and Baltic civilization will expand northward.

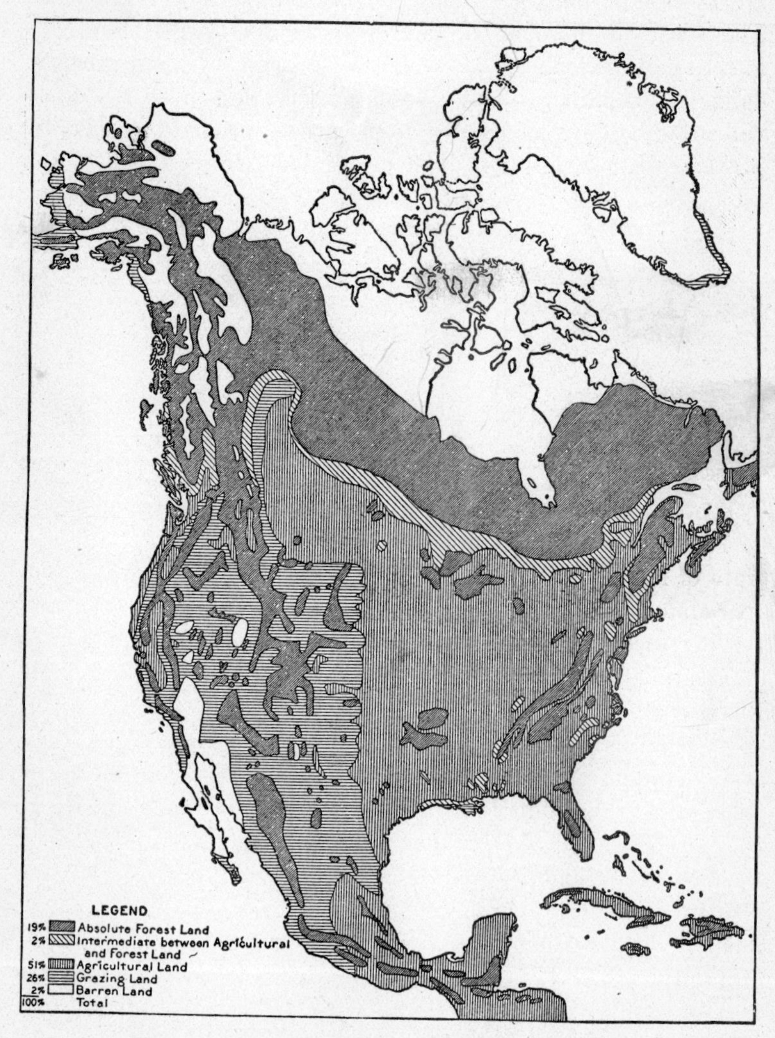

Fig. 335.—Probable future use of land. (*U.S. Forest Service.*)

The people of the United States and Canada have fallen heir to the largest fortune in unoccupied land and undeveloped resources that ever fell to the lot of any historic people. They are even now only beginning to understand how large it is. The sense of unbounded and inexhaustible wealth tends to foster an extravagant spirit which is the source of their greatest danger. Scientific utilization and conservation of all resources will extend the existence of one or more great nations in temperate North America through uncounted centuries.

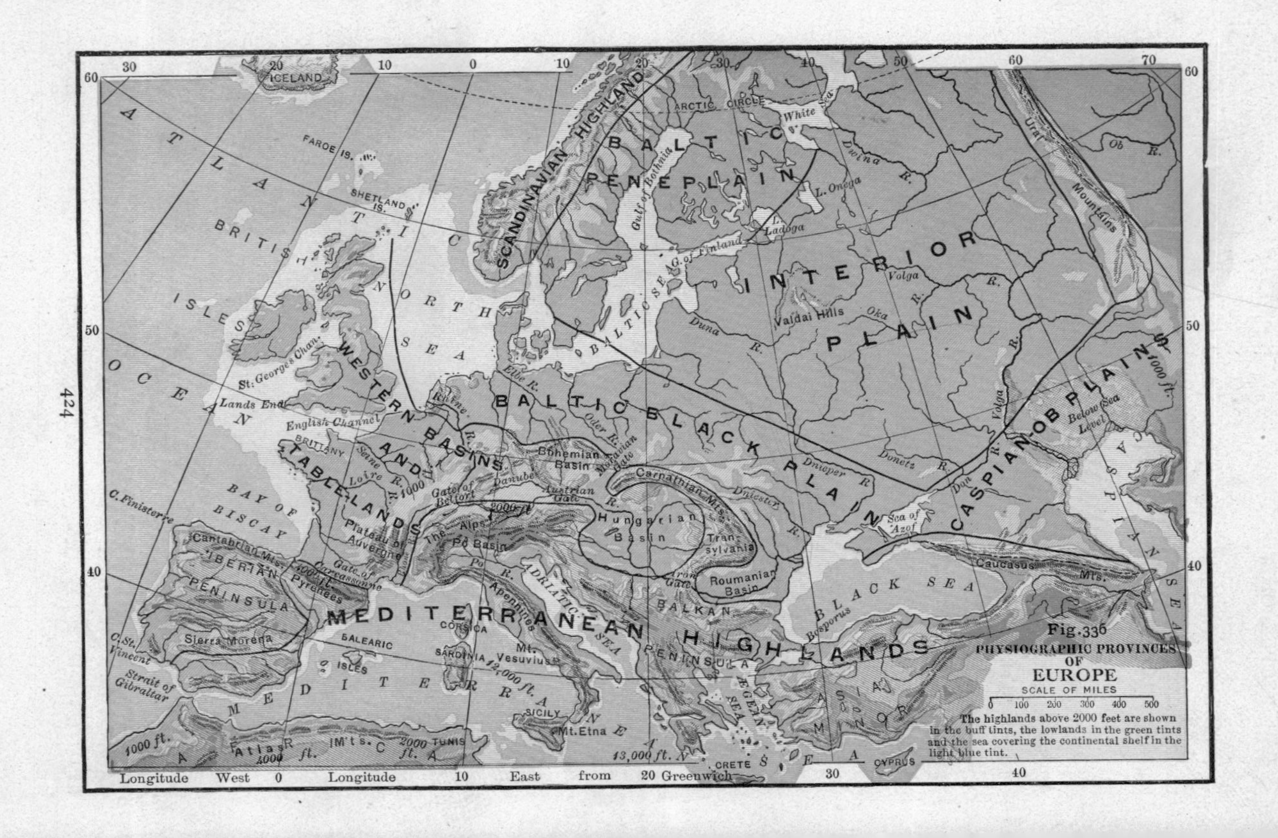

Fig. 336 PHYSIOGRAPHIC PROVINCES OF EUROPE

The highlands above 2000 feet are shown in the buff tints, the lowlands in the green tints and the sea covering the continental shelf in the light blue tint.

CHAPTER XXIX

THE WEST EUROPEAN PROVINCE

Physiographic Provinces of Europe. — The *Baltic peneplain*, invaded by the White Sea, has a structure and relief almost identical with those of the Laurentian peneplain (pp. 45, 118), invaded by Hudson Bay. The *Scandinavian highland* corresponds substantially with the plateau and coast mountains of Labrador. The *Interior* and *Baltic-Black plains* of Europe are quite similar to the Interior plain of North America. The *Western province* of Europe, a complex assemblage of broken blocks, some depressed and some elevated (p. 63), with vestiges of old folded mountains and including the British Isles, is homologous with the Appalachian highland, including Newfoundland. The *Mediterranean region*, with its folded, curved, and branched mountain ranges, volcanoes, peninsulas, islands, and sunken sea basins, resembles the Caribbean ranges in structure more than maps alone can show. By cutting out the Gulf of Mexico with its coastal plain and moving the Caribbean ranges northward to the border of the continent, the geographic correspondence between Europe and North America east of the Rocky Mountains becomes very striking.

Climates. — The climates of the European provinces have been previously described (pp. 218–221), and may be briefly characterized as Atlantic, continental, and Mediterranean. The Atlantic climate is temperate and moist. The small range is due especially to mild winters. The rainfall is generally above 30 inches and almost perennial, with a small excess in autumn and winter. . The continental climate is extreme and dry. The range is large, a long, cold winter in the north and a long, hot summer in the south overlapping midway. The rainfall is generally less than 30 inches, with a large excess in summer. The Mediterranean climate is hot, with a wet and temperate winter. The rainfall varies with exposure, being above 30 inches on western coasts and slopes, and below 30 inches on eastern.

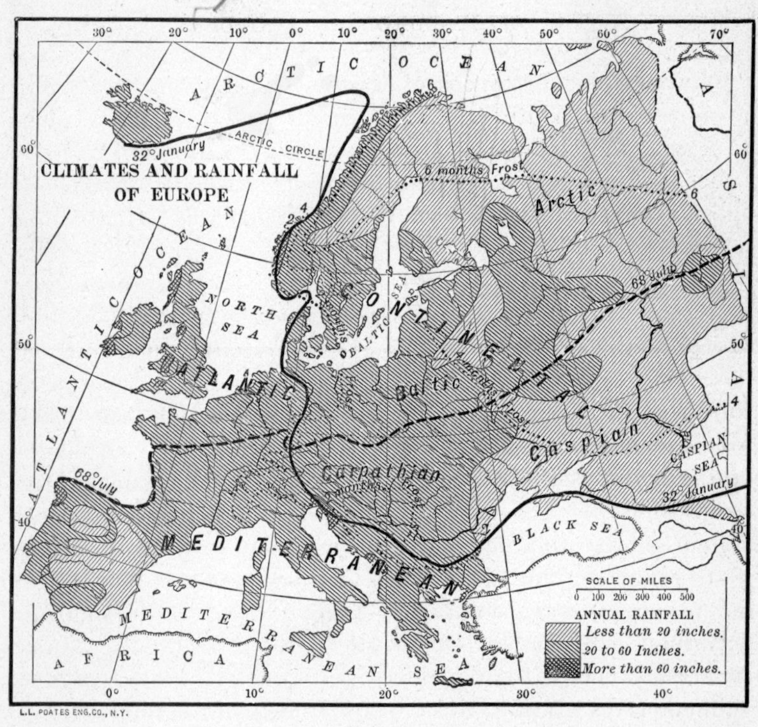

Fig. 337.

Natural Provinces of Europe. — Those portions of Europe which are more than sparsely populated (Fig. 236), and which are occupied by the leading nations of the world, lie, with trifling exceptions, in provinces of the Oregon, Californian, and Mississippian types. On account of differences in the position and trend of mountain ranges, the arrangement and relations of the

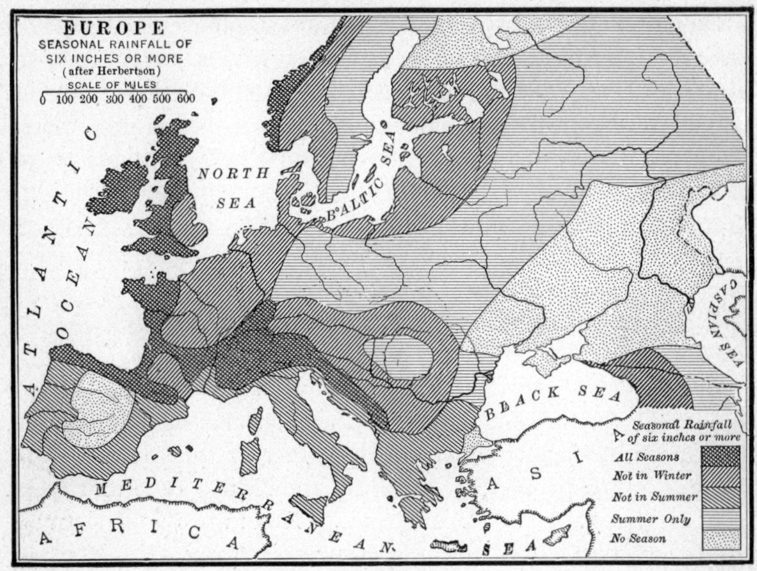

Fig. 338.

European provinces differ from those of the American. The Mediterranean (Californian type) province is sharply separated on the north from the West (Oregon type) and Central (Mississippian type) European provinces, by an almost continuous system of east-west mountain ranges. The absence of north-south ranges permits the climatic conditions of the West province to extend eastward with very gradual change to the Central.

Natural and Human Divisions. — In contrast with North America, occupied by only three great political units, Europe, with two fifths the area, was in 1914 divided among some twenty rival states. Of these thirteen have survived the World War without loss of territory. The rest have been more or less broken up, with the formation of ten new states. The new political division has been made, as far as possible, according to community of racial type, language, and religion. Figure 339, and the table on page 429, show how far this plan has been carried out.

In the West province, Great Britain, France, and Germany have long led the world in industry, commerce, wealth, science, literature, and political power, with no formidable rival previous to the recent expansion of the United States. Switzerland, Belgium, the Netherlands, and Denmark are of minor importance only because of small territory and population. The Baltic racial type and the Teutonic languages — English, German, Dutch, Danish, and Swedish — prevail except in France, where there is a large admixture of Alpine and Mediterranean stocks, and French, the most important of the Romanic languages, is spoken.

The Central province is occupied by Russia, Roumania, Bulgaria, and the new states of Poland, Ukraine, Czechoslovakia, Jugoslavia, Hungary, Austria, and other fragments of former empires. The people are largely of the Alpine type and speak a great variety of Slavic languages. There are many Germans in the western part, and the Roumanians speak a Romanic language.

The Mediterranean province includes mainly Italy, Spain, Portugal, and Greece. The people are nearly all of the Mediterranean type. Italian, Spanish, and Portuguese are, like French, Romanic languages, derived from the ancient Latin. In Greece a modification of ancient Greek is spoken. The Turks are Asiatic Mongolians and speak a language very different from those of genuine Europeans.

The British Isles

Between 50° and 60° N. Lat., the continental shelf of western Europe projects far out to sea (Figs. 16, 336) and bears upon its surface a group of two large and many small islands. Separated from the mainland by the English Channel, a shallow strait from 100 to 21 miles in width, they are almost peninsular rather than insular. They stand in front of the Baltic entrance and the mouth of the Rhine, and command the

RACES, LANGUAGES, AND RELIGIONS OF EUROPEAN PEOPLES

<table>
<tr><th colspan="4">Caucasian Race</th><th rowspan="3">Mongolian Race</th></tr>
<tr><th>Prevailing Type Baltic</th><th>Prevailing Type Mediterranean</th><th colspan="2">Prevailing Type Alpine</th></tr>
<tr><th>LANGUAGES TEUTONIC</th><th>LANGUAGES ROMANIC</th><th>LANGUAGES SLAVIC</th><th>LANGUAGES SLAVIC</th></tr>
<tr>
<td>Protestant and Roman Catholic
Germans 69,000,000
Irish 4,400,000
Protestant
English 34,000,000
Scotch 4,700,000
Welsh 2,000,000
Dutch 6,600,000
Danes 3,000,000
Swedes 5,700,000
Norwegians . . 2,400,000
Roman Catholic
Flemings 3,200,000
Total . . . . 135,000,000</td>
<td>Roman Catholic
French 41,000,000
Walloons . . . 3,000,000
Italians 35,500,000
Spanish 19,000,000
Portuguese . . 5,500,000
Greek Catholic
Roumanians . 13,000,000
LANGUAGES NOT ROMANIC
Greeks 5,000,000
Jewish
Jews 10,000,000
Total . . . . 132,000,000</td>
<td>East Slavs
Greek Catholic
Great Russians 80,000,000
White Russians 5,000,000
Little Russians or Ukrainians 30,000,000
South Slavs
Bulgarians . . 4,200,000
Serbians 9,500,000
Croats 2,000,000
Roman Catholic
Slovenes . . . . 1,300,000</td>
<td>West Slavs
Roman Catholic
Poles 17,100,000
Czechs 5,600,000
Moravians . . 1,700,000
Ruthenians . . 3,500,000
Protestant
Slovaks 2,500,000
Total Slavs 162,400,000
LANGUAGES NOT SLAVIC
Lithuanians . 3,500,000
Letts 2,000,000
Roman Catholic, Greek Catholic, and Mohammedan
Albanians . . . 1,100,000
Total Alpine 169,000,000</td>
<td>Mohammedan
Turks }
Tatars } 6,000,000
Roman Catholic
Magyars 10,000,000
Protestant
Finns 3,000,000
Esths 1,000,000
Total . . . . . . 20,000,000</td>
</tr>
</table>

Total for Europe, 456,000,000

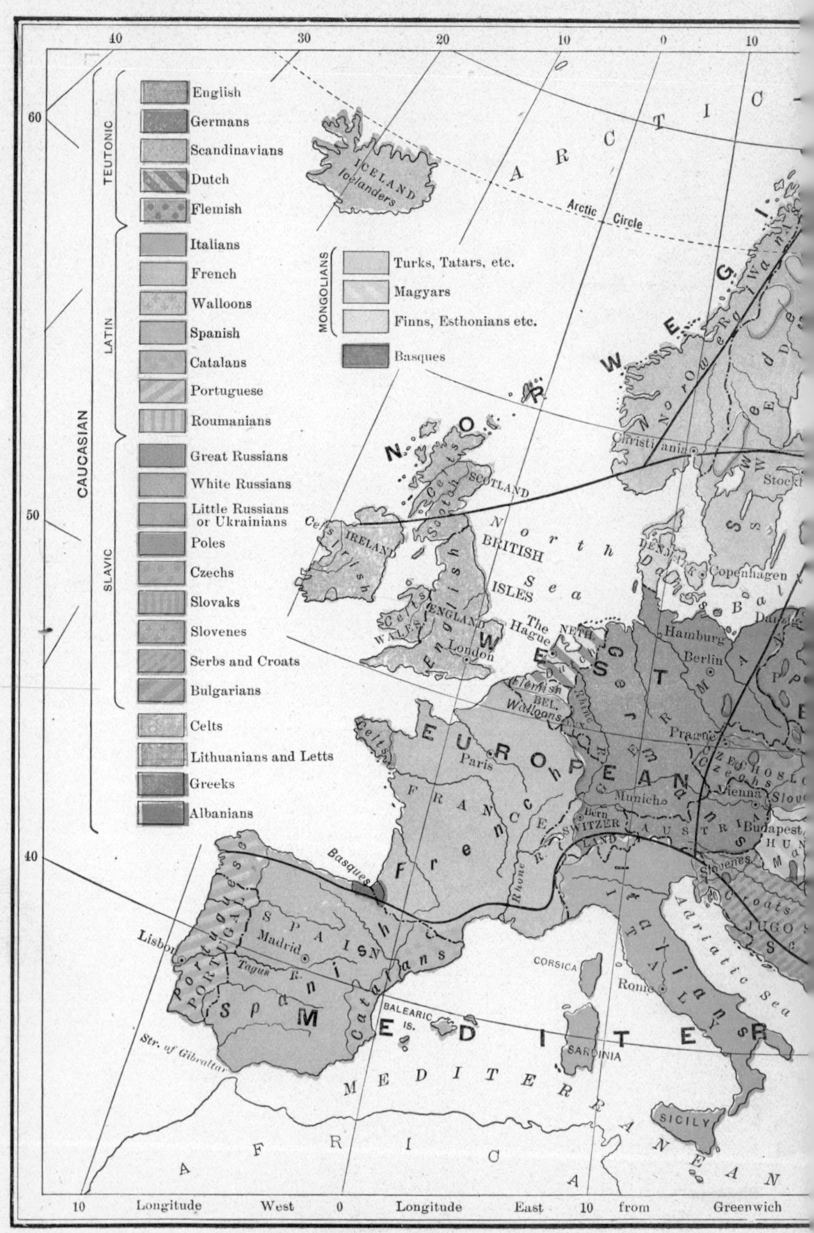

CAUCASIAN
TEUTONIC
English
Germans
Scandinavians
Dutch
Flemish
LATIN
Italians
French
Walloons
Spanish
Catalans
Portuguese
Roumanians
SLAVIC
Great Russians
White Russians
Little Russians or Ukrainians
Poles
Czechs
Slovaks
Slovenes
Serbs and Croats
Bulgarians
Celts
Lithuanians and Letts
Greeks
Albanians
MONGOLIANS
Turks, Tatars, etc.
Magyars
Finns, Esthonians etc.
Basques
ICELAND
Icelanders
Arctic Circle
ARCTIC
NORWEGIAN
North Sea
BRITISH ISLES
SCOTLAND
IRELAND
ENGLAND
WALES
London
The Hague
NETH.
BEL.
Flemish
Walloons
Paris
FRANCE
French
WESTERN EUROPEAN
Germans
Hamburg
Berlin
Prague
Munich
Vienna
Budapest
Bern
SWITZERLAND
AUSTRIA
Christiania
Copenhagen
DENMARK
Danes
Stockh
Danzig
Slovenes
Croats
Basques
Lisbon
PORTUGAL
Portuguese
SPAIN
Madrid
Tagus R.
Spanish
Catalans
BALEARIC IS.
CORSICA
SARDINIA
SICILY
Rome
ITALY
Italians
Adriatic Sea
Rhone R.
Str. of Gibraltar
MEDITERRANEAN
AFRICA
Longitude West
Longitude East from Greenwich

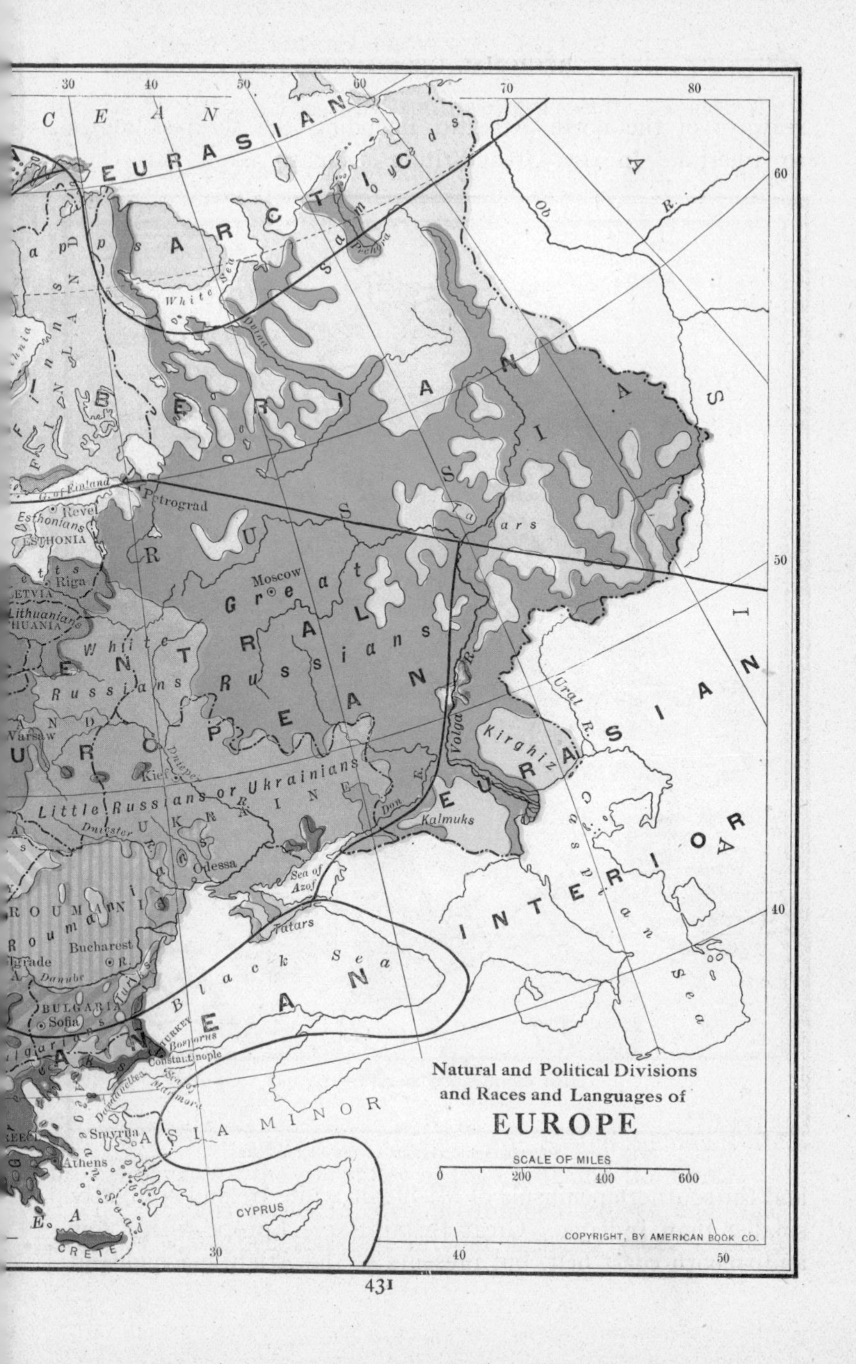
Natural and Political Divisions
and Races and Languages of
EUROPE
SCALE OF MILES
0 200 400 600
COPYRIGHT, BY AMERICAN BOOK CO.
EURASIAN
ARCTIC
Samoyeds
White Sea
Dwina
Petchora
Ob R.
Petrograd
Revel
Esthonians
ESTHONIA
Riga
LETVIA
Lithuanians
Moscow
Great Russians
White Russians
CENTRAL EUROPEAN
RUSSIA
Tatars
Warsaw
Kief
Dnieper
Little Russians or Ukrainians
UKRAINE
Dniester
Odessa
Sea of Azof
Don R.
Volga R.
Ural R.
Kirghiz
Kalmuks
EURASIAN INTERIOR
Caspian Sea
ROUMANIA
Roumanians
Bucharest
Danube
BULGARIA
Sofia
Black Sea
Tatars
TURKEY
Bosporus
Constantinople
Sea of Marmora
Dardanelles
ASIA MINOR
Smyrna
Athens
CYPRUS
CRETE
MEDITERRANEAN

near together in pairs. London and Bristol are 110 miles apart. Liverpool and Hull are separated by the same distance, while Glasgow is only 40 miles from Edinburgh. There is no point in the island as much as 100 miles from the sea. Nature has planned it for a center of maritime commerce and sea power.

Physiography and Economics. — The physiographic regions of the British Isles are shown in Fig. 340.

The Scotch Highlands are a faulted and glaciated plateau of crystalline rocks, of about 3000 feet in elevation, dissected by narrow valleys containing many beautiful "lochs." It is a region of rugged heights, barren moors, and grass- and heather-clad slopes, given up to cattle and sheep pastures and game preserves, with a few farms in the valleys. There are no towns and few railroads, except along the east coast, where a narrow lowland and the North Sea fisheries support most of the population. It is rich in wild and picturesque scenery which attracts thousands of tourists.

The Rift Valley Lowland, about 50 miles wide, studded with many protruding ridges and "craigs" of volcanic rock, has very productive land in the valleys of the Tay, Forth, and Clyde. Its chief source of wealth lies in beds of coal and iron, and its facilities for ocean commerce, which make it a manufacturing and trading district of dense population. The business center is Glasgow (1,111,000), made a first-class seaport by the improvement of the Clyde, and engaged largely in steel ship building and sugar refining. Edinburgh (334,000), the ancient capital of Scotland, "the Athens of the north," built upon and around three volcanic craigs, is famous for its picturesque site, streets, and buildings, its law courts and ancient university.

The Southern Uplands and *Pennine Range* are not high enough to present a serious barrier to the passage of railroads and canals. They are well fitted for sheep raising and general farming in the valleys; but the coal fields on both flanks of the Pennines are far more important. The presence of coal and iron, and the shipping facilities on two seas, here form the natural basis upon which has developed the greatest manufacturing district of the world. The western slope, accessible for supplies of American cotton through the ports of Liverpool (747,000) and Manchester, is devoted to cotton spinning and weaving, carried on in many large towns, of which Manchester (715,000) is the commercial center. On the eastern slope Bradford (289,000) and Leeds (446,000) are the centers of great woolen manufactures; and farther south, Nottingham (260,000) and Leicester (227,000) manufacture fine hosiery, ribbons, and silks. Sheffield (469,000) has a world-wide reputation for cutlery. Near an outlying coal field in the midland gap, Birmingham (870,000), "the Pittsburgh of England," produces railroad rails, armor plate, structural steel, and iron goods of many kinds. The concentration of industries and population is so great that the "black country" contains about 8,000,000 people. In the north of England on the east coast, the towns on the Tyne and Tees have coal and iron and do a large business in iron smelting and the building of steel ships.

Fig. 342. — Coal fields of Great Britain.

The Central Lowland furnishes easy routes of transportation between ports and industrial centers on three sides of England.

The Lake District, in northwestern England, resembles the Scotch highlands, and is even more famous for beauty of scenery (Fig. 119). *The Welsh Mountains* repeat most of the features of the Scotch highlands except the lochs. The anthracite coal field on their southern coast is a great smelting district for iron, copper, tin, and other ores from many foreign sources. Cardiff (182,000) and Swansea (115,000) are the principal ports.

The Southeast Lowland. — A line drawn from the mouth of the Severn to the mouth of the Tees, with a curve toward the east, divides Great Britain into two contrasted parts. The region on the northwest contains all the highlands and most of the coal and iron, and is given up to manufacturing industries on the largest scale. The region on the southeast is a lowland varied by gentle hills and rolling downs, and is largely agricultural. Wheat, oats, hay, and turnips are the principal crops. Cattle, horses, and sheep of the finest varieties are bred. Near the south coast, apple orchards, hop yards, and vegetable, fruit, and flower gardens flourish. A large portion of the area is occupied by the parks and country estates of the wealthy, who maintain them solely for beauty and pleasure. Bristol (357,000), Southampton (120,000), and Portsmouth (231,000) are important ports, especially for American trade. Hull (278,000) is the center of the North Sea fisheries.

London. — The metropolis of the world now numbers over 7,250,000 people. Situated at the head of tide water on the Thames, it is more convenient for European trade than for American. At present it holds a rank near the first among seaports. From the Norman walled city of the eleventh century, about one mile in diameter, it has grown in all directions, absorbing town and country, until now it covers an area extending 5 to 10 miles from the original center. The old town, locally known as " the City," is now given up to official and financial business, and has a permanent population of only about 30,000. Probably 1,000,000 people may be found there during business hours. It contains the general post office, the Bank of England, the stock exchange, the Mansion House or residence of the Lord Mayor, the Guildhall, St. Paul's Cathedral, the Norman fortress called the Tower, Billingsgate fish market, St. Bartholomew's Hospital, and many other famous buildings.

London is rather sharply divided into an "east end" and a "west end." East London is the seaport, largely occupied by docks, warehouses, markets, factories, and the appurtenances of trade on a large scale. It is also the home of about a million paupers, who seldom see a day in which they have enough to eat. West London is the home of aristocracy and wealth, where

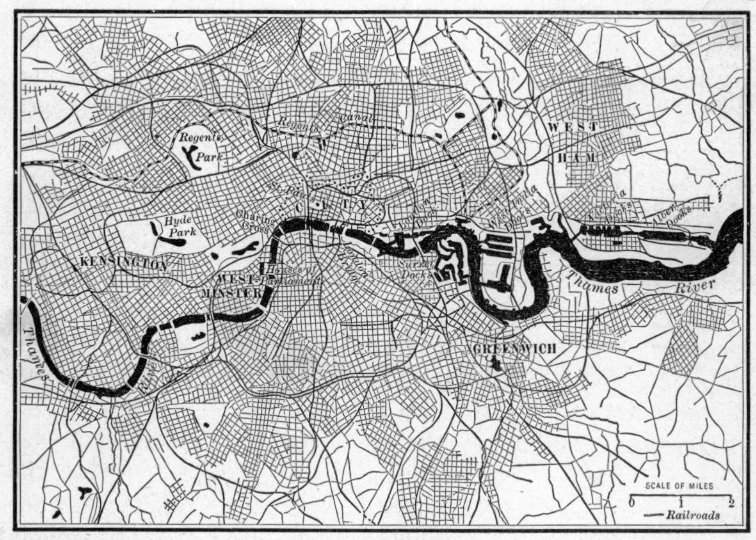

Fig. 343. — London.

another million live in luxury. The south side of the Thames is neither pauper nor aristocratic, but is occupied by people of moderate means. The center of the west end is the formerly distinct city of Westminster, the seat of government and religion and the real capital of the British Empire. West London contains the Houses of Parliament, Buckingham Palace (the town residence of the sovereign), Westminster Abbey, where the sovereigns are crowned, the government offices, the law courts, museums, art galleries, theaters, hotels, club houses, many palatial public and private buildings, and the fashionable retail shopping district. In the midst of it Hyde Park, Regents Park, and other smaller parks occupy large spaces devoted to outdoor recreation and pleasure.

London is governed by a legislative and executive body known as the London County Council. The movement of the people is effected by lines of surface cars and an extensive system of underground electric railways. The thousands of omnibuses and cabs in use a few years ago are now to some extent displaced by autocars. London is one of the greatest railway centers of the world. Trunk lines enter from all sides, and stations of the largest capacity receive and discharge passengers. London is the financial center of the world, where bonds, stocks, notes, bills, checks, drafts, coin, paper money, and securities of all kinds from every part of the world find a market.

London is a world by itself, which may be analyzed and roughly divided into many cities occupying to a greater or less extent the same territory, as follows:

1. Marine London, including all persons employed in shipping by water and in handling and storing goods.

2. Manufacturing London, including all persons employed in any capacity in manufacture.

3. Mercantile London, including all wholesale and retail merchants and their employees.

4. Financial London, comprising all persons who deal in public and private securities, and are engaged in banking and brokerage.

5. Official London, comprising all those engaged in the administration of imperial, royal, and municipal government.

6. Social London, made up of people of many classes, who live there because of the social, educational, and artistic advantages.

7. Professional and servile London, comprising all those who render personal service by caring for the health, property, welfare, and comfort of the population.

8. Pauper London, comprising a large number of people who have no regular or visible means of support.

Ireland, "the Emerald Isle," so called because of perennial greenness due to the mildness and humidity of its climate, consists of a central plain with highlands around the borders. It is very poor in mineral resources, and peat is the common fuel. The peasants raise potatoes, pigs, and dairy cattle. Flax is grown in the north, from which the famous Irish linen is manufactured at Belfast (393,000). Cork has an excellent harbor on the south coast, and its port of Queenstown is a place of landing for American passengers and mail. The population of Ireland has been decreasing for more than a century by emigration, chiefly to the United States.

Economic Conditions. — Little more than a century ago the British were an agricultural and pastoral people numbering about 9,000,000. The progressive utilization of their mineral resources has been the chief factor in an increase of population to 45,000,000, of which 70 per cent are engaged in manufactures and commerce and only 12 per cent in agriculture. The population of England and Wales is 36,000,000 giving a density of 634 to the square mile. Of these 78 per cent live in cities. Of the area 41 per cent is pasture, 32 per cent arable, and 11 per cent occupied by roads and buildings. If the islands could be blockaded so as to cut off foreign food supplies, the stock on hand would last but a few months, and half the population would suffer from hunger in a short time. The mills of Great Britain spin one fifth of all cotton grown and supply more than half of all cotton goods exported. One fourth of the world's wool clip is manufactured there. In production of iron and steel it stands next to the United States. In exports of manufactured goods it leads all countries. Its total foreign trade amounted in 1916 to the enormous sum of $7,400,000,000.

Such an economic condition demands a world-wide market and a great merchant marine. The market is found largely in the colonies and dependencies which form the British Empire, of which India, Egypt, Canada, Australia, and South Africa are the most important. The tonnage of all merchant vessels carrying the British flag is nearly half the total of the world. British ships not only carry away manufactured goods and bring home foodstuffs and raw materials, but do a large part of the carrying business of other countries, especially of the United States. Such a fleet requires protection; hence the British navy about equals in fighting strength those of France and the United States combined, and holds the empire of the seas. The success of this vast scheme requires the possession of coaling and repair stations on the high seas and open trading ports on all coasts. Hence many of the "keyholes" and "crossroads" of the world are British. Gibraltar, Malta, Suez, and Aden command the Mediterranean-Suez route; Singapore and Hongkong the trade of the China seas; Cape Town, Mauritius, and Ceylon the Indian Ocean; Halifax, Bermuda, Barbados, and Jamaica the western Atlantic; and many islands in the Pacific are British. Thus "Britannia rules the waves."

The British people have acquired great wealth from profits on raw materials imported, manufactured, and exported, from profits on goods imported, repacked, and distributed abroad, from the carrying business done by sea for other people, and from banking and exchange. The capital thus accumulated is largely invested abroad in bonds of various governments, and the stocks of industrial enterprises. The geographic basis of British power and prosperity lies in a unique combination of conditions: (1) the position and coast line of the British Isles, which furnish unequaled advantages for foreign trade; (2) the "silver streak" of water which has protected the country from foreign invasion for eight hundred years; (3) the complex structure of the land, accompanied by low or moderate relief; (4) the mild, moist, and equable climate; (5) the large supply of coal and iron. The first four are permanent; the fifth is temporary, and is liable to become seriously impaired within the present century.

World Power. — The British people have exerted a greater influence upon the world than any other since the fall of the Roman Empire. This is due to their stable and enlightened government, free and democratic institutions, mechanical and inventive skill, success in war, shrewdness and integrity in trade, rapid increase in numbers, and their colonizing policy. British civilization now prevails over one third of the habitable globe, and the English language is spoken by one tenth of the human species, more in America than in the Old World.

France

France would extend from the Ohio River to the Gulf of Mexico and cover the area of Kentucky, Tennessee, Alabama,

Georgia, and Florida north of the 30th parallel. It is a "bridge" country, lying between the Mediterranean and the Atlantic and connecting the central plateaus of Europe with the Iberian peninsula. Its position between two seas, with ample coast line on both, gives it commercial advantages scarcely second to those of Great Britain.

Coast Features. — France is bounded by mountains and seas except on the northeast. The coast opposite England is a chalk cliff (Fig. 128), but several artificial ports accommodate the large transit between the two countries. A tunnel twenty miles long under the Strait of Dover is a proposition seriously maintained by engineers. Havre, at the mouth of the Seine, has been prepared by elaborate harbor works to receive the shipping too large to go up the river. Cherbourg is a port of call for steamships to and from British, Dutch, and German ports. The granite upland peninsula of Brittany has many small harbors frequented by fishing vessels. St. Nazaire and Nantes on the Loire are important maritime marts, while Bordeaux (262,000) on the Garonne is the port of the southern wine district. Between the Gironde and the Pyrenees a remarkably straight and smooth belt of bars, lagoons, and dunes preclude access from the sea. On the south coast, Marseilles (551,000), commanding the outlet of the Rhone valley, is the principal seaport on the Mediterranean and the second city of France.

Relief and Drainage. — Apart from the boundary mountains, the highland of France lies in the south, where the plateau of Auvergne occupies an oval area about half as large as Tennessee. It is a broken and tilted block, bounded on the east by a steep escarpment known as the Cévennes Mountains, and sloping westward halfway to the Atlantic. Its surface is studded with hundreds of *puys*, or volcanic cones (Fig. 53). The Cévennes are continued northward by a lower escarpment which curves to the east and joins the Vosges at the head of the Saone-Rhone valley. West and north of these highlands a somewhat undulating plain extends to the coast, parted by low divides into the basins of the Seine, Loire, and Garonne. In the northeast a narrow area is drained by the Meuse and Moselle to the Rhine. Physically distinct from the rest of France, the Saone-Rhone valley opens a broad highway from the Mediterranean northward to the gate of Belfort, where a gap in the highlands gives easy passage to the Rhine at Basel. In the extreme south, the gate of Carcassonne connects the Mediterranean with the Garonne basin.

Climate and Agriculture. — The climate of the French lowlands is everywhere mild and genial, with little frost and a moderate rainfall. The peninsula of Brittany is cloudy and foggy, with no frost and a perennial vegetation. It furnishes dairy products, small fruits, and flowers for the London and Paris markets. Most of the people live near the coast and are engaged in sardine fishing. From north to south the number of rainy days decreases, and the warmth and dryness of the summer increase. In the basins of the Seine and Loire large crops of wheat, barley, and sugar beets are grown. Orchards, vineyards, and hop yards are extensive and profitable. The Garonne basin is famous for wine, tobacco, corn (maize), and the mulberry. The Mediterranean climate and products extend far up the Rhone valley, which is devoted to the culture of olives, oranges, almonds, figs, grapes, and the mulberry for feeding silkworms. The central plateau is bleak, wet, windy, and generally unproductive except of pasture.

Half the area of France is arable, and more people are engaged in agriculture than in any other industry or business. The land is cultivated in small plots and holdings, largely by hand labor, and in a very thorough and intensive manner. Stock is seldom turned out to pasture, but cattle and horses are kept by soiling with fresh fodder in stables. Hedges or fences of any kind are rare. There are no waste or untidy places, the roadsides and stream banks being fully utilized. The country resembles a well-kept garden. The French peasants are among the most industrious and thrifty people in the world. France leads all other countries in the production of wine, which has amounted in good years to 1,500,000,000 gallons. Much wine is imported from the United States, flavored with French wine, and reëxported with French labels. The wheat crop of about 370,000,000 bushels ranks third in the world, and is consumed at home. France produces one tenth of the beet sugar and one fifth of the raw silk used in the world. In variety and richness of agricultural products France is a highly favored country.

Minerals and Manufactures. — In the extreme north an extension of the Belgian coal field into France is a center of textile industry in cotton, woolen, linen, hemp, and jute. Lille (218,000) is the chief city. France uses one fourth of all wool manufactured. Fine laces woven by hand and of fabulous value are produced around Valenciennes, Alençon, and other towns. Small coal fields in the Rhone valley made possible the establishment of the greatest silk and velvet industries in the world at Lyons (524,000) and St. Etienne, now carried on by hydroelectric power. They use one fifth of all raw silk manufactured. Coal and iron ore at Creusot in the northern part of the central plateau, and at Nancy and Verdun in the northeast, locate there the chief iron works. Grenoble in the southern Alps has water power and is the seat of the largest fine glove manufacture in the world. Limoges, on the western edge of the plateau, and Sèvres, near Paris, are celebrated for fine china and porcelain, and Rouen for decorative glass.

These manufacturing centers are surpassed in value of product by Paris, which makes a specialty of articles of luxury, or fancy goods. These include brandies, cordials, essences, perfumes, paintings, clocks, mirrors, bronzes, gilt and inlaid furniture, jewelry, tapestries, carpets, millinery, ladies' dresses, and a great variety of articles which require and display artistic ability. The raw materials of such goods form a small part of their cost, and the profits are very large, because their high value lies in the beauty or attractiveness conferred by human skill.

Transportation. — The large rivers of France are all connected by canals and form an extensive system of navigated waterways. On account of the swift current, the Rhone is less available than the rest. One fifth of the total movement of goods is by

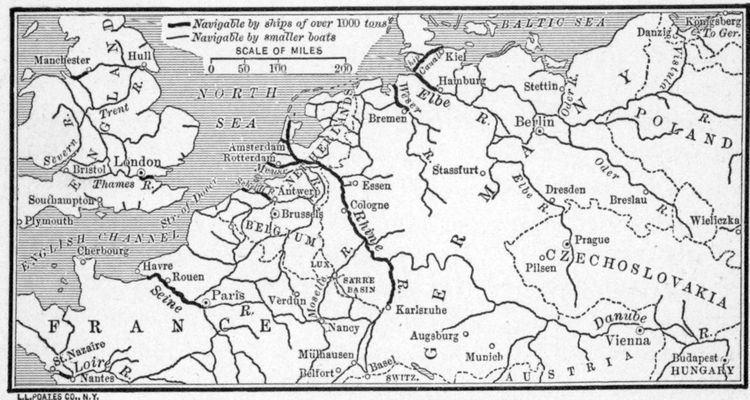

Fig. 344.—Waterways of Northwestern Europe.

water. The 30,000 miles of railway are organized in five great systems radiating from Paris. Those from the north through Paris to the east and southeast form a part of transcontinental lines to Marseilles, Genoa, Brindisi, Constantinople, and all parts of the Mediterranean.

Alsace-Lorraine. — In 1919 Germany restored to France the province of Alsace-Lorraine, having an area about as large as Connecticut and Rhode Island and a population of 1,870,000, most of whom speak German but have French sympathies. Thus the territory of France is extended to the Rhine, but a more important change is the transfer to France of the iron deposits of Lorraine, the largest in Europe, from which

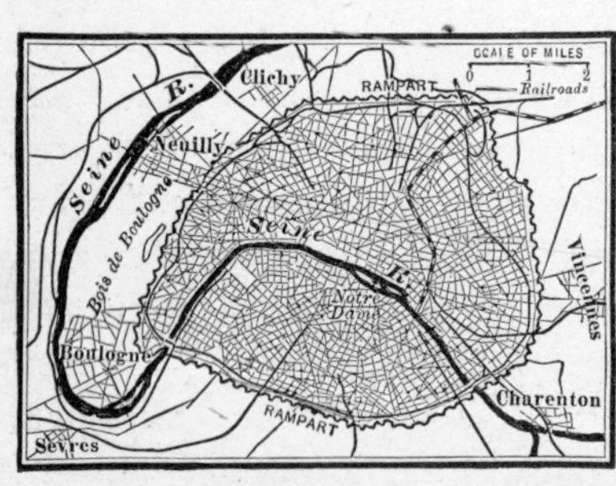

Fig. 345.—Paris.

the Germans obtained three fourths of their ore. As reparation for coal mines destroyed in northern France, Germany also cedes to France the ownership of the mines of the Sarre basin adjoining Lorraine. These changes may compensate for the almost total destruction of the northern textile industries of France and give her a leading position in manufactures.

Alsace contains rich deposits of potash and is the seat of cotton manufactures at Mulhouse and Colmar. The Rhine, now under international control, with numerous canals and railroads, makes this region a thoroughfare of communication between north and south and east and west. The principal cities are Strasbourg and Metz.

Paris (2,888,000), situated at the point of convergence of large tributaries of the Seine, is the third city of the world in population. As the capital of the French republic, it exerts a greater influence in the government than does the capital in any other country. It is a seaport and a great manufacturing center, but its fame rests more upon its beauties than its industries. Beginning as a fishing village on a small island in the Seine, it was fortified because of its strategic importance at a river confluence and the crossing of great highways of travel. The inclosing walls have been repeatedly enlarged in circumference, and the city is still surrounded by a rampart, now used as a boulevard. In the last fifty years it has been systematically rebuilt, care being taken to use historic palaces, churches, and public buildings to the best advantage. Museums, art galleries, opera houses, hotels, cafés, parks, avenues, boulevards, bridges, arches, columns, fountains, statuary, and all the devices of urban architecture are combined on a scale of magnificence scarcely approached by any other city. These features, together with the resources for education and amusement, and the artistic display of the shops, attract visitors and residents from all parts of the world, and form a valuable economic asset.

People. — On account of its "bridge" position, France has been the crossroads and meeting place of migrations for centuries, and the people are racially much mixed. They are prevailingly Baltic in the north, Alpine in the center, and Mediterranean in the south. The number is now about 40,000,000 and practically stationary, the increase in 40 years having been only 6 per cent. During that period, at peace under a republican government, they accumulated a greater wealth per capita than was possessed by any other people. In 1916 they imported foodstuffs and other materials worth above $5,000,000,000 and exported wine and manufactured articles, chiefly of silk and wool, amounting to $1,160,000,000. In foreign commerce and naval strength France stands third. In education and in artistic ability and products it is second to none.

Colonies. — In area of foreign possessions France is second only to Great Britain, but they are far less valuable than the British. Algiers and Tunis are practically outlying parts of France. Most of west Africa from the Mediterranean to the Kongo, Madagascar, and eastern Indo-China are under French control and exploitation.

Belgium

In natural conditions, people, language, and industries, southeastern Belgium is closely allied to northern France. It is a country of low hills, rich in coal, iron, zinc, and silver-lead, and dotted with mines and factories producing railway materials, firearms, machinery, glass, and chemicals. The inhabitants, called Walloons, speak French. Northwestern Belgium, or Flanders, is a marshy plain, little above sea level, and resembles Holland in being traversed by canals and protected by dikes. The inhabitants, called Flemings, speak a language differing little from Dutch. It is a center of extensive textile products of all kinds, of which Brussels carpets, Ghent linen, and Mechlin lace are the most noted. The soil of Belgium is generally productive and 60 per cent of the area is under cultivation in small farms. Cereal grains, potatoes, flax, and sugar beets are staple crops. Draft horses and dairy cattle are bred. Antwerp (321,000) on the Scheldt is accessible by the largest steamships and is the first seaport in tonnage in Europe. The position of Belgium makes it a natural gateway for central Europe and insures a large trade in goods passing through. Brussels (650,000), the capital, resembles Paris on a small scale.

Fig. 346. — Antwerp.
River and canals shown in black.

At the outbreak of the World War Belgium was a hive of industry, with the greatest density of railway mileage and population in Europe. In an area smaller than Massachusetts and Connecticut, it supported nearly 8,000,000 people in comfort and prosperity. During German occupation (1914–1918) it shared the fate of northern France. It was plundered of machinery and other movable property, many of its towns were destroyed, and large areas of its farm lands were laid waste. At the close of the war, Germany ceded to Belgium three small frontier districts and undertook obligations to repair a portion of the damages. With characteristic courage and industry, the Belgians are making good progress toward a restoration of their country to its normal condition.

Belgium controls the Kongo State in central Africa, having a population of 15,000,000, and is developing its resources by means of railroads and waterways.

Germany

Germany, with an area smaller than France, is by nature less favorably situated and endowed. The boundaries on the west and northeast are artificial, but in the south and southeast are mountainous. The Baltic and North sea coasts are bordered by barrier beaches and dunes, but broken by estuaries of great rivers. The Baltic plain has a glacial soil (Fig. 117), less fertile than that of the western lowlands, and includes large tracts of marsh and heath. The highlands south of the glacial boundary are a complex mosaic of low block plateaus, ridges, and basins. The principal ridges form an X, with a center at 50° N. Lat. and 12° E. Long., and have peaks between 4000 and 5000 feet in height.

Climate. — Germany lies on and beyond the eastern border of the West European province, and of Atlantic climate. It is a region of transition from oceanic to continental conditions, and the changes from west to east are marked. The North Sea ports are always open, while those of the Baltic are frozen from one to four months in the year. On account of the increase of elevation toward the south, the mean annual temperature is no higher at the foot of the Alps than on the Baltic shore. The warmest situations are in the southwestern valleys. Some of the western and southern slopes have a rainfall of 40 inches, but the average is less than 30 inches.

Use of the Land. — Ancient Germany was heavily forested. Under scientific forestry regulation, one fourth of the area is still devoted to growing timber, about one third oak, beech, and other hard woods, and the remainder larch, pine, fir, and spruce. Half of the land is arable. Rye, oats, potatoes, and sugar beets are the staple crops of the Baltic plain; wheat, barley, hops, grapes, and tobacco of the south. Rye is the common breadstuff. Germany leads the world in the production of potatoes and sugar beets. Potatoes serve not only for food but as a source of alcohol for fuel. Sugar and the famous Rhine wines are exported. Barley and hops go to make great quantities of beer, in brewing which Munich (595,000) is the leading city. Dairy cattle are bred in the lowlands, and sheep and horses on the highlands. Beet pulp from which the sugar has been extracted takes the place of corn in fattening hogs. Agriculture is highly scientific, and fertility is maintained by the use of artificial fertilizers, made from the slag of iron furnaces smelting phosphatic ore, potash salts mined at Stassfurt, and nitrate manufactured from air (p. 304). Nearly two fifths of the people are engaged in agriculture. Nevertheless there is an increasing importation of foodstuffs.

Minerals and Manufactures. — The coal fields of Germany are small, but in conjunction with iron ores and water transportation are made efficient. The chief iron district is on the Ruhr, a small tributary of the lower Rhine, where the famous Krupp steel works are located at Essen. The same district contains textile centers, — for silk at Crefeld, for woolen at Aachen, and for wool, cotton, and linen at Barmen and Elberfeld. Mining and manufactures are not confined to the lower Rhine. The mines of the Hartz and Erzgebirge (ore mountains) yield lead, silver, and copper. Saxony, of which Dresden (547,000) is the capital, is a hive of industry in textiles, metals, sugar, and chemicals. Germany surpasses other countries in the manufacture of chemicals, especially dyes from coal tar, medicines, electric apparatus, optical glass, and scientific instruments.

Transportation. — The remarkable industrial development of Germany has been made possible by an improved system of inland transportation, in which the waterways (Fig. 344) supplement the railways. All the great rivers traverse the blocks and ridges with little reference to present relief and are navigable nearly to their sources. The Rhine, Weser, and Elbe flow through the highlands and across the plain to the west of north. The Elbe, Oder, and Vistula are connected on the plain by a system of east-west cross valleys, the channels of ancient glacial drainage, which furnish easy routes for canals and railways. The river channels have been cleared, deepened, and straightened, the banks protected by masonry, and the natural routes connected by canals, providing in all over 8500 miles of waterway. As a great commercial highway from the Swiss frontier to the sea, the Rhine is now no less remarkable than for its picturesque scenery and romantic tradition. Cologne (516,000) is the principal German port on the river. There are 38,000 miles of railway, nearly all owned by the government and centering at Berlin.

Foreign Commerce. — The Baltic ports, Danzig, Stettin, and Kiel, have been connected with the North Sea by the Kaiser

Wilhelm ship canal, 61 miles long, from Kiel to the mouth of the Elbe. Harbor improvements at Hamburg (p. 169) have made it the second greatest seaport on the continent and the third in the world, while Bremen holds second place in Germany. The total value of foreign commerce has amounted to more than $3,900,000,000 annually. The largest imports are foodstuffs and raw materials, mostly from the United States. Of the exports 70 per cent is manufactured goods, of which Great Britain is the largest buyer.

Fig. 347. — Hamburg.
River and canals in black; the free port is inclosed by dotted line.

Cities. — There are twenty-three German cities of over 200,000 inhabitants and seven of over 500,000, of which Berlin, with 2,000,000, is first, and Hamburg, with 932,000, is second.

Political and Social Conditions. — The German Republic consists of twenty-six federated states, of which Prussia is the largest. The population of about 60,000,000 gives a high density, amounting in Saxony to 820 to the square mile. To support such a population, it is necessary to make the most of the rather meager resources of the country, to maintain efficient industries and to extend foreign commerce.

The Netherlands, Denmark, and Sweden

The kingdom of the Netherlands, commonly called Holland (*holtland*, woodland), the delta land of the Rhine, Meuse, and Scheldt, about as large as the southeastern quarter of Louisiana, which it resembles, has reclaimed three eighths of its territory from the sea by building 1000 miles of dikes. The lands thus held are called polders, and are drained by constant pumping. The soil is very rich, and is used for meadows and dairy cattle, and for the culture of grain, potatoes, sugar beets, flax, and flowers. Gardens of tulips, dahlias, and hyacinths cover hundreds of acres. Half the land is pasture and one fifth sand dunes and heaths. The common fuel is peat. Many of the cities are built upon a foundation of piles made from timber floated down the Rhine. The means of internal communication are the most complete in the world. There are 3000 miles of navigable waterway, including 2000 miles of canals, 9500 miles of roadway, and 2000 miles of railway. On the canals barges are propelled by wind, animal, and human power. Many of the people live in boats. Wind power is used so extensively that Dutch domestic economy may be said to be based on wind and water. "God made the rest of the world, but man made Holland."

The wealth and importance of Holland are due to its position commanding the trade of the Rhine and the Baltic plain. The Dutch were for centuries the chief distributors of Oriental goods to western Europe, and they now take toll both ways of goods in transit to and from Germany and Russia. Their great seaports of Rotterdam (500,000) and Amsterdam (641,000) are connected with the ocean by ship canals. Amsterdam is built upon 90 islands connected by 300 bridges. The principal streets are double, with a canal in the middle, bringing land and water into the closest possible relations. Holland forms an insular base for over-sea traffic inferior only to Great Britain.

Fig. 348. — The Netherlands.

Foreign Possessions. — To the home country the Dutch East Indies form an appropriate and valuable annex. They include Java, Sumatra, Celebes, parts of Borneo and New Guinea, the Moluccas, and many other small islands, having an aggregate population of about 47,000,000. The

Dutch are very successful in the management of the native peoples, in conducting with their aid plantations of sugar cane, coffee, cocoa, tea, rubber, tobacco, cinchona, and spices, and in mining tin.

The 6,700,000 people of the Netherlands have a density of 535 to the square mile, rising in some provinces to over 1000. Coöperation in creating and maintaining their land against the assaults of the sea has transformed a horde of fishermen and pirates into a highly prosperous and civilized people. The existence of this little kingdom in the midst and in the way of more powerful neighbors is made possible in part by the defensible nature of the country. Cutting the dikes would cover half the land with water too shallow for shipping and too deep for infantry and cavalry. Invasion would be possible only in the winter, when land and water are frozen.

Denmark is a little larger than Holland, but has less than half the population. It comprises a peninsula and islands which command the entrance to the Baltic Sea. Its position accounts for its independence and neutrality, and for the commercial importance and population of its capital, Copenhagen (506,000). The land, once covered with beech forests, is poor, but in no other country has scientific dairy farming become so general and successful. Sugar beets are the chief crop, but most of the land is under grass and the principal exports are butter, eggs, and bacon.

Sweden. — Most of the people of Sweden live in the southern part of the country, which is a lowland highly diversified by hills, lakes, marshes, eskers, and moraines. Forests of fir, pine, and beech cover the rougher parts and constitute an important source of wealth. Nine per cent of the total area of Sweden is under cultivation and supports more than half the population. The principal crops are oats, rye, and potatoes. Sweden is rich in minerals, especially iron, the deposits of ore at Gellivara, north of the Arctic circle, being among the largest and purest in the world. The notable exports are iron ore and metal, timber, furniture, wood pulp, paper, and matches. The natural waterways have been improved by canals and form a steamer route by way of the lakes, Wenner, Wetter, and Mälar, through the heart of the country. The capital, Stockholm (413,000), built on the islands and shores of Mälar, is one of the most beautiful cities in Europe.

CHAPTER XXX

THE CENTRAL EUROPEAN PROVINCE

Physiography and Climate. — The northern part of the Central European province lies upon the Interior and Baltic-Black plains, the southern among broken-block basins and folded mountains (Fig. 336). The prominent relief features are the eastern Alps, the Bohemian basin between the eastern arms of the X (p. 448), the Hungarian basin within the sickle-shaped curve of the Carpathians, the Roumanian basin between the Transylvanian Alps and the Balkans, and the mountainous plateau of the Balkan Peninsula. The plains portions contain a hydrographic center above 1000 feet, from which rivers flow northwest to the Baltic and southeast to the Caspian and Black seas. Among the latter is the Volga, the longest river in Europe. The southern portion is "Danube land," drained by the largest river in Europe to the Black Sea. The climate is continental and extreme, with a rainfall not much above or below 20 inches. In summer thunderstorms are frequent, and the winters are long, with persistent snow.

Russia and Its Successors

European Russia lies in the Arctic, Siberian, Central, and Interior provinces and extends over the Interior, Baltic-Black, and Caspian-Ob plains (Fig. 336). The area is about 1,600,000 square miles and the population about 121,000,000.

Soil and Vegetation. — More than half of Russia is covered with good glacial soil resembling that of the glacial plain of North America (Fig. 117). Near the margin of the glacial drift, and extending beyond it between the Volga and Dniester rivers nearly to the Black Sea, is the "black earth" region, where the soil and vegetation resemble those of the American prairies. The northern half of Russia is covered by tundra and the great Siberian coniferous forest (Fig. 192). Southward the vegetation changes successively to mixed forest, then summer forests of oak and ash, then a belt of prairie, passing finally into arid steppes around the Caspian Sea. The products are in the north almost exclusively timber and furs; in the cleared lands south of latitude 60°, rye, oats, flax, and hemp; and on the black earth, wheat and sugar beets; while the treeless steppes are suitable only for grazing. Roughly, about one third of Russia is forest, one third arable, and one third grazing land. The Russian plain produces four fifths of the flax, three fifths of the hemp, half the rye, one fourth of the oats and barley, one fifth of the potatoes and sugar beets, and one sixth of the wheat of the world. It supports 20,000,000 horses, 30,000,000 cattle, and 40,000,000 sheep and goats. Nine tenths of the people are employed in agriculture, but the methods are generally primitive and the yields per acre small. The land is held in great estates by the nobility or by peasant communities, called *mirs*. Ignorance, poverty, and a state little above serfdom prevail among the masses.

Minerals and Manufactures. — Russia is rich in minerals. Gold, copper, and platinum are mined near the Urals. Coal and iron are abundant and occur near together in three districts, — in the east near the Ural Mountains, in the center south of Moscow, and in the south on the Donetz and Dnieper rivers. In the extreme southeast, on the shores of the Caspian, is one of the richest petroleum fields in the world (Fig. 288). Its burning springs have been held sacred by the Fire Worshippers for centuries. The iron industry is largest in the central and southern districts. Cotton is manufactured around Moscow and Petrograd, and linen, hemp, and wool in many cities. The domestic supplies of timber, grain, sugar, and hides give rise to corresponding industries. Along the border of forest and prairie, leather is tanned with birch bark. Distillery and brewing products are of greater value than any other class of Russian manufactures.

Transportation. — The Russian plain is so flat that drainage is poor, and much of it is marshy and liable to floods during the spring melting of snow. The fall of the rivers is slight, and they are consequently slow, shallow, and crooked. During several months of the year they are blocked by ice. Materials for road construction are scarce, and means of communication are everywhere inadequate. Winter, when land and water are solid, is the season of active movement of men and goods, by horse sledges. In spite of the difficulties, the great rivers are the principal highways, and are navigated to the total extent of 50,000 miles. Canals between the Volga and Neva connect the Baltic with the Caspian, and between the Vistula, Düna, and Dnieper connect it with the Black Sea. The Volga system is the most important waterway, but it does not give access to the open sea. A canal 40 miles long from the Volga at Tsaritsyn to the Don would remove this difficulty. A ship canal from the Baltic to the Black Sea is quite feasible and would repay a very large cost. Railway construction presents few difficulties, but the mileage is less than that of Germany, and the tonnage little more than that of France. Moscow and Petrograd are the principal railroad centers, and the network is closest in the agricultural region. Petrograd is the western terminus of the Siberian Railway, extending 5000 miles across Eurasia to the Pacific coast. It is a competitor of the American railways and of the Suez and Panama canals, for trade between the Orient and western Europe.

Foreign Commerce. — Russia has no port on the high seas except Archangel and Alexandrovsk on the Arctic Ocean. The Baltic port of Petrograd (Fig. 349) has been artificially improved and is most important for trade with western Europe and America. On the Black Sea, Odessa is the chief port for exports of wheat. Astrakhan, on the Caspian, is the center of important sturgeon fisheries.

Cities. — In Russia there are twenty-five cities of over 100,000 inhabitants, of which Petrograd (2,133,000), Moscow (1,817,000), and Odessa (631,000) are the largest. Petrograd was built by Peter the Great in the eighteenth century upon islands in the marshes of the Neva, in order to remove the capital from inland Moscow to a site on the Baltic. It is now the principal port, with a channel deepened to 20 feet. In winter powerful ice breakers are used to keep the harbor open.

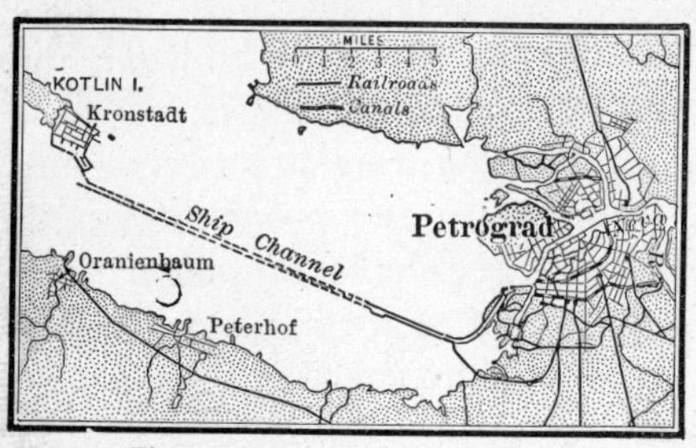

Fig. 349. — Petrograd and vicinity.

Asiatic Russia. — Russia has no foreign possessions, and does not need any, because of her vast contiguous Asiatic empire, sparsely inhabited and with plenty of room for expanding population. Siberia, Turkestan, and other Asiatic provinces have an area of 6,294,000 square miles and a population of 30,000,000. The area of the whole Russian Empire is nearly equal to that of North America, or more than one seventh of the land surface of the globe, and its population is one tenth of the human species.

People. — Three fourths of the people of European Russia live in the Central European province, west of the Volga-Don and south of the Siberian railway. In the west there are many Germans and Jews, and in the east many Tatars and other Mongolian peoples.

The backward state of civilization in Russia is due to several causes, all arising primarily from geographic conditions. The territory is continental and interior, shut in from stimulating contact with the sea (p. 158). The Urals and the Caspian form no effective barrier on the east, and the Russian plain is an extension of the great plains of Asia, from which successive waves of human invasion have swept westward. All the large rivers lead toward Asia or the Arctic and encourage intercourse away from the European and Atlantic centers of enlightenment.

The vast forests and marshes, the scarcity of materials for road construction, and the severe winters enforce upon each community an unfavorable degree of isolation.

In 1917 the tyrannical rule of the Czar was overthrown. The government fell into the hands of workmen's soviets, or trade union councils, controlled by leaders who seem to be even more oppressive than the Czar. The nobility and people of wealth and education have been generally plundered or killed. The masses are illiterate and so ignorant that their struggle for liberty and justice is likely to be a long one. How much of the territory of the former Russian Empire will remain under Russian control is uncertain. Out of it several new and independent states have been erected or projected.

Poland

The old Kingdom of Poland, once a great power extending from the Baltic to the Black Sea, was divided more than a century ago between Russia, Prussia, and Austria. A territory about as large as Ohio, Indiana, and Kentucky, in which a majority of the population are Poles, numbering about 15,000,000, has been declared an independent republic. It stands between Germany and Russia and extends from the Carpathians to the Baltic. Its boundaries are not fully determined, but it certainly includes some of the most valuable provinces of the three former empires, — Russia, Germany, and Austria. Most of the country lies in the basin of the Vistula River, and while there are many lakes and marshes, the soil is as productive as any part of the Baltic Plain. The chief cereal crop is rye, while oats, potatoes, and sugar beets are extensively grown. Much of the land is held in large estates by German, Polish, or Russian owners and worked by poor Polish peasants. In the south, along the foot of the mountains, mines of coal and iron form the foundation for industrial centers of the first rank. The southwest corner contains a system of mines and mills producing a variety of iron and steel wares. Not far away, cotton manufacture has made

Lodz (500,000) grow as rapidly as some American cities. Warsaw (900,000), the old capital and chief railway center, is the seat of a variety of factory products, especially leather and sugar. Its university is an ancient center of learning.

On the Baltic coast the German province of East Prussia is cut off from the rest of Germany by Polish territory. At the mouth of the Vistula, the German city of Danzig has been made independent, but its use by Poland as a seaport has been secured. The Poles have been subjected to the influence of west European culture and in intelligence, religion, and spirit resemble the French more than they do the Russians. The resources, industries, and communications of Poland favor the maintenance of a strong and prosperous state. As a buffer between Russia and Germany, it holds a difficult position. The present population of about 25,000,000 may be doubled by annexation of adjoining Russian and Lithuanian territory.

The Baltic States and Finland

The eastern coastland of the Baltic formed a part of the old Russian Empire but is not occupied by Slavic people. In the south, adjoining Poland, the Lithuanians and Letts, numbering about 5,500,000, are descendants of a primitive Caucasian people not closely related to other Europeans. On both sides of the Gulf of Finland the Esths and Finns (about 4,000,000) are Mongolian peoples, allied to the Tatars and Turks. Of these regions Finland, in the Siberian natural province, is the most advanced and important. It lies on the Baltic Peneplain, is studded with low, rounded hills and lake basins, and is largely forested, resembling the region south of Hudson Bay (pp. 117–119, 342). The population is concentrated near the coast and has been much modified in body and mind by Swedish blood and culture. Oats, potatoes, rye, and barley are raised. Horses and dairy cattle are bred. The most valuable products are timber and wood pulp. Abundant hydroelectric power favors textile mills and other mechanical works recently established. The people are thrifty and intelligent, Helsingfors (170,000), the capital, being the seat of a famous university. The Finns have never willingly submitted to Russian rule and have now established an independent republic about as large as Wisconsin and Michigan.

The Baltic States, Lithuania, Letvia, and Esthonia, though now independent, are weak and in an unsettled condition. They are not willing to submit again to Russian rule. The Lithuanians are equally unwilling to unite with Poland. The loss of these provinces is a severe blow to Russia, since it cuts off access to the Baltic Sea and Atlantic Ocean through the ports of Riga, Reval, and Libau, and leaves Petrograd, its only remaining Baltic port, on the extreme border of the state.

Ukraine

The oldest center of civilization in Russia is not Moscow but Kief (610,000), the holy city of the Ukrainians or Little Russians. These people, about 30,000,000 in number, occupy an area in southern Russia nearly as large as Texas. It includes a large part of the famous black earth region, "the granary of Europe," and produces most of the wheat exported through the port of Odessa (630,000). It is a smooth plain, green in spring and summer, a brown waste in autumn, and white with snow in winter. The villages extend along the streams where water is perennial. Windmills are everywhere used to grind grain. In the east the richest Russian coal and iron fields occur on the Donetz River. In the west the middle and upper classes are largely Polish and in the northeast Great Russian, and in the cities are many Jews.

In 1917 the Ukrainians set up an independent republic, which they have hardly been able to maintain against either the Germans or the Great Russians. A stable Ukrainian state would be one of the largest and strongest among the new nations of Europe. It would be as disastrous to Russia as the secession of the southern states would have been to the United States. A Russia cut off from the Black Sea and the Baltic would cease to be a European power and become practically Asiatic.

The Successors of Austria-Hungary

The former dual empire of Austria-Hungary contained an assemblage of races and languages as diversified as its physical features. It was held together chiefly by the personal power of the Hapsburg rulers and, as a result of their defeat in the World War, their " ramshackle empire " fell to pieces. The fragments have been reorganized on the basis of race and language and the new boundaries have been better adjusted to the physical features.

Czechoslovakia. — The Czechs and Slovaks of the northern provinces of Austria-Hungary have shared with their Polish kinsfolk the advantages of long contact with western civilization and have acquired marked superiority to the East Slavs. They occupy the basin of Bohemia, the plateau of Moravia-Silesia, and the mountain region of the western Carpathians. Bohemia is a depressed block surrounded by a high rim and its dominant position between the Baltic Plain and the Danube valley has given it the name of " the citadel of Europe." The central plain is a land of rich, well-cultivated farms and orchards, noted for cereals, potatoes, sugar beets, hops, fruit, and bees. The highland rim contains almost every useful mineral, of which coal and lignite are the most valuable. Along the faulted margin of the block are numerous mineral springs, of which those at Karlsbad and Marienbad have a world-wide reputation. Moravia and Silesia are natural counterparts of Bohemia, though somewhat less highly favored. A dense and industrious population has developed an industrial life unsurpassed in central Europe. To the staple industries of iron, steel, textiles, and sugar has been added the manufacture of leather, paper, chemicals, and beer. Bohemian glass and porcelain have been famous for centuries. Bohemia is drained by the upper Elbe, which escapes through the mountain rim by the Saxon gate; Moravia by the March southward to the Danube. These are the natural outlets for commerce.

The people of these lands comprise about 6,000,000 Czechs, who are among the best educated people in Europe, and about 3,300,000 Germans, who occupy solidly the mountain rim and form a large part of the town population. The Slovaks, a relatively backward, peasant people, numbering about 2,000,000, living in the Carpathian uplands and valleys, have united with the Czechs to form a Czechoslovak republic. This may also include 2,000,000 Ruthenians, or Little Russians, on the slopes of the middle Carpathians. The new state has an area a little larger than New York and a population of about 13,500,000, sparse in the mountains and very dense in the industrial districts. It is a vigorous, well-equipped nation, subject only to the commercial disadvantage of inland position, with trade connections through the territory of rival or hostile neighbors. The internationalization of the Elbe, Oder, and Danube is designed to secure their free use by all nations. Prague (225,000), at the head of navigation on the Moldau, a branch of the Elbe, is the capital city, noted for its university, medical schools, and hospitals.

Austria. — The new Austria, the heart of the old empire, is left almost without a body. It includes only the northeastern spurs and slopes of the Alps and the lowlands of the Danube valley in the Austrian gate between the Alps and Bohemia. It is a little larger than South Carolina and has a population of about 6,500,000 Germans. Two thirds of it is mountainous and resembles closely in scenery and conditions of life the Alps of Switzerland (pp. 469–470). There are mines of lignite, iron, and other metals. The lowlands are similar to those of Bohemia. Vienna (about 2,000,000), at the intersection of roads and waterways leading to the natural gates of "Danube land," has been the political and commercial center of that region for a thousand years. Under the Hapsburgs, the city attained a wealth and magnificence scarcely second to those of Paris. Since its tributary area and population have been reduced to one eighth of their former dimensions, Vienna seems doomed to stagnation and decay.

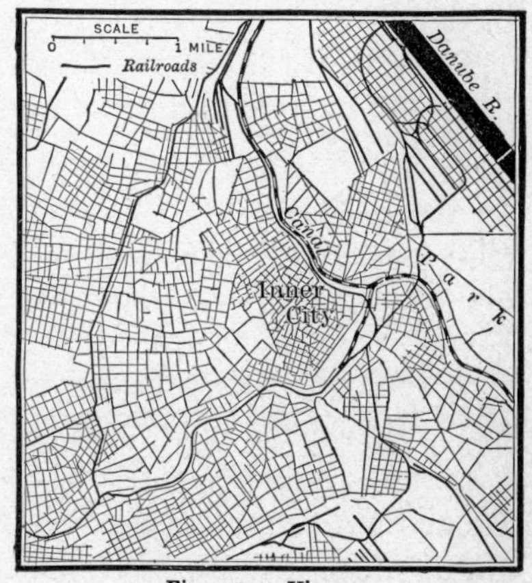

Fig. 350. — Vienna.

Hungary. — The Hungarian Basin, the largest of the down-faulted blocks of Europe and about the size of Nevada, is walled in by the Carpathians on the north and east, the Alps on the west, and a rugged plateau on the south. Its surface is so flat that the rivers are crooked, sluggish, and subject to overflow. The climate is continental and aggravated by the reduction of the rainfall to 20 inches or less. It is a treeless steppe, covered with tall grasses and flowers in spring, hot and dried up in summer and autumn and swept by cold winds in winter. The basin, with its surrounding slopes, is occupied by about 10,000,000 Magyars, or Hungarians, descendants of a Mongolian people who invaded Europe in the ninth century. More or less mingled with them on the borders and also forming solid enclaves, or distinct islands of population, are nearly as many Slavs, Roumanians, and Germans. About half the land is arable and seven tenths of the people are farmers. The country was given over to great herds of sheep and horses and both are still bred; but as in the American steppe region, the grazing lands have been invaded by the plow until they have become one of the largest sources of corn and wheat in Europe.

After the World War, territories occupied by large masses of Germans, Slavs, and Roumanians were included in other states and the area of the new Hungary was reduced to that of Indiana. The population of about 8,500,000 is strongly Magyar with a considerable German element. Budapest (880,000), a double city united by bridges across the Danube, is the capital and commercial center, noted for large flour mills. Its tributary area has been reduced to one fourth and its tributary population to one half their former magnitude. Like Austria, Hungary is now of less importance than its neighbors, having small resources, surrounded by unfriendly rivals, and with no outlets except through their territories. Like the Rhine, Elbe, Oder, and Vistula, the Danube has been internationalized and removed from control by any local power. The rapids at the Iron Gate are passed by a canal and the river is navigable to the German frontier.

Roumania

While the former great powers of Central Europe have been broken up by the World War, the area and population of Roumania have been more than doubled. The Roumanian people are quite distinct from the Slavs and Magyars who surround them, owing to descent from a body of Roman soldiers colonized on the lower Danube in the second century A.D. Their features, language, customs, and name show their Italian origin. Their total number is about 13,000,000. Their homeland is the basin between the Balkans and the elbow of the Carpathians, an extension of the south Russian plain. Its alluvial soil, built up from the waste of the mountains, is even richer than the black earth. Hence Roumania is one of the granaries of Europe, producing crops of corn, wheat, barley, and oats comparable with those of Ohio. Beans, potatoes, sugar beets, and tobacco flourish, and the lower mountain slopes are planted with orchards and vineyards. A continuous petroleum field extends along the mountain front, making Roumania second to Russia in the production of European oil. The same area also contains coal, iron, copper, lead, and other minerals. The streams from the mountain cañons furnish water power. The Roumanian is by inheritance a peasant farmer and herdsman and does not take kindly to machinery; hence manufactures are poorly developed.

Driven back and forth by pressure from the Magyars, Turks, and Russians in turn, the Roumanians have spread eastward into Bessarabia, across the mountains into Transylvania, and westward over the edge of the Hungarian Plain. These territories have now been added to the original Kingdom of Roumania, although they contain large enclaves of Magyar, German, and Turkish people. The mountains are generally covered with forests of oak, beech, and pine, and, besides supplying timber, support herds of goats, sheep, and swine. Transylvania is a plateau with level upland pastures and fertile open valleys. Bessarabia is adapted to grain, with high grade steppe pasture in the south. With a backbone of forested mountains rich in minerals, flanked on three sides by wide and fertile plains, few countries in the world possess such a balanced variety of surface and resources.

Roumania commands the mouth of the Danube and the Black Sea ports of Galatz, Sulina, and Constantza. The capital, Bucharest (340,000), is proud of its title " the Paris of the East." Greater Roumania is about as large as New York, Pennsylvania,

New Jersey, and Maryland, and has a population of about 16,000,000. Protected from interference by more powerful neighbors, it is equipped to maintain a high degree of prosperity.

The Balkan Peninsula

The Balkan Peninsula forms a physical unit strongly contrasted with the plains which bound it on the north. Few regions in the world possess a structure and relief so varied and confused. As a whole, it is a plateau broken into a large number of small elevated blocks and depressed basins and traversed by two main mountain ranges. On the western border the Dinaric Alps rise abruptly from the Adriatic. They are mainly a mass of porous limestone, into which the rainfall sinks, leaving the surface arid and bare. Drainage is generally underground and the lack of transverse valleys renders the region almost inaccessible from the sea. The precipitous coast is bordered by rocky islands, which have been compared to gnawed bones. In the east the Balkan mountains form a continuation of the Carpathian system, curving eastward from the Iron Gate to the Black Sea and sending a spur southward to the Ægean. Midway between these mountain systems, the valleys of the Morava and Vardar rivers form a continuous and easy passage from the Danube to the Gulf of Salonica, with a branch southeastward to Constantinople. The Black Sea coast is smooth and without good natural harbors. The climate, vegetation, and agricultural products are continental, passing into Mediterranean near the coast.

The population of the Balkan Peninsula consists of people of diverse races, languages, and religions, mingled together in extreme confusion. The people of the town generally differ widely from those of the surrounding country. The inhabitants of neighboring villages are, in some cases, so unlike that they have nothing to do with each other. The original Slavic population was subjected for centuries to Turkish plunder, massacre, and misrule and, unable to act together, has suffered from political and social unrest. With relief from foreign oppression, an opportunity has come for self-government and national development.

Jugoslavia. — The South Slavs of the former Austro-Hungarian provinces have united with those of Serbia and Montenegro to form a Serb-Croat-Slovene state, commonly known as Jugoslavia. Its territory includes the western plateau and mountains and a part of the Hungarian Plain. It is about four fifths as large as Roumania and has a population of about 11,000,000, of which seven tenths are Slavic. The plateau portion is a land of wooded hill pastures and fertile river valleys, industriously tilled by hardy farmers, although their methods are rather primitive. The staple crop is corn, but the other cereals are important. Orchards of plums, from which a native brandy is made, form a special feature. Live stock is more important than crops. The hills are grazed by sheep and goats, and pigs are fattened on the acorns and beechnuts of the forest. The common draft animals are cattle. There is considerable mineral wealth as yet slightly developed. The coast of the Adriatic is practically inaccessible except at the port of Fiume, which is claimed by Italy, but may be made a free city and port like Danzig. Jugoslavia has trade outlets also by way of the Danube and the Vardar valley. The capital is the Serbian city of Belgrade on the Danube.

Bulgaria. — Bulgaria comprises the main Balkan ranges and intervening basins and borders the Black Sea. Admixture with Mongolian invaders has made the Bulgarians more Asiatic than the other South Slavs, with whom they are not friendly. The main resources of the country are obtained from farms and forests. Roses grown for the manufacture of perfume are a special product of the southern slopes. Bulgaria is crossed by the Oriental Railway from Paris and Vienna to Constantinople and Bagdad and has ports on the Black Sea. The Bulgarians dispute with Roumania possession of the Dobrudja, a sterile plateau between the Danube and the Black Sea, and lay claim to a part of Thrace on the Ægean coast. Bulgaria is the size of Ohio and has a population of about 4,300,000. Sofia (103,000) is the capital. There are no other large cities.

Albania. — About 1,000,000 people of an ancient race, very distinct from their neighbors, inhabit the rugged mountains at the southeastern end of the Adriatic Sea. These Albanians are shepherds and small farmers, divided into many tribes and clans, having little intercourse with one another and no political unity. They are fierce fighters and have never been subjugated even by the Turks. They resist foreign control, but their territory, a little larger than Massachusetts, is claimed by the Jugoslavs, Greeks, and Italians. The Italians have possession of the region around Valona, a good seaport which commands the entrance to the Adriatic. An independent Albania may come into existence.

Macedonia and Thrace. — The Ægean coastland of the Balkan Peninsula has a strikingly ragged border of fingerlike projections, gulfs, and islands. The people consist of a confused mixture of Slavs, Turks, Greeks, and Jews, numbering about 2,000,000. The principal value of the region lies in its ports, of which Salonica, the natural outlet of the whole Balkan Peninsula, is a point of great commercial and military importance. This port, with Macedonia, including most of the coast region, is now a part of Greece. In the east Thrace has been removed from the control of Bulgaria and Turkey and assigned to Greece.

Constantinople (1,000,000). — No city in Europe has a more eventful history or a more commanding site than Constantinople on the Bosporus. It is the toll gate through which the commerce of the Black Sea, including that of Russia and the Danubian countries, must pass, and it is a bridge between Europe and Asia. The rival and successor of Rome in world supremacy, it became the religious center of the Mohammedan world and has been held by the Turks since 1453, but for a long time past only because the Christian powers were unwilling to trust it to any one of their own number. It remains the seat of the Turkish government and the residence of the Sultan, but the city and strait are virtually under international control.

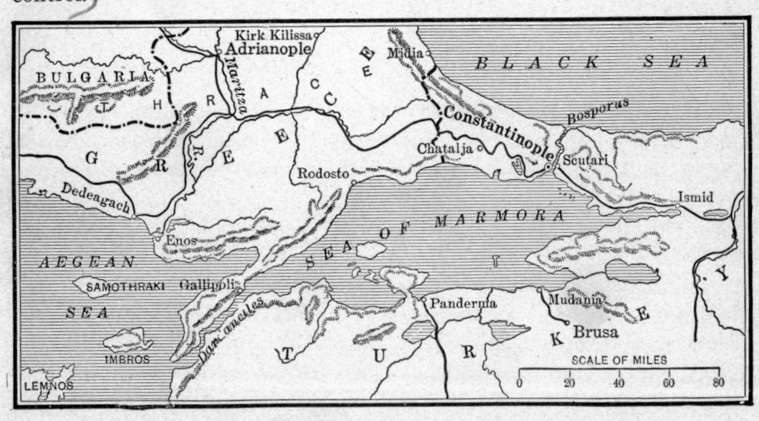

Fig. 351. — Constantinople and vicinity.

CHAPTER XXXI

THE MEDITERRANEAN PROVINCE

The Mediterranean Sea and its coast lands are the theater in which has developed the oldest, highest, and most enduring civilization the world has ever seen. Such a civilization could arise and persist only under favorable geographic conditions. The sea itself is a great cleft in the continental platform due largely to the subsidence of detached blocks of the earth crust, leaving ridges upstanding between. It is almost cut in two by the ridge of the Apennine-Atlas mountains. It consists of three basins, each of which is more than two miles deep (Fig. 336). The eastern and largest basin opens westward through the shallow strait between Sicily and Tunis. The middle and smallest basin is nearly inclosed by Italy, Sicily, Sardinia, and Corsica. The western basin is connected with the Atlantic by the Strait of Gibraltar, only 15 miles wide. The Mediterranean is more than 2000 miles long, and its area is about 1,000,000 square miles. The shallow arm of the Adriatic extends northward 500 miles, while in the northeast the Ægean, Dardanelles, Marmora, and Bosporus connect with the basin of the Black Sea, which extends 700 miles eastward and has an area of 180,000 square miles. The Mediterranean washes the shores of three continents which it at once separates and connects, after the balanced fashion of minor oceanic waters (p. 157).

The northern coast lands of the Mediterranean are high and traversed by the curved and branching ranges of the Spanish Sierras, Pyrenees, Alps, Apennines, Pindus, Rhodope, Taurus, and other lesser mountains. The Rhone valley and the Dardanelles-Bosporus depression are the only considerable gaps in the barrier. The African coast land is mountainous from

Gibraltar to Tunis, but the eastern basin is bounded by the desert lowlands of the Sahara to the delta of the Nile. The eastern parts of the Mediterranean and the adjacent countries are often called *the Levant*.

The climate of the Mediterranean province, already described (p. 218), owes much of its genial character to the vast body of water, the surface layer of which, 1200 feet thick, has a temperature of about 70°, and acts in winter as an efficient hot-water heating plant. The Sahara on the south and the mountains on the north include between them a physiographic, climatic, economic, and human unit, in which European, African, and Asiatic characters are well blended.

The Alps. — The Alps sweep in a great hook-shaped curve from the Gulf of Genoa, west, north, and east to the Danube at Vienna. The outer margin measures 820 miles, and the inner 470 miles. The width varies from 80 to 150 miles, and the area is about 90,000 square miles, equal to that of Great Britain. The Alps are not a wall but a broad slab with steep edges about two miles thick, an incised plateau lifted into the higher layer of the atmosphere. The central core of the system is of crystalline rocks, with limestones and sandstones on the flanks, all folded, crumpled, contorted, and thrust over and under one another in the most complex manner. The highest peaks are in the central French-Swiss-Italian portion, and are from 13,000 to over 15,000 feet high. The boss of St. Gothard is a center from which streams flow in all directions to the Rhone, Rhine, and Po. The waste of the Alps has contributed to build up the plains of France, Holland, Germany, Hungary, Roumania, and Italy. In the western and central Alps the passes are 6000 to 7000 feet above the sea. In the eastern Alps the peaks and passes are somewhat lower than in the central. The climatic, economic, and human conditions change abruptly at the southern margin of the Alps from Atlantic, temperate, and German to Mediterranean, subtropical, and Italian.

The Alps are a region of scenic beauty perhaps unrivaled in

the world. Sharp, frost-riven peaks, horns, and needles rising above snow- and ice-filled cirques, glacier-worn valleys, waterfalls, and deep, narrow, or winding lakes form a combination of elements which seem to belong to another world (Figs. 61, 102, 103, 105). The Alps are crossed by many carriage roads (Fig. 295) and footpaths, and by six trunk-line railroads. One French line passes through the Mont Cenis tunnel, 7.6 miles long, at an altitude of 4380 feet, and another by way of the broad upper Rhone valley to the Simplon tunnel, 12.3 miles long, and

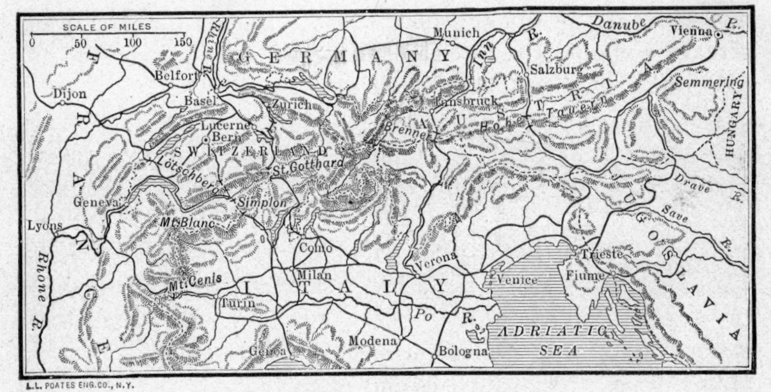

Fig. 352.—Railroads and passes in the Alps.

only 2300 feet above the sea. One German line passes up the valley of the Reuss and through the St. Gothard tunnel (Fig. 296), 9.3 miles long, at a height of 3785 feet, and another by the valley of the Inn crosses the Brenner pass at a height of 4470 feet. An Austrian line from Salzburg crosses the Hohe Tauern through a tunnel 5.3 miles long at a height of 4000 feet. A 9-mile tunnel to connect Bern with the Simplon line has been opened at Lötschberg. In each case, the descent on the Italian side is accomplished by way of steep and difficult valleys. The line from Vienna to Venice by the Semmering pass, 2970 feet above the sea, has easier grades.

The rainfall in the Alps varies from 20 to 90 inches, and the temperature from subtropical to polar. The northern valleys are favored by winds which descend the slope and are warmed by compression.

Alpine Economics. — Alpine climates, products, and life vary chiefly in a vertical direction. The small areas of arable land in the valleys below 2500 feet produce rye, oats, potatoes, and hay, and on the southern slope the vine and the mulberry. Cattle and goats are pastured on the middle slopes and furnish butter, cheese, and condensed milk. Above the pastures are forests, and uninhabitable waste land amounting to more than half the whole area. Dairying is the chief occupation. Cattle and goats are wintered in the valleys, and in spring are driven by the men and boys up to the high Alps (pastures), following the retreating snow. The women remain in the valleys to cultivate the crops, while the men and boys make butter and cheese on the mountains. Most of the high pastures and chalets can be reached only by footpaths, and this entails a heavy burden of porterage in getting dairy products to market and provisions to the herdsmen. Every peasant man, woman, and child is a beast of burden, carrying a conical basket of appropriate size fastened to the shoulders. Hay and firewood are often gathered from difficult and dangerous places and carried home in bundles.

Fig. 353. — Porterage in Switzerland.

Switzerland includes not only the central Alps, but the low limestone folds of the Jura (Fig. 39) in the west and the hilly plateau between. The plateau is much superior to the mountains in soil, climate, and products, yet the country imports cereals, meat, wine, and timber, as well as minerals, and pays for them largely with cotton, silk, and straw goods, machinery, and small articles, such as watches, clocks, and jewelry. Wood carving, straw plaiting, lace making, and other hand industries are carried on by the peasants in their homes during the winter. Water power is used, especially in electrochemical works. Many of the people are engaged in caring for the millions of tourists and foreign visitors, who are a source of large income. There is no great wealth and little poverty among the people. The railways include many cogwheel and cable roads, designed for sight-seers; some of them reach a height of 10,000 feet. Nearly all the lines, as well as many miles of post roads, are owned and managed by the state.

The Swiss Confederation is composed of twenty-two cantons, and the government is the most democratic in the world. The public school system, including seven universities, is not inferior to that of Germany. Zurich, Basel, and Geneva are the only towns having more than 100,000 people. The population is 3,750,000, of which about 70 per cent speak German, 20 per cent French, and 8 per cent Italian. This small state, filling a chink between four great powers, has been able to win and maintain its independence because mountain lands are not very attractive to invaders and are easily defended, while mountain life fosters a hardy and liberty-loving people.

Italy

"Beyond the Alps lies Italy" is a concrete expression of the joys which follow after passing through hardships and perils. A European peninsula 600 miles long, which lacks but 100 miles of joining Africa, Italy holds a commanding position in the Mediterranean. It is nearly twice as large as Florida, but smaller than the British Isles. The southeastern slope of the Alps and the plain of the Po constitute a continental portion, from which the Apennine chain, 7000 to 9000 feet in height and, with its forelands, about 100 miles wide, extends southeastward in the form of a top boot. The narrow Strait of Messina separates the toe of the boot from the large triangular island of Sicily. The northern Apennines are comparatively smooth and traversable by open valleys. The central part, of fissured limestone, and the southern, containing knots of old igneous rock, are shattered by intersecting fault lines, along which displacement is still going on. It is one of the most active earthquake regions in the world (Fig. 56). The western side of the peninsula, including Sicily, is highly volcanic. Vesuvius (4000 feet),

Fig. 354.—Bay of Naples and Mt. Vesuvius.

Etna (11,000 feet), and the Lipari islands between the two, are frequently in eruption. The Adriatic coast is smooth, but the western coast is a succession of promontories and cuvettes (p. 169). The 4000 miles of coast line make Italy resemble a gigantic pier thrust out into the currents of human civilization. The islands of Sardinia, Corsica, and Elba are physically fragments of the Italian land.

Climate and Vegetation. — Mountain walls on the north and Mediterranean water on both sides give to "sunny Italy" a genial climate with little or no frost or snow, becoming almost tropical in the south. The *sirocco*, a hot, moist, and oppressive wind from the south, and the *tramontana*, a cool, bracing wind from the north, are occasional features. The rainfall varies from about 45 inches in the north to 27 inches in the south. The summers are so dry that many streams disappear. Irrigation is practiced more extensively than in any other European country. The conspicuous natural vegetation consists of small, leathery-leaved evergreen trees and shrubs growing in clumps (p. 233). The chestnut flourishes and is an important source of food. Cactuses, introduced from America, especially the prickly pear, are common in the south. Grass is generally poor, hence goats are more numerous than cattle.

Agriculture. — All crops are grown in Italy. The Po plain is covered with the waste of the Alps, and is growing out into the shallow head of the Adriatic. The river is subject to great floods, which are completely controlled by levees. The river banks and road grades are many feet above the level of the fields, and the water is used for irrigation. Wheat, corn, rice, and hay which is cut many times a year on the same land, are the main crops. Cattle and horses are numerous, and poultry, eggs, and cheese are exported. South of the Apennines olive orchards and vineyards, the vines being trained over mulberry trees, occupy about 12,000 square miles. The south, especially Sicily, is one of the great tropical fruit- and nut-growing districts of the world, yielding oranges, lemons, figs, citrons, walnuts, almonds, and pistachios. Corn is the staple food of the common people. Excellent hard wheat is grown in the southeast and used for making macaroni. One third of the whole country is mountainous, and about three eighths under cultivation.

Minerals and Manufactures. — Italy is a young land, poor in minerals. Marble from the northern Apennines and sulphur from Sicily are the most important. Lead, zinc, and iron are mined in Sardinia and Elba. Coal is imported from England. The abundance of cheap labor and water power has made possible a remarkable development of manufactures. The making of silk thread from domestic and foreign cocoons is a leading industry. Cotton, woolen, and leather goods are made beyond the home demand. Elba iron ores are smelted. Water power is used in steel and chemical works. Italy, like France, excels in artistic hand-made products, among which glass, lace, coral and shell work, woodwork, marble sculptures, and paintings are famous.

Fig. 355.—The Grand Canal, Venice.

Communications and Commerce. — On account of the difficulty of the passes, central and southern Italy are crossed by but two railroads. The principal lines follow the coast. The network is closest in the Po plain. The total mileage is about 10,000, of which four fifths is state-owned. Italy is naturally adapted for maritime commerce, but is retarded by a narrow and mountainous hinterland. The Alpine railways (Fig. 352) bring to Genoa a large trade from southern Germany, and it is now the second port on the Mediterranean. Venice, built upon the islands of a barrier beach and having canals for streets, has lost much of the commerce which once made it the wealthiest and most luxurious city in Europe, but by the Brenner pass it shares in the transalpine trade. Naples has a magnificent bay and is the terminus of many American steamship lines. Brindisi, reached by rail from the north, is a port of embarkation for the Levant and Orient. The principal Italian exports are raw and woven silk, cotton goods, fruits, wine, cheese, olive oil, and sulphur. The imports are coal, wheat, raw cotton, raw silk and cocoons, iron, steel, machinery, and fish.

Fig. 356. — The Colosseum, Rome.

Cities. — There are thirteen urban communes having a population of over 100,000. Naples (698,000) is made attractive by the most beautiful bay in the world and the proximity of the most famous volcano. Milan (663,000) and Turin (452,000) lie at the convergence of many transalpine routes and are the trade centers of the prosperous and progressive Po plain. Rome (591,000), the former mistress of the world, the seat of the Holy See and residence of the Pope, and the capital of the kingdom of Italy, is a strange combination of the ancient and modern, where the Colosseum, or circus of the Roman emperors, and St. Peter's church, each the largest building of its kind in the world, confront each other. No other city possesses equal historic and artistic interest. The old city, encumbered with colossal ruins, has been transformed into a clean, elegant, and well-equipped modern city suited to the life of the present day. Palermo (346,000) is the chief port for the Sicilian fruit trade. Florence (242,000) and Venice (168,000) are rich above all the rest in treasures of architecture and art. The importance of Italian towns cannot be measured by their population alone. Italy lives largely upon its past, and many towns, though small, are not obscure. Their names are written into the world's history, literature, and art. Climate, scenery, and many of the greatest works of human achievement combine to render Italy the most attractive country in Europe to the traveler.

People. — Italy has been in the way of streams of human migration, and the arena of repeated foreign conquest for thousands of years. The mass of the people are the descendants of slaves brought from every part of the known world during the long sway of the Roman Empire. Consequently the Italians have strains of blood derived from every branch of the white race. The mixture has been well blended and unified, speaking one language, and since 1871 under one government. Northern Italy is industrial, progressive, democratic, and prosperous. Southern Italy is agricultural, reactionary, feudal, poor, and ignorant. This difference is due as much to the natural wealth of one region and the poverty of the other, as to racial and historical influences. The south Italian at home lives upon *polenta*, or corn-meal mush without salt, and black bread baked twice a year, and seldom tastes meat. The emigration is very large, amounting in some years to over 600,000 persons, of whom two thirds go to the United States, Brazil, and Argentina. Many return after a time, bringing home money and new ideas, but the total number of Italians living abroad probably amounts to five or six millions. The population of Italy is 37,000,000, strongly condensed near the coast.

As a result of the World War Italy has redeemed several districts inhabited chiefly by Italians. Austria has ceded to Italy the Trentino, a triangular area on the southern slope of the Alps, and the peninsula of Istria, which includes the great port of Trieste (230,000) at the head of the Adriatic (Fig. 352). This places the Austro-Italian frontier at the crest of the Alps. Italy also lays claim, as necessary for her adequate protection, to Dalmatia, a long, narrow strip of the east Adriatic coast inhabited by Slavs and including the port of Fiume and a few other small Italian cities, thus cutting off Jugoslavia from the sea.

Spain and Portugal

The Iberian Peninsula is a compact land mass twice as large as Italy. Seven eighths of its boundary is seacoast, and the remainder is formed by the abrupt and unbroken wall of the Pyrenees, 10,000 feet high. Three fourths of the peninsula is an old block plateau about 2500 feet in elevation, with steep escarpments on the south and northeast (Fig. 57). It is traversed diagonally by block mountains 7000 to 8000 feet in height. The eastern edge is also mountainous. The margins of the block are rich in minerals. The Sierra Nevada on the south and the Cantabrian-Pyrenees on the north are young mountains folded up against the old block. The large lowland areas are in the valleys of the Guadalquivir, Guadiana, and Tagus in the southwest. The coast line is generally high and little indented. Although peninsular, this region has all the characteristics of a continental land on a small scale.

Climate and Vegetation. — On account of the form and relief of the peninsula, the climate, in its range of temperature, great and rapid changes, and general dryness, is more continental than that of any other Mediterranean country. The northwest corner enjoys a typical Atlantic climate with heavy perennial rainfall, while the southeast is hot and almost rainless. The northern and central mountains are covered with summer forests containing groves of chestnut and cork oak, the interior is a treeless steppe, while in the southern half Mediterranean evergreen shrubs appear.

Agriculture. — In the Mediterranean belt the irrigated valleys produce luxuriant tropical fruits, — oranges, dates, pomegranates, olives, and Malaga grapes. Rice, cotton, sugar cane, corn, and vegetables are also grown. The principal crop of the plateau is wheat. In summer the dry pastures support flocks of sheep, which are driven down to the valleys in winter. Outside the irrigated areas, methods of agriculture are extremely inefficient, land lying untilled or being cultivated in a destructive manner. The population is generally poor and ignorant.

Minerals and Manufactures. — Spain is the richest mineral region in Europe. Lead and silver are mined in the southeast, copper in the southwest, and excellent iron ore near the northern coast. Although large coal fields lie near, they are not much worked, and the ore is sent to Wales to be smelted. About two fifths of the world's supply of mercury comes from Almaden. A considerable industry in textiles, leather, and paper is carried on in the northeast, where the people are more progressive.

Communications and Commerce. — The high margins of the plateau offer obstructions to navigation on the rivers, and to railway building. The upper river courses are in gorges and cañons which render them useless and difficult to cross. A trunk line, connecting with the French system, passes the west end of the Pyrenees to Madrid and Lisbon, and another follows the east coast to Gibraltar. Foreign trade is very small, the exports consisting chiefly of wine, fruits, cork, and metallic minerals, and the imports of coal, cotton, foodstuffs, and machinery.

Portugal. — The southwestern plains, separated from the plateau by gorges and cañons in the rivers, belong largely to Portugal. They are maritime and Atlantic, and are the best part of the peninsula. Wine, the most important product, is shipped under the name of *port* from the city of Oporto. Lisbon (435,000), at the mouth of the Tagus, has one of the finest harbors in the world.

Cities. — Madrid (649,000), the highest capital in Europe, arbitrarily located in the midst of a desolate plateau, with a severe climate both summer and winter, has the advantage of a central location commanding mountain passes, and has become the political, commercial, and railroad nucleus of the peninsula. Barcelona (621,000) is the second city and most vigorous commercial and industrial center. It carries on a large trade with France. Valencia (246,000), Malaga, Cadiz, and Seville are very old cities and have had an eventful history. They are now the outlets for tropical fruits from the irrigated gardens around them.

People. — The Iberian peninsula has been invaded by peoples from the south, east, and north, and the struggles between them for possession continued through 1500 years. Consequently the population is derived from many different elements, — Mediterranean, Celtic, Roman, Teutonic, Arab, and Moorish. The population of Spain and Portugal is now 27,000,000. In the sixteenth century the Spanish and Portuguese obtained possession of South America, North America nearly to the Missouri-Mississippi, and of large parts of Africa, and have left their languages and the impress of their character upon one sixth of the land area of the globe. Most of the colonies have become independent, and the mother countries have sunk into a state of apathy and insignificance. Since the loss of their foreign possessions, they have had an opportunity to develop their domestic resources. Spain is Mediterranean and African in most of its physical and human conditions, while Portugal looks toward the north Atlantic, and is well situated to take part in the life of which that ocean is the center.

Greece

Greece, about as large as Pennsylvania, is "the greatest country in the world of its size," but its greatness lies almost wholly in the past. Here the southern end of the Dinaric system frays out in many branches, which finally break up into an archipelago. The valleys are partly drowned, and the land has been characterized as "standing up to its knees in water." The southern part is nearly severed from the northern by the Gulf of Corinth, and the separation has been completed by a ship canal four miles long across the isthmus. The position, relief, and climate of Greece had much influence upon the extraordinary development of politics, philosophy, science, literature, and art which characterized its early history, but they are not sufficient to keep its people above the average level of the Mediterranean standard. The climate is much like that of southern California. Irrigation is necessary, the principal products being olives, wine, and so-called currants, which are really small seedless grapes. Many sheep and goats are kept, and some iron ore is mined and exported.

As a result of the World War, Greece has gained important accessions by the annexation of Thrace, former Turkish territory around the port of Smyrna (375,000) in Asia Minor, and of the Ægean islands, where the people are largely of Greek blood and speech. The total area of Greece exceeds that of New York and the population is about 7,000,000.

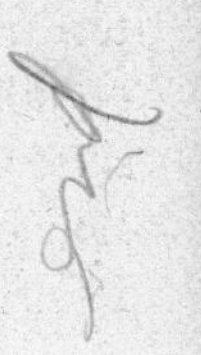

CHAPTER XXXII

THE MANCHURIAN AND CHINESE PROVINCES

The Manchurian and Chinese provinces closely resemble the Mississippian and Floridan provinces of North America. The Manchurian corresponds in position with the country between the Gulf of St. Lawrence and the Gulf of Mexico and extending westward to Lake Huron and the Mississippi. To this are added the islands of Japan, which would stretch from Nova Scotia to Florida, at a distance of 125 to 500 miles offshore. The Chinese province has a position and area corresponding to the Gulf of Mexico. The two are separated by an east-west mountain range as high as the southern Blue Ridge. The mainland portion of the two provinces includes the densely peopled parts of the Chinese Republic.

China

The mainland portion of the Manchurian province is largely occupied by two extensive plains, besides the mountainous peninsula of Korea, corresponding in position with the Delaware-Chesapeake peninsula, but much larger. The loess deposits of the province are very extensive (p. 144). The alluvial plain of the Hoang, five times as large as that of the Mississippi, is extremely fertile but subject to disastrous floods. The mouth of the river has shifted repeatedly a distance of 300 miles. The Chinese province is a mountainous plateau inclosing isolated valleys belonging to the Yangtze, Min, and Si rivers. The highlands bordering the Chinese plain contain very extensive beds of anthracite and bituminous coal, which have hardly been touched. The plateau contains coal, copper, silver, lead, and tin, all of which are mined to some extent.

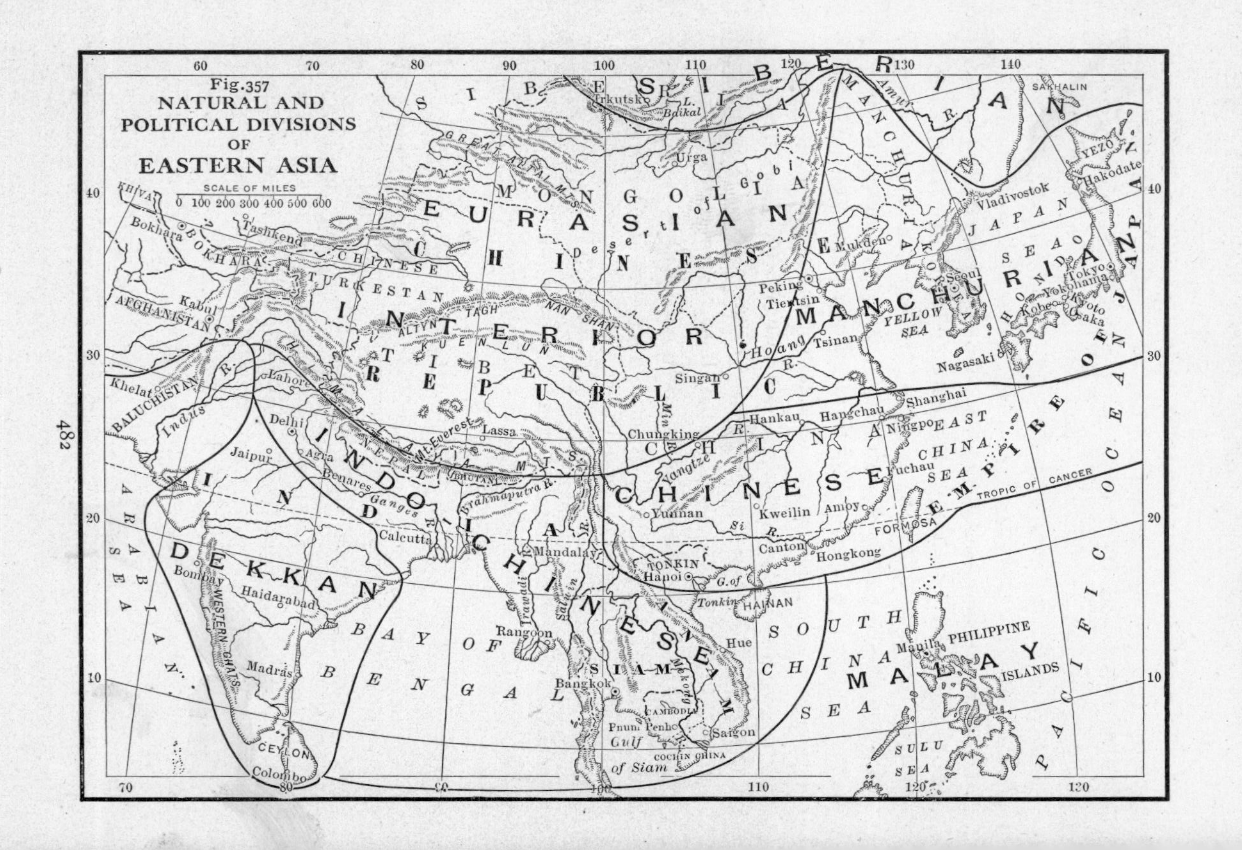

Fig. 357 NATURAL AND POLITICAL DIVISIONS OF EASTERN ASIA

Climate and Crops. — The range of temperature is somewhat greater than on the Atlantic coast of North America. The southeast monsoons bring an excessive rainfall in summer, which causes floods in the rivers. Manchuria is a region of open forest, prairie, and steppe, resembling Manitoba and adapted to wheat growing and grazing. The Chinese plateau and mountains were originally covered with temperate rain and summer forests, but have been almost entirely denuded. Bamboo is used for most purposes in place of timber. In the Chinese plain and plateau valleys, agriculture of a very intensive character prevails, the slopes being terraced and cultivated in some places to a height of 7000 feet. Irrigation is generally practiced, both from streams and from wells, and the warmth and rainfall of summer enable two crops a year to be harvested. Rice is an almost universal crop, and the main food of the people. It is supplemented by beans and fish. The loess soils are so porous that in a dry season the crops fail and serious famines occur. The silk industry is very important, both from domesticated "worms" and those which exist in a natural wild state. China produces about 30 per cent of the world's supply of raw silk. China has long been famous for its tea plantations, for which the warm, moist summer, winter without severe frost, and red, friable, well-drained soil of the Chinese province are very favorable. Cotton and opium are also grown, but in quantities insufficient for domestic consumption. Manufactures include cotton and silk fabrics, straw matting, and porcelain "chinaware."

Transportation. — Roads in China are very poor, especially in the plateau provinces, and transportation is mostly by porterage, wheelbarrows, pack animals, and bullock carts. Wheelbarrows are used because it is easier to find a passable track for one wheel than for two. They are propelled by hand, sometimes with a donkey or a sail to assist. The great rivers are the arteries of commerce and are supplemented by canals. Of these the Yangtze is the most important, being navigable by ocean steamers for 680 miles, for river steamers 1000 miles, and for small craft 500 miles farther. Millions of people make their home in boats, which are towed, when the wind fails, by men "tracking" along the shore. Railroads are much needed, but as yet only about 5000 miles are open. It often happens that the people of one province starve while there is abundance in another, because food cannot be got to them.

Foreign Commerce and Seaports. — The foreign commerce of China amounts to about $1,000,000,000 annually, the chief exports being silk, beans, and tea, and the imports cotton goods, opium, sugar, rice, petroleum, and metals. Of the ports open to foreign trade, Shanghai is by far the most important, handling about one third of the whole. The second is Canton, with about one tenth. The British colony of Hongkong includes an island and adjacent mainland at the mouth of the Si River. The city of Victoria on the island has one of the finest harbors in the world, and handles nearly as much trade as Liverpool.

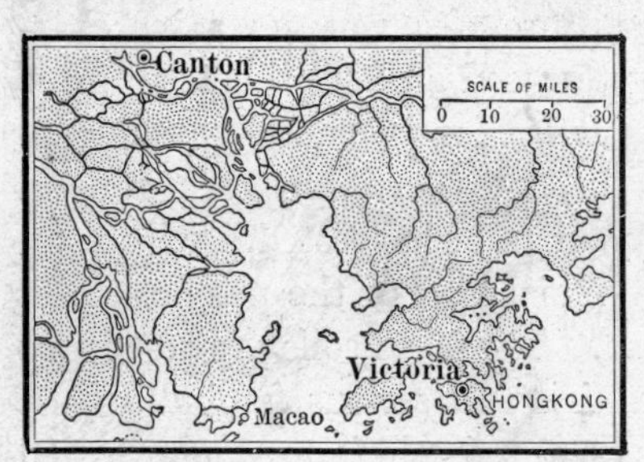

Fig. 358. — Delta of the Si River.

People of China. — No accurate census of China has ever been taken, and estimates of population vary from 270,000,000 to 439,000,000. The country is populated to the maximum density which it can support. There are eleven cities with a probable population above 200,000 and seven above 500,000, of which Canton exceeds 1,000,000. The Chinese are industrious, skillful, thrifty, and honest, but overcrowding keeps the masses in poverty. The standard of living is low and generally upon the very edge of the means of subsistence. The Chinese emigrate in large numbers to India, Indo-China, the Malay Archipelago, and the islands of the Pacific, and constitute the "yellow peril" from which the United States and Australia protect themselves by exclusion laws. The mineral resources of the country and the abundance of cheap labor favor an enormous industrial development whenever railroads and foreign capital and machinery can gain access. China may yet be the greatest manufacturing country of the world. Under a deadening

Fig. 359. — Street scene, Peking, China.

religion and a corrupt government, China has made little progress for thousands of years. Some measure of escape from these seems to be at hand, and the natural conditions are favorable for development to the rank of a great world power.

Japan

The island empire of Japan has no natural analogue in the world except possibly New Zealand. It has been compared to the British Isles, but the contrasts are on the whole greater than the resemblances. It consists of a chain of four large islands, with hundreds of smaller ones, extending from Kamchatka to Formosa, and now includes also the southern half of Sakhalin and the peninsula of Korea. The islands are the summits of an old mountain range, rising from the profoundest depths of the Pacific and crowned with many volcanic cones 8000 to 12,000 feet above the sea. They are the most active earthquake area in the world (p. 69), and waves in the earth crust and sea, volcanic eruptions, and typhoons (p. 208) would seem to make the country difficult of habitation. Three fourths of the land is mountainous and heavily forested, and less than 16 per cent is under cultivation. Bays and harbors are numerous, and the southern islands border a long strait called the Inland Sea. Coal is plentiful and copper is mined for export.

Climate and Vegetation. — The islands are exposed to the southeast monsoons in summer and to northwest winds from the continent in winter. The consequent large range of temperature is somewhat modified by branches of the warm Japan current flowing on both sides. The rainfall varies below and above 60 inches. April to September is a wet season, November to January dry. The northern island, Yezo, is snow-covered in winter and foggy in summer. The southern islands have little frost at sea level, and the bamboo and sago palm flourish. Familiar American and European trees, such as the pine, elm, chestnut, oak, and maple, grow in great luxuriance, but are mingled with peculiar species of cedar, laurel, paper mulberry, and many others. Oranges, figs, and large persimmons are characteristic fruits. The cherry and plum are grown chiefly for their blossoms. Rice, barley, millet, and beans are the staple food crops. The farms are so small that garden culture prevails, and domestic animals are few. In the production of silk Japan now surpasses China, and Japan and Formosa teas are of superior quality. About 3,000,000 people live by fishing, and whale meat is more common in market than beef or mutton. Houses are built of bamboo, paper, and other light materials, and are thus comparatively safe from destruction by earthquakes (Fig. 55).

Manufactures and Transportation. — Generations of hand labor, combined with native talent, have made the Japanese superior in many lines of handicraft, and rivals of the French in beauty of artistic work. Their art products include wares in paper, matting, silk, porcelain, lacquer, enamel, gold, silver, bronze, and steel. Ironworks and shipyards are maintained by the government. Cotton, silk, and woolen mills using coal and water power have been established at Osaka. Transportation is largely by porterage and pack horses. In cities two-wheeled handcarts, called *jinrikishas*, take the place of cabs and cars. The railroad mileage is about 5000.

Fig. 360. — Street scene, Yokohama, Japan.

Commerce. — Yokohama (429,000) is the chief port for American trade. Nagasaki (137,000), on the south island, and Kobe (498,000), on the Inland Sea, handle the Asiatic trade.

The Japanese take as naturally to the sea as the British, and have had long experience as fishermen. They have the ambition and the natural facilities to carry on most of the shipping trade of the north Pacific. Tokyo, the capital, has a population above 2,200,000, Osaka above 1,400,000, and Kyoto 540,000.

People. — The Japanese are the ablest of Mongolian peoples. Within the last fifty years they have abandoned a long-continued policy of seclusion and a feudal government, and have adopted European education, science, arts, industries, customs, and government. That a whole people should be willing to throw away their native, ancestral civilization and adopt almost bodily that of foreigners is a marvel surpassed only by their success in doing so in little more than one generation. In fighting strength of army and navy, Japan has taken a high rank among the great world powers. In the Japanese Islands the population of 56,000,000 in an area no larger than that of South Carolina, Georgia, and Florida is overcrowded, and expansion to the sparsely populated lands of Korea and Manchuria, and a change from agriculture to industrial occupations, are as desirable as they are inevitable. That little Japan rather than big China should be the dominant power in eastern Asia is favored by the oceanic accessibility of the one and the continental isolation of the other.

CHAPTER XXXIII

THE MEXICAN AND CARIBBEAN PROVINCES

Mexico

The Mexican Province is a subtropical plateau 5000 to 7000 feet in elevation, with marginal mountain ranges. It includes the greater part of the area and people of the republic of Mexico. Its elevation gives it a temperate climate with a hot season. The winters are dry and the summer rainfall is nowhere much above or below 20 inches. A large part of it is semiarid and requires irrigation. The natural vegetation is tropical forest of the thorn scrub variety (p. 234). It is sometimes called "the land of the cactus" on account of the number and variety of plants of that family found there. This plateau is probably the original home of the corn (maize) plant, which has always been the most important agricultural product, and with beans supplies the food of the common people. Wheat and cotton are grown, but not sufficient to supply the home consumption. Several species of agave, of which the century plant is one, yield valuable fibers, and another species is the source of pulqué, the national intoxicating drink. Chili, or red pepper, is universally used as a condiment.

Indians. — At the time of European discovery, the plateau of Mexico was occupied by the Aztecs and related tribes, who had attained a higher degree of civilization than any other Indians of North America. Corn, cotton, and agave formed their economic basis. Without iron or domestic animals except the dog, irrigation and hoe culture were highly successful. Their manufactures of dyed cotton cloth and ornamental articles of feathers, silver, and copper were highly artistic. Their buildings of stone, their lofty artificial mounds for religious purposes, and their mines and irrigating works showed considerable engineering skill. The Spaniards ruled and plundered Mexico for three hundred years, but never really colonized it. They introduced cattle, sheep, horses, and donkeys. Cattle and sheep raising are now important industries, while the donkey and mule have become the common beasts of burden.

Mining. — Mexico has always been "the land of silver" and now produces more than any other country. The native mines were developed by the Spaniards, who derived from them fabulous wealth. Some of them are still worked by primitive methods, the ore being hoisted in sacks on the backs of men, who climb notched logs or ladders. The ore is broken by a heavy stone disk rolled around by animal power, and finally reduced to powder by dragging stone blocks over it. The crushed ore is mixed with water and chemicals in a stone tank and trodden by animals and men until the silver is extracted. In recent times modern mining machinery and methods have been introduced. Mexico is also an important source of copper.

The Mexican petroleum fields near Tampico produced in 1918 about 55,000,000 barrels, giving that country a rank next to the United States and Russia. The oil resources of Mexico are estimated to fall little short of those of the United States and may prove of greater value than metals.

Manufactures. — The scarcity of fuel has restricted manufacture by power machinery, and domestic hand work prevails. Water power is being used to run cotton mills, and at Monterey blast furnaces burning coke from native coal are in operation. The natives are skillful artisans and produce blankets, cloaks, laces, leather goods, jewelry, and carved woodwork among the best of their kind.

Transportation and Commerce. — Primitive methods of transportation still largely prevail. Much of the hoisting and carrying is done by porterage. The typical native is of moderate stature and light build, yet habitually walks rapidly, carrying burdens over rough trails which few white men could undertake. In the mines loads of 200 to 350 pounds are carried up ladders of 1800 rounds, ten trips being made in six hours. A backload of 150 pounds is often carried 20 miles to market. In the cities, most of the work done in the United States by horse and electric trucks and drays is done upon men's backs. Most of the roads are only foot trails, and on great highways the porters, burros, pack mules, and clumsy oxcarts are more numerous than modern vehicles.

Fig. 361. — Market, city of Mexico.

Since 1880 some 15,000 miles of railroad have been built, largely by foreign capital. More than half is under government control. Two main lines traverse the plateau from north to south, connecting with the United States system at several points. Transverse lines are difficult and costly, and only two extend from sea to sea. The network is most dense in the south.

Seaports. — Vera Cruz and Tampico on the Gulf coast are the principal gateways to the sea. Acapulco and Manzanillo on the Pacific have good harbors, but are difficult of access from the land.

City of Mexico. — The metropolis of Spanish North America and the capital of Mexico is situated in a valley surrounded by volcanic mountains, near the southern edge of the plateau, at an elevation of 7400 feet. It was originally built in a shallow lake and reached by causeways. The valley is now drained by a canal 30 miles long, including a tunnel of 6 miles. The climate is agreeable and the scenery magnificent. The city contains many fine public buildings and has a population of 470,000.

Southern Mexico. — The southeastern part of the republic of Mexico belongs to the Caribbean province. High temperatures, heavy rainfall, and tropical forests prevail. It has been an important source of mahogany, rosewood, and other cabinet woods, but the supply is now greatly diminished. Sugar, coffee, cocoa, and bananas are the staple food products. Rubber is obtained from both wild and cultivated plants. The peninsula of Yucatan is a low limestone plain, with subterranean drainage. A species of agave which yields *sisal*, an excellent fiber for cordage and bagging, is here indigenous and extensively cultivated. The Mexican

Fig. 362. — Agave plantation, Mexico.

government has recently completed a railway across the Isthmus of Tehuantepec, 192 miles long, with adequate harbor facilities. The summit level is only 700 feet above tide. This route between northern Pacific and Atlantic ports is much shorter than the Panama route, and will hold a large share of the traffic.

People. — The population of Mexico is about 15,000,000, and is most dense in the states near the capital. About one fifth are of European, chiefly Spanish, descent, two fifths are pure Indian, and two fifths are of mixed blood. Many tribes, some numbering 500,000, maintain their original habits and language with little change. In Mexico the Indian has not been exterminated or dispossessed, as in English-speaking America. There he still forms the great mass of the common people, is not a slave or an outcast, and occasionally contributes an able president to the republic. He has developed his own peculiar abilities and resources under favorable conditions, and has shown himself superior to most of the black, and equal to some of the yellow and white peoples.

Caribbean Lands

The Caribbean Province. — The lands which surround the Caribbean Sea are fragmentary or marginal, mountainous, and largely volcanic. They consist of four parts: (1) *Central America* (with part of Mexico), a zigzag band of alternating isthmuses and peninsulas 1200 miles long, which connects the Mexican plateau with the Andean; (2) *the Greater Antilles*, a range of large islands extending eastward an equal distance; (3) *the Lesser Antilles*, a chain of small volcanic islands connecting (2) and (4); (4) *the South American coast ranges*, between the Caribbean and Orinoco basins. These lands present a variety of structure, elevation, and exposure, but agree in having a high temperature, heavy summer rainfall, and a tropical vegetation. The climate is tempered near the coast by trade winds and monsoons from the sea, and in the interior by altitude.

The banana, manioc, yam, and sweet potato are perennial and very prolific, and form the basis of the native food supply. Coconuts, oranges, pineapples, and many other fruits grow wild. The forests contain cabinet woods, dyestuffs, medicinal plants, and rubber trees of great value. Cattle raising is an important industry on the highlands, where the forest gives way to grass. Four great staples are grown for export, — sugar cane, bananas, coffee, and tobacco. The province produces about one fourth of the world's crop of cane sugar, chiefly from the Cuban plantations. It is the source of all the bananas in the markets of North America. The climate of the uplands between 1000 and 1200 feet in elevation is perfectly adapted to coffee growing, and the 12 per cent of the world's crop produced might be largely increased. Tobacco flourishes everywhere as a winter crop.

Central America. — The Caribbean coast lands of Central America are low, marshy, and unhealthful. The highlands lie near the Pacific, and, in spite of volcanic eruptions and earthquakes, are densely populated, especially in the northern part. On the plateaus and mountain slopes, oak and pine forests and grassy savannas sustain the principal occupation of cattle raising. Coffee of extra fine quality is grown and marketed in Europe. One third of the 5,000,000 people are pure Indian, and nearly all the rest of negro and mixed blood.

The Panama Canal. — The Isthmus of Panama possesses no importance as a bridge between two continents, but as a barrier between two oceans it is a strategic point in world commerce and politics second to none. In 1855 the Panama Railroad was completed, and until the opening of transcontinental lines in the United States was an important route of traffic between the Atlantic and Pacific states. After unsuccessful attempts in Nicaragua and by the French at Panama, the United States government undertook to construct along the line of the railroad a ship canal which was opened in 1914. The work included not only the cutting of a canal 45 feet deep and 50 miles long, across a divide 250 feet high, but the construction of the largest dam in the world to control the floods of the Chagres River, of locks to reach the summit level, 85 feet above tide, and of a harbor at each end (p. 159, Fig. 149). The mechanical problems which were solved were hardly greater than the sanitary one of maintaining an adequate force of laborers in one of the most unhealthful regions of the tropics. Their successful solution constitutes the greatest achievement yet accomplished by man in overcoming natural barriers to progress. The naval forces of the United States on two oceans, instead of being divided by a six weeks' voyage, are now able to unite quickly on either coast. The cheapening of transcontinental freight rates has stimulated industry on both sides of the continent. The Gulf ports and the West Indies have acquired new importance. The Pacific coast of South America has been brought into close relationship with the Atlantic ports of North America and Europe, some of the trade of the Orient has been diverted from the Suez route, and the westward and eastward movements of civilization now meet and overlap.

Cuba. — Half the area and two thirds of the white population of the West Indies are found in Cuba. The highlands of the island reach a maximum elevation of 6800 feet near the southeast coast. The principal crop is sugar cane, which on the limestone soils of the central provinces requires replanting but once in seven years. Cuba exports one sixth of the cane sugar used in the world. Of less value but equal fame is the tobacco of the Havana provinces. The coasts are generally bordered by an elevated coral reef, but abound in landlocked harbors. Havana, the metropolis of the Caribbean province, on an excellent harbor, is a clean and beautiful city of 350,000 people. Cuba, with a population of 2,628,000, is an independent republic under the protection of the United States.

Haiti, the Hispaniola of Columbus, is traversed by four parallel mountain ranges with peaks above 10,000 feet, and is naturally one of the most magnificent and attractive of the West Indian islands. The native population was exterminated by the Spaniards in about fifty years and replaced by slaves imported from Africa. Haiti is now occupied by about 3,225,000 negroes, organized in two independent republics. White men are denied civil and political rights. Industry and commerce are greatly hampered by bad government.

Porto Rico, now a territory of the United States, resembles Cuba in products and people. It is densely populated (1,246,000) and highly cultivated. It is better adapted to the growing of high-grade coffee than any other crop, but the coffee produced is exceeded in value by the sugar and tobacco.

Jamaica, called from its position " the key of the Caribbean," is famous for beautiful scenery and delightful winter climate. The Blue Mountains rise above 7000 feet. Its special products — rum, ginger, and pimento — are now being displaced in commercial importance by bananas, oranges, tobacco, and cacao. About 95 per cent of the people are colored and are peaceful and prosperous under British rule.

The Lesser Antilles extend in a sweeping curve of about 1500 miles from Porto Rico to Point Gallinas on the South American coast. Most of them are true oceanic islands of volcanic and coral structure. All the West Indies, except Cuba and Porto Rico, are overwhelmingly African in population. They are at present in a state of commercial decline as a result of the abolition of slavery and the competition of European beet sugar. They suffer also from being politically divided. The coast margin of South America is the outlet for the rich coffee and cocoa plantations of Venezuela and Colombia.

On account of its position, climate, salubrity, fertility, and variety of products, the Caribbean province is by nature competent to supply North America with all kinds of distinctly tropical products. That its possibilities have never been realized is due to human rapacity, political jealousy, and economic mismanagement. It is reasonable to hope that the opening of the Panama Canal and the expanding influence of the United States may enable it to occupy the place in the economy of the world which naturally belongs to it.

CHAPTER XXXIV

INTERTROPICAL PROVINCES OF SOUTH AMERICA

The Brazilian Province. — The larger part of Brazil is a highland 700,000 square miles in area and forming an "island" surrounded by the ocean and the continuous valleys of the Amazon-Madeira and Paraguay-Parana rivers. Near the southeastern coast it is bordered by a mountain system which reaches a height of 10,000 feet. Behind the mountains denuded plateaus descend westward from 4000 or 5000 feet to 2500 feet. Many of the "serras" or mountain ranges shown on the map are flat-topped escarpments of the plateau. The eastern slopes have a heavy rainfall and are forested. The interior is dry and occupied by campos (p. 237) and catinga (p. 234). The large stream valleys are wooded. Much of the interior of the "Brazilian island" is uninhabited and unexplored.

Coffee Culture. — The Brazilian plateau produces about 1800 million pounds of coffee annually, or three fourths of the world's crop. The coffee district lies just north of the tropic and within 200 miles of the sea, at an elevation of about 2000 feet. The soil is laterite (p. 145), produced by the decay of eruptive rocks rich in potash and iron, and locally called *terra rossa* (red earth). The region is near the southern edge of the equatorial belt, with about half the year hot and half temperate. The rainfall is between 40 and 60 inches, three fourths of which is brought by the equatorial calms between October and March. The summer, therefore, is the wet growing season, and the dry, warm winter, when the trade wind blows, is the season for harvesting and curing. The fruit of the coffee tree is a red berry about the size of a small cherry and containing two seeds. The pulp is removed by soaking in water, and the seeds are dried in the open air on cemented or tiled floors painted black to increase the absorption of heat from the generally unclouded sun. After drying, which requires from one to many days, according to the weather, the grains are run through a machine which removes the hulls, assorted, and put up in bags weighing 132 pounds. The labor on the coffee plantations is now performed mostly by Italian colonists.

Cities of Brazil. — The Brazilian province exemplifies the rule that in tropical America the largest cities are, with few exceptions, situated upon the plateau, while the seaports are relatively small. São Paulo, 32 miles from the sea and 2500 feet above it, has a population of 400,000; its seaport, Santos, the greatest coffee-shipping port in the world, has but 35,000. Of the eleven independent nations of intertropical America, but one, Brazil, has a capital which is at sea level, Rio de Janeiro (1,128,000). This contrast with the countries of temperate climates suggests the possibilities of future development of tropical lowlands, when, by the application of science, their peculiar diseases may be eliminated and the depressing effects of their climate relieved.

The Orinoco Province comprises the highlands of Guiana, Venezuela, and northern Brazil and the llanos of Venezuela and Colombia. The highlands form a plateau rising by precipitous escarpments to 8000 feet. They are covered with tropical forests and savannas and are inhabited only by a few Indians and fugitive negroes. The llanos (p. 237) are low plains lying in the rain shadow of the highlands and including some tracts of sandy desert. Most of the area is clothed with luxuriant grass. The winters are hot, but so dry that nearly all vegetation dies. The chief occupation of the people is cattle raising.

The Andean Province. — The Andean Cordillera north of the tropic consists of two or more parallel ranges separated by high plateaus. The system is studded with knots of giant volcanoes (Fig. 56), some above 20,000 feet, and covered with perpetual snow even under an equatorial sun. Earthquakes are frequent and violent. The intermont valleys are divided by transverse spurs into a series of basins with floors between 8000 and 13,000 feet above the sea, most of which are drained through cañons eastward to the Amazon. The largest basin, about 300 miles long and 100 miles wide, contains Lake Titicaca, 50 by 130 miles in extent, and 12,545 feet above the sea. This mountain system stretches a band of cool temperate to polar climate, 2500 miles long and 250 miles wide, across the equatorial belt. The rainfall brought by the trade winds is heavy on the eastern slope, scanty on the plateaus, and next to nothing on the western slope. The conditions are similar to those of the Mexican province, but on an exaggerated scale.

Aboriginal Andean People.— The Andean plateaus were the seat of an aboriginal civilization in some respects superior to that of Mexico. The people cultivated corn and the potato, indigenous to the region, both of which attained a perfection unknown elsewhere. The almost intractable llama (Fig. 222) was domesticated as a beast of burden, and herds of alpacas and vicuñas, pastured on the luxuriant *ichu* grass which clothed the lower slopes, were kept for flesh and wool. Gold, silver, copper, and tin were plentiful, and the best implements were of bronze.

Under three centuries of Spanish oppression and plunder, the native population of 10,000,000 was reduced to less than 1,000,000. Early in the nineteenth century the people threw off the Spanish yoke and organized the present Andean republics. Three fourths of the population are of Indian blood, but, owing to centuries of isolation and slavery, remain in a condition inferior to that of the Mexicans. The native economic basis of corn, potatoes, grass, llamas, alpacas, and vicuñas has been extended by the introduction of wheat, cattle, donkeys, and horses. The Andean province contains some of the richest deposits of silver, copper, tin, and mercury in the world. Since the beginning of Spanish possession, the hill of Potosi has yielded silver to the value of $1,500,000,000. Many of the mines can be reached only by mule trails over passes 10,000 feet or more in height, and are difficult to develop.

Previous to the completion of the railroad in Ecuador, about 1,000,000 people were dependent for connection with the outside world upon a single dangerous mule trail, and had hardly any foreign commerce. The people of the Andean province exist in a state of naturally extreme isolation. In spite of great difficulties, railroads, climbing from the coast over passes of 15,000 feet in elevation, now penetrate the basins of Quito, Titicaca, and Cuzco.

The Amazon Province. — The area of equatorial forest — lying in the basins of the Amazon and Parana rivers in Brazil, Colombia, Peru, Bolivia, and Argentina — is more than half as large as the United States. It is accessible only by the rivers, of which the Amazon is navigable for steamers to the foot of the Andes, a distance of about 2000 miles. Its tributaries add as much more waterway for large craft, and an uncalculated distance for small boats. It is sparsely populated by native tribes of Indians in a state of savagery more or less modified by contact with the whites.

There are no towns except a few trading posts. Manioc and fish are the staple articles of food. Manioc is cultivated in rude fashion and the roots are ground, washed, pressed, and dried into a cake, which is sometimes ground into flour. The principal commercial product is rubber, gathered from several species of wild trees, and exported chiefly from Para, at the mouth of the Amazon. This province furnishes about three fifths of the world's supply.

CHAPTER XXXV

INTERTROPICAL PROVINCES OF ASIA AND AFRICA

The Dekkan, or " southland," forms the core of the peninsula of India. It is a triangular plateau bordered on the west by the steep seaward escarpment of the Ghats (steps), 4000 to 6000 feet high, and sloping to a narrow coastal plain on the east. A belt of hilly country separates it from the Ganges plain. The northwestern third of it is covered by ancient lava sheets, which have weathered into a rich black soil. The remainder is composed of eruptive and metamorphic rocks which produce laterite. There are some valuable coal fields in the north. The temperature is tropical, modified by elevation and subject to a range of 25 degrees. The rainfall brought by the southwest monsoon of summer, screened off by the Ghats, averages on the plateau from 20 to 40 inches, but is variable and uncertain from year to year. The northeast monsoon of winter brings light rain to the eastern margin. The Ghats and hills are wooded; the rest of the plateau is a savanna, green during the rainy season, brown, bare, dusty, and very hot in spring and early summer. The natural conditions are essentially similar to those of the Mexican plateau.

The basin of the Ganges and lower Brahmaputra lies between the Dekkan and the Himalayas, opening southward to the Bay of Bengal. It is an alluvial and delta plain about four times as large as that of the Mississippi. The summer monsoons sweep up the valley bringing a deluge of rain, amounting in the east to 50 or 60 feet a year, the heaviest in the world. More rain sometimes falls in one day than in the northeastern United States in a whole year. Three fourths of the rainfall occurs in three summer months, and the winter and spring are dry. The plain is traversed by many rivers which rise in the mountains. These conditions account for extensive irrigation works (p. 148) in a region of heavy rainfall.

India. — The Dekkan, the Ganges plain, and some bordering territory constitute the empire of India, of which the British king is sovereign. An area little more than half as large as the United States supports a population of 315,000,000, the density in many parts exceeding 500 to the square mile. About half the area is arable, 6 per cent of which is under irrigation. Two thirds of the people are engaged in agriculture, carried on by village communities, which cultivate the same land through successive generations. Rice, wheat, millet, beans, and cotton are the principal crops. Cattle are the most numerous domestic animals and are used for milk and draft. The eating of flesh is forbidden by the religion which many of the people profess. Fine cotton goods and sacking and cordage made from jute are the largest factory products. Jute, cotton, rice, wheat, oil seeds, hides, tea, and opium are exported. The large rivers, canals, 32,000 miles of railroad, and about 200,000 miles of improved wagon roads furnish internal communication.

People of India. — The aboriginal inhabitants of India were Dravidians, a very ancient people whose origin and racial affinities are uncertain. Successive Caucasian invasions from the northwest have driven them into the Dekkan and established "many distinct and independent communities owning no brotherhood of religion, language, race, or social intercourse." Ten religions and twenty-five languages are officially recognized. The overpopulation of the empire and the consequent occasional famines are due in part to the peace and good order maintained among these discordant elements by British rule. The government is administered by a Viceroy and subordinate officials, the total British population being less than 100,000, of whom more than 75,000 are soldiers. The climate is very unhealthful for Europeans, who, as far as possible, leave the lowlands in summer. Calcutta (1,222,000), on a distributary of the Ganges,

Bombay (979,000), and Madras (519,000) are the principal cities and seaports. Some of the ancient cities, such as Delhi, Agra,

Fig. 363. – Street scene, Jaipur, India.

and Benares, are famous for beautiful architecture and as centers of religious veneration.

Indo-China. — The peninsula of Indo-China occupies a position in Asia corresponding to that of the Caribbean province in North America. The complex relief and outline of the land are due to parallel mountain ranges, separated by the valleys of great rivers, which thrust out deltas into the sea. Tropical and monsoon forests and bamboo jungle prevail, with savannas in protected localities. The valleys are densely populated by various Mongolian peoples, who live along and upon the rivers, which furnish almost the only practicable routes of travel. The staple products are rice in the valleys, and millet on the uplands. The great forest resources of the mountains include the invaluable teak timber, which is extensively utilized. The elephant is used for labor and for display (Fig. 257). Siam is an independent kingdom, and the eastern part of the peninsula is a French protectorate.

The Malay Province. — The islands of the Malay province present a greater variety of human than of natural conditions. Most of them have been in contact with Europeans for centuries, and some are under complete political and economic control by white men. New Guinea has been very imperfectly explored, and the natives are in a state of primitive savagery. Java has been systematically and thoroughly developed by the Dutch. The United States has undertaken a similar task in the Philippines, while the Hawaiian Islands are as highly civilized and modernized as Jamaica.

Java, midway between Asia and Australia, holds the commanding position of the archipelago. It consists essentially of a line of volcanoes, 600 miles long, which have poured out sufficient material to build a continuous island about the size of New York. Many of the volcanoes are still active and destructive to life and property, but the land owes its superior fertility to frequent showers of volcanic dust. The island is a vast plantation where the natives grow rice for themselves and coffee, sugar cane, tea, quinine, and indigo for their Dutch rulers. About 40 per cent of the area is under cultivation, and over one half of that is devoted to rice. Coffee was formerly grown under a system of compulsory labor, and is still in part a government monopoly. Java coffees bring a high price on account of superior flavor. Java stands next to Cuba in the production of sugar. The cultivation of the cinchona tree, introduced from South America, now yields 86 per cent of all the bark used in the world. These crops, together with tea, rubber, tobacco, and indigo, receive the closest attention from the scientific bureaus of the government, and yield a large profit to the Dutch merchants.

The population is 34,000,000, or more than half that of Australasia and all the intertropical islands. The density is 680 to the square mile. The Javanese live in villages built of bamboo and other light materials, which are not injured by frequent earthquakes. They are moderately industrious but improvident.

The Hawaiian Islands, on the tropic, 2000 miles southwest of San

Francisco, consist of eight large volcanic masses rising from profound ocean depths, and having an area about the size of Connecticut and Rhode Island. They are under the economic control of sugar planters, and send to the United States 550,000 tons of sugar annually. Their position at the cross-roads of the Pacific makes their possession of prime importance in the politics and commerce of that ocean. The native Hawaiians are the most advanced among Polynesian peoples, but are diminishing in numbers, and are now outnumbered four to one by Chinese and Japanese.

Fig. 364. — Sugar plantation, Hawaii.

The Kongo Province. — The equatorial forests of Africa have an area about the same as those of South America, chiefly in the basins of the Kongo and Niger, but the province is more accessible because of its long coast line. It is nearly all under Belgian, British, French, or Portuguese administration. The native negro population is estimated at about 50,000,000, which gives a density nearly equal to that of the United States as a whole. The climate is extremely fatal to white men. The region has been called the banana zone, because the means of subsistence lie in spontaneous fruits, of which the banana, plantain, and oil palm are in themselves sufficient. Domestic animals are very uncommon. Dogs are fattened for food, and monkey flesh is a delicacy. The coast and river people pay much attention to fishing. There is little hunting, except among the scattered tribes of pygmies, a race of dwarfs who live in the dense forest by the chase and by bartering game for bananas. The craving for meat and its scarcity led to the general prevalence of cannibalism, which Europeans have not been able entirely to suppress.

The British and French have built short railways on the Guinea coast, and a Belgian road 250 miles long around the rapids of the Kongo gives a rail and steamer route of 1500 miles into the interior, with branches on the tributaries. The European exploitation of the country can hardly be called a development, for like native life it depends upon collective economy. The province furnishes more than one fourth of the world's supply of rubber. Other valuable exports are ivory, palm nuts and oil, gold, and timber. The cultivation of cotton, corn, cocoa, coffee, tobacco, and spices is encouraged and meets with some success.

Fig. 365. — Baobab tree, central Africa. (Schimper.)

The Central African Province. — In central Africa an area about the size of the United States, lying between 20° S. Lat. and 15° N. Lat., has a general elevation between 2000 and 4000 feet. Near the eastern border the plateau rises to 5000 and 8000 feet, and volcanic peaks above 18,000. The climate is tempered according to elevation, and the rainfall, varying between 20 and 60 inches, is distributed in one or two rainy seasons. The region contains the most extensive savannas in the world. Forests occur along the streams, on the slopes of the mountains, and near the coast exposed to the trade winds. The baobab tree (Fig. 365) with its swollen trunk, and the peculiar candelabra-shaped euphorbias, are characteristic.

The abundance of large animal life before noticed (p. 236) is in striking contrast with the poverty of the Brazilian province.

People. — The province is peopled by many tribes of negro stock, modified in the north by Caucasian admixture. Some are cattle and goat herders, but agriculture is the general occupation. The principal food crops are millet, corn, and bananas. Hoe culture is universal, animals being kept for flesh, milk, and hides. Clothing is at an irreducible minimum, consisting at most of a single scanty garment of skin or cotton cloth. Cotton growing for exportation is one of the possibilities of the future.

Political and Economic Conditions. — The plateau of Abyssinia, in the extreme northeast, has been the seat of an independent empire of Caucasian and Christian people from a remote period. The rest of the province is now under the control of the British, French, Belgians, and Portuguese. Slavery has been abolished and peace and good order are maintained. The British territory is penetrated by four railroads, one from the east coast to Lake Victoria, one from the coast to Lake Tanganyika, one from Cape Town to the upper Kongo River, and one in the west across the Niger. There are some short lines in the French and Portuguese possessions. Habits of industry and thrift are encouraged and readily acquired, and the natives are being educated in agricultural and mechanic arts. Both Catholic and Protestant missionaries have met with considerable success, and much is being done to develop the resources of the country, and to improve the condition of the people. However, the civilization of races sunk for centuries in savagery cannot be accomplished in a few generations.

The Madagascar Province. — The large island of Madagascar forms the only province of the Caribbean type in the southern hemisphere. It consists of an interior mountain range surrounded by a belt of lowland. The trade winds bring ample rainfall to the eastern side. The mountain heights and the western side are drier. The winter is relatively dry and cool. An almost unbroken forest borders the shores and surrounds the central highlands. The flora is rich, varied, and peculiar, three fourths of the species being unknown elsewhere. There are no large native animals, but Madagascar is the home of the lemurs (allied to the monkeys), chameleons, and many peculiar birds. The living forms show it to be a very old land, long isolated, and, like Australia (p. 254), preserving types elsewhere extinct. The people are of mixed races, but the semicivilized descendants of ancient Malay invaders are dominant. The island is a French colony, and produces cloths, bags, and mats made by hand from a variety of fibers, cattle, hides, rubber, rice, timber, coffee, sugar, and vanilla.

CHAPTER XXXVI

TEMPERATE PROVINCES OF THE SOUTHERN HEMISPHERE

The Plata Province. — The temperate grasslands of the southern hemisphere differ somewhat from those of the northern in being less clearly distinguished as savanna, steppe, and prairie.

The *pampas* of Argentina and Uruguay were in recent geologic times the bed of an inland sea which received drainage from a large area to the northward and was covered with a rich, red

Fig. 366. — Cattle ranch, Argentina.

clay soil. Its emergence above sea level occurred so recently that forests and large animals have never reached it. Thus grasses and herbaceous plants grew and decayed almost untouched for ages, adding humus to the soil. The rainfall varies from about 30 inches near the coast to less than 10 in the interior. The temperatures are not extreme, but violent winds from both north and south are frequent. Dense tufts of tall, stiff grass rise like islets above the brown loam and bear silvery, plumose spikes of flowers. The bare spaces between are covered at certain seasons with more delicate grasses and herbaceous plants, forming a combination of savanna and prairie. This passes on toward the interior into steppe and scrub.

Cattle and horses brought by the Spaniards from Europe, finding unlimited pasture and few enemies, multiplied rapidly in a wild state and were slaughtered for their hides only. This business was carried on by native Indian *Gauchos*, superb horsemen who preferred their meat cooked with the hide on. The breeds of stock have been greatly improved and are now raised on well-equipped ranches. Butter, frozen meat, tallow, hides, and extracts of beef are exported in large quantities from the moist eastern portion. In the drier west, sheep are more numerous than cattle. The province is second only to Australia in wool clip. As railroads are extended the grazing lands are coming more and more under the plow, wheat and corn being the principal crops. Although Argentina raises only about one fifth as much wheat as the United States, the home consumption is so small that exports are nearly as large. The possibilities of the country for food production are so great that it has been called the world's most valuable future asset.

Fig. 367. — The Plata estuary.

The Plata province, on an area one fourth as large as the United States, has a population of only 7,600,000. There are many Italian colonists. Buenos Aires (1,560,000), on the Plata estuary, is the largest city in the southern hemisphere. Montevideo (378,000) is nearer the sea and has a better harbor.

The South African Province. — That part of South Africa which includes the provinces of Transvaal and Orange Free State lies upon a plateau 4000 feet above the sea. The winters are almost rainless, and the country is a rather barren steppe fitted for a limited amount of grazing. Ostriches are bred for their plumes. The most important economic features are the gold mines of "the Rand" and the diamond mines of Kimberley. The Rand is the outcrop of beds of conglomerate called *banket*, 45 miles long, in which gold occurs not in veins or lodes, but generally diffused throughout the mass. It is mined like coal and extracted by the cyanide process (p. 303). The yield per ton is small, but the quantity of banket is so large, and the mining operations so certain and cheap, that the Rand yields more gold than any other district in the world. The annual output is now about $193,000,000, or two fifths that of the world.

Fig. 368. — Diamond mine, Kimberley.

About 70 square miles around Kimberley furnish nearly the whole of the world's supply of diamonds, amounting to more than $37,000,000 annually. The diamonds occur in large "pipes" or chimneys in the country rock, filled with a sort of blue clay, and of unknown depth. They may be old volcanic vents.

The native Kafirs, formerly employed in the gold and diamond mines, have now been largely displaced by imported coolies from India and China.

The Queensland Province includes most of those parts of Australia where the rainfall is between 10 and 20 inches. North of the tropic it is savanna, and south of it steppe, with areas of "bush" or thorn scrub. The steppe south of the tropic is the greatest sheep and wool region in the world, supporting about 75,000,000 sheep, and yielding one fifth of the world's wool supply.

The New Zealand Province. — *The East Coast of Australia* south of the tropic is flanked by the continuous Dividing Range, 4000 to 7000 feet high, and exposed to the southeast trade winds, which bring a mild and equable climate, with a rainfall of 20 to 60 inches, heaviest in autumn. The vegetation is open, parklike forest of gigantic evergreen eucalyptus trees interspersed with savanna. The chief products are wheat, wool, and timber. These conditions prevail in the most densely populated parts of the states of Queensland, New South Wales, and Victoria, and of the continent. Sydney, on a spacious landlocked harbor, with a population of 637,000, is the third city in the southern hemisphere and the chief Australian port for European mail steamers. Melbourne has a harbor scarcely inferior to that of Sydney, and a population nearly as large. The people are of almost pure British stock, and yellow people are rigidly excluded.

New Zealand, a mountainous and volcanic archipelago, 1000 miles long and a little larger than Great Britain, lying 1200 miles off the southeast coast of Australia, forms a geographic unit almost distinct enough to be reckoned as a miniature continent. Longitudinal ranges traverse the islands near the west coast in the south and the east coast in the north. The Southern Alps overhang the sea with peaks above 12,000 feet, from which glaciers descend almost to sea level. The coast is fiorded like Alaska (pp. 163, 164). The north island has active volcanoes, geysers, hot springs, and volcanic lakes. Coal and gold are the most important minerals.

New Zealand is exposed to the strong westerly winds which bring to the west coast a rainfall as high in some places as 120 inches. On the east side the rainfall ranges from 30 to 50 inches. The temperature is higher and more equable than that of the British Isles. Half the area is heavily forested with a peculiar flora, among which the kauri pine and tree ferns are conspicuous. The rest is open and covered with wiry grasses and native flax.

The leading occupations are herding sheep and cattle, and the allied industries in cheese, butter, meat, wool, and leather. Many frozen sheep carcasses are exported to Great Britain. Auckland, Wellington, and Lyttleton are the chief seaports. There are no large cities.

New Zealand is a semi-independent colony of the British Empire, and the colonists, numbering about 1,000,000, are almost entirely British. The native Maoris, physically and mentally the best of the Malay peoples, survive to the number of 50,000, but are slowly diminishing. They enjoy equal political rights with the whites. On account of its remote position New Zealand is destined to play a modest part, but it has become famous as a political and economic experiment station, where the most advanced ideas are successfully practiced.

Tasmania, an island about as large as Scotland, 150 miles south of Australia, is an old mountainous plateau, rich in coal, iron, tin, and copper. Its climate and vegetation are similar to those of New Zealand. It is one of the states of the Australian Commonwealth.

The area of Australia is almost exactly the same as that of the United States. While the region of less than 10 inches of rainfall amounts to about 11 per cent of the United States, it is 44 per cent in Australia. The other 56 per cent has a population of about 4,000,000. Temperate South America, Australia, and New Zealand are largely unoccupied and undeveloped lands, which await a migration of people from the northern hemisphere. Such a movement is sure to result in time from the increase of population and overcrowding of northern lands and resources, and will be one of the great events of the future.

CHAPTER XXXVII

COLD TEMPERATE AND POLAR PROVINCES

THE cold belt with a temperate season stretches across North America at its widest part, and measures, from the Labrador coast to Bering Sea, more than 4000 miles. It includes the whole of the Laurentian peneplain except the northern margin, Newfoundland, the Mackenzie plain, the northern Rocky Mountains, the Yukon plateau, and the northern Pacific coast ranges. It is divided into an oceanic and a continental province of very unequal extent. The western slope of the Pacific mountains is exposed to the sweep of the westerly winds from the ocean and has an abnormal climate for its latitude, with cool summers, mild winters, a range of about 20 degrees, and a rainfall reaching in places 190 inches, including 100 feet of snow. East of the mountain crest the climate is extreme, with a range of 50 to 80 degrees and scant rainfall, raised to more than 20 inches in the east by cyclonic winds. The region as a whole is best characterized as the coniferous forest belt, broken by innumerable lakes, "muskegs," or marshes, patches of tundra and prairie, and in the mountains by areas of permanent ice and snow.

The Alaskan Province. — The Pacific coast of North America, from the Strait of Fuca to the Alaskan peninsula, is a ragged belt of islands, canals, and fiords (p. 163), behind which the mountains stand with their feet in the sea (Fig. 106). The valleys are filled with ice, which overflows in more than 200 large glaciers. The slopes below the snow line, where not too steep, are heavily wooded with hemlock, spruce, and cedar, but the timber is inferior in size and quality to that farther south.

Mining and Fisheries. — Juneau, the capital of the territory of Alaska, owes its existence to veins of gold-bearing quartz in

Fig. 369. — Coast of Alaska.

the neighboring islands, which have been worked since 1880. The whole province now yields about $6,260,000 a year. Copper mines exist, but are only beginning to be developed. Extensive deposits of high-grade coal occur near the coast in the extreme northern part, but are as yet little used. The most productive industry of the province is its salmon fisheries. The salmon are sea fish which enter every river mouth in the spring and ascend to the headwaters to spawn. During this journey of hundreds or even thousands of miles they eat nothing, and all die after spawning. The young fry float downstream tail first and go out to sea. The adult fish weigh from 10 to 100 pounds, and are caught in the rivers with nets and traps, and taken to canneries established near the coast. More than 29,000 people are employed in the business, and the value of the product is about $46,000,000 annually. The United States government has established hatcheries and enacted rules regulating the salmon industry, to prevent waste and conserve the supply.

Transportation and Trade. — Several lines of ocean steamships and river boats in summer furnish regular and fairly rapid transportation to and from Seattle and Vancouver. Ten local railways, varying in length from 7 to 258 miles, connect important points with one another and with the coast. The United States government has built hundreds of miles of stage roads and established cable and telegraph lines to all the principal centers in the territory of Alaska. Mail service is maintained throughout the year. The total exports of the territory of Alaska amounted in 1918 to about $87,000,000, and the imports to more than $44,000,000. Nearly all of this trade was with the United States. These amounts will certainly increase indefinitely in the future, but the greatest, most generally available, and only inexhaustible resource of the country cannot be estimated in dollars, and lies in its magnificent scenery of sea, fiord, mountain, forest, cataract, and glacier.

The Norwegian Province. — In Europe the high western coast of the Scandinavian peninsula surpasses the Alaskan province in the number and magnitude of its fiords and in the countless islands which guard it from the waves. The oceanic winds bring to it an even more equable climate and a heavy rain and snow fall. Owing to the lower altitude of the plateaus and mountains, the snow fields and glaciers are much less extensive. Land resources are scant, and the inhabitants have always been compelled to take to the sea. In the Middle Ages they were sea rovers and pirates, and in modern times are sailors and fishermen. The cod and herring fisheries, of which the Lofoden Islands are the chief center, employ a larger proportion of the people than in any other country. Timber of excellent quality is exported. Norway has water power enough to run the machinery of the world. It is beginning to be utilized, and in the future this province may become a great manufacturing district.

The Scotch Highlands exhibit all the natural features of Norway, except glaciers, on a small scale. In beauty of scenery and number of summer visitors, Norway and Scotland stand second only to the Alps.

The Southwest American Province. — Chile, from 40° S. Lat. southward, presents a high, glaciated mountain chain, cut by fiords and canals into a swarm of islands, all of the genuine Alaskan type. Owing to the cold west wind drift in the Pacific, the temperatures are lower than in the corresponding northern latitudes, and the climate is very stormy at all seasons. In Tierra del Fuego snow falls every month in the year, yet no month is too cold for the native inhabitants to go almost without clothing or shelter. The population of degraded savages is very small, and the conditions of human life are probably more miserable than in any other inhabited land.

The Canadian Province. — The Lake Superior iron district has been discussed in Chap. XXV. (p. 369). The economic basis of the permanent inhabitants of the rest of the Canadian province lies chiefly in its animal life, which is very abundant. The number of species of birds and mammals in summer equals that of any part of the temperate zone. They include the moose, the largest mammal in North America, caribou, musk ox, wood bison, several species of bear, puma, lynx, and mountain sheep and goats. These make the country famous as a hunting ground for sportsmen. A herd of 30,000 musk oxen has been seen on the east side of Hudson Bay, and 50,000 caribou have been known to cross the Yukon at Caribou Crossing. As many as 80,000 caribou skins have been bought by traders in a single year. In winter these animals feed upon the "moss" or air plants which grow upon the trees in the forest, and in summer they migrate to the tundra. Caribou meat and skins furnish the staple materials for food and clothing. The lakes and rivers abound in excellent fish, which form a food supply for great numbers of small fur-bearing animals.

Trapping and Hunting. — The population of nearly the whole Canadian province consists of Indians and half-breeds, engaged in trapping, hunting, and bartering to white traders the furs which constitute the chief product of the country at present marketable. The Hudson's Bay Company has maintained for 250 years forts or trading posts throughout the region for the purpose of collecting furs. In summer steamers on the large rivers make regular trips from post to post, but travel is mostly by canoe.

The Indian birch-bark canoe is one of the most remarkable achievements of savage man. The bark of the paper birch is stripped off in large sheets as thin as cardboard and sewed to a light wooden frame, the seams being made water-tight by means of pitch. The finished canoe has beautifully curved outlines, and is of such shape as to move through the water with little resistance. It will carry a load of 1000 pounds, yet is so light that a man can carry it easily across the numerous portages from stream to stream. The Indians display great skill in paddling and steering this fragile craft through rapids, where to graze a rock means disaster. Travel in winter over the heavy mantle of snow is possible only on snowshoes, which are almost as ingenious in construction as the canoe, and might be called snow boats. An elliptical frame of wood a foot and a half wide, and from three to six feet long, is covered with a network of rawhide, in the middle of which the wearer stands with his toes inserted in a loop or pocket. The snowshoe is not lifted but slid forward at each step, and prevents the wearer from sinking, while any snow upon the top falls through the meshes. Transportation is by dog sledges. A team of ten dogs will draw a load of 1000 pounds twenty miles a day.

Lumbering. — The Canadian forest is one of the most valuable in the world. Its vast resources are as yet but little utilized, but, with the rapidly diminishing supply in the United States, must be more and more largely drawn upon. Lumbering is carried on chiefly along the southeastern margin, where logs can be floated down the numerous streams to the lakes and the St. Lawrence.

The Canadian Pacific Railway traverses the province from Montreal to Winnipeg, and the Grand Trunk Pacific is under construction from Quebec along a line farther to the north.

Mining. — The native animal and human life of the Canadian province has not been seriously disturbed by the fur trader, whose interest it is to conserve the population and make it as productive of wealth as possible. The lumbermen do not penetrate far into the forest because timber cut in remote parts cannot be got to market. The case is far different with the miner. The whole country, as far as explored, is very rich in minerals, of which gold, silver, copper, and iron have been extensively mined. Of these, gold, on account of its high value in small bulk, is utilizable wherever found, and a strong man can carry $20,000 worth on his back.

Gold has been mined in Alaska and British Columbia for fifty years, but the history of the Klondike gold field on the upper Yukon is the most interesting and typical. Mining began there in 1896, and the gravel along many streams was found to be very rich.

The gold occurs in the form of fine dust or small grains or nuggets disseminated in alluvial sand and gravel, from which it is separated by washing. Along the Yukon the gravel is frozen to the bottom, a distance of fifteen to forty feet. The upper layers thaw out in summer but contain little gold. The gravel has to be thawed by building a fire upon it, shoveling out the loosened material, and building another fire in the bottom of the hole. In this way the rich bottom deposits are reached and taken out by running tunnels in all directions. Washing is done only in summer, when water is plentiful. The simplest process is by "panning." An iron pan is filled with gravel and water, and, by skillful shaking, rinsing, and pouring, the dirt is washed out, leaving the heavier particles of gold in the bottom of the pan. The work is done more rapidly by means of a "cradle" or "rocker," which is a wooden box open at one end and mounted so that it can be rocked while water is poured in. The same object is accomplished on a larger scale by "sluicing," or running a stream of water over gravel in a long trough. The most improved mining machinery is now in use.

The Klondike field yielded, up to 1918, gold to the value of about $196,000,000, as much as $22,000,000 having been taken out in one year.

Most of the stream gravels of the Yukon plateau contain gold, and in many fields sufficient to make mining profitable. The most important of these are the Iditarod and Fairbanks districts on southern tributaries of the Yukon in Alaska, which yield about $7,500,000 annually. Here the city of Fairbanks is provided with all the conveniences of civilized life, — electric light, telephone, mail service, water supply, banks, churches, and newspapers, — and is the principal commercial center of interior Alaska. In a district on the coast of the Seward peninsula, of which Nome is the center, gold is obtained from the sands of the seashore and coastal plain to the amount of $3,000,000 annually.

Fisheries. — To the Canadian province belong some of the most productive marine fishing grounds in the world. The wide continental shelf, including the Gulf of St. Lawrence and the banks of Newfoundland, covered with shallow, cold water, is the feeding ground of myriads of cod, halibut, herring, and mackerel, which furnish occupation for a large part of the coast population. Hundreds of vessels from Canadian and United States ports go out every season to catch and cure fish. Cod are caught with trawls, which are lines sometimes half a mile long, anchored at the ends, and carrying hooks about four feet apart. Men go out every day in small boats to take off the fish and rebait the hooks, and are often prevented by fog and storm from regaining their vessel.

The Siberian Province. — In Eurasia a region in almost every respect the counterpart of the Canadian province stretches from the Baltic to the Pacific. West of the Yenisei River it is a low plain, very poorly drained, covered with coniferous forest and inhabited by fur-bearing animals. East of the Yenisei it is diversified with hills, plateaus, and mountains, terminating in the great volcanic chain of Kamchatka. The Arctic rivers are choked with ice most of the year, and their valleys are subject to great inundations in the spring. None are of much value for navigation except the Amur, which on account of its southerly position is more open, and leads to the Pacific. Lake Baikal, about half the size of Lake Superior, is the largest body of fresh water in Eurasia, and the deepest in the world. Northern Sweden contains immense deposits of high-grade iron ore. Along the southern border of the province in Asia, and in the Ural Mountains, a rich mineral belt yields gold, silver, platinum, iron, and coal. The Siberian Railway skirts the southern boundary as the Canadian Pacific does that of the Canadian province (p. 455).

The American Arctic Province. — The northern part of North America, including most of the Arctic archipelago, is a lowland underlain by ground perpetually frozen to the depth of 100 feet or more. The surface thaws during the short summer, but for want of underdrainage remains soft and marshy. This region forms the *tundra*, locally known as the "barren grounds." There are no trees, but a carpet of mosses and lichens, with a few herbaceous plants and stunted shrubs, covers the ground. In winter the whole is blanketed with several feet of snow. Such vegetation renders some abundance of animal life possible. Musk oxen, hares, wolves, bears, and foxes are permanent inhabitants, and large herds of caribou find here summer pasture. Flights of wild fowl, geese, ducks, and divers sometimes darken the air. They arrive in May, nest and breed in the marshes, and depart southward in September. They are accompanied and preyed upon by hawks and eagles.

The musk ox and caribou possess special adaptations to their environment. Their food consists chiefly of the so-called "reindeer moss," a species of lichen. Their hoofs, which are spreading, curved and concave beneath, with sharp edges, give a foothold on slippery surfaces, prevent sinking in the snow, and form an efficient implement for scraping away the snow in search of food. The musk ox is enabled to endure any degree of cold by his winter undercoat of dense, fine wool, and overcoat of very long hair.

The tundra is the home of a few Eskimos, who wander inland from the coast, but it has been invaded by Indians from the south.

The Eurasian Arctic Province. — Arctic Eurasia is a lowland tundra like that of Arctic America, and is inhabited by various tribes, similar to the Eskimos in race, character, and habits of life. They are nearly all subjects of the Russian Empire. The Lapps of northern Europe keep large herds of domestic reindeer for draft, flesh, and milk, and for that reason are the most advanced of Polar peoples.

The Greenland Province. — The Greenland ice moves slowly outward toward the coasts and sends glacial tongues through numerous fiords to the sea. The discharged icebergs form a barrier which renders access to the east coast exceedingly difficult. They drift southward, and in the spring often interfere with the traffic between America and Europe, before they finally melt in the warm waters of the Gulf Stream. The ice floes which cover the Arctic Ocean in winter, and never break up completely, constitute a portion of the rock sphere, many feet in thickness, floating upon the water, and may be considered as a peculiar part of the land. The land and sea ice are incapable of supporting life of any kind. The sea constitutes the base of supplies. In its waters minute floating organisms are abundant and furnish food for fish, which in turn support mammals and great flocks of sea birds. The birds migrate southward in winter, but the seal, walrus, and polar bear are permanent inhabitants of the water and sea ice. The bare, rocky cliffs of the coast afford a perching place for birds and men, and the ice-free areas of land at the north support herds of musk oxen and caribou. Timber is obtained from the driftwood originally brought to the sea by the American and Asiatic rivers. Metals are obtained only from foreign visitors.

Under these hard conditions human life is reduced nearly to its lowest terms, but is maintained by about 10,000 Eskimos, originally Mongolian

Fig. 370. — Dog sledge and kayak, Greenland.

emigrants from Asia. Agriculture in any form is impossible, and vegetable food is scarcely known. Men must live, if at all, much as the other animals do. The seal is their main dependence for food, clothing, and fuel. The necessities of seal hunting have developed a remarkable degree of ingenuity and skill. It is carried on largely by means of the *kayak*, a long, narrow boat made of skins and completely closed except for a hole in the deck, which permits the hunter to sit on the bottom. His skin jacket is fastened to the margin of the hole in such a manner as to render the boat practically a water-tight, floating garment. The kayak is managed with a paddle and is easily capsized, but the experienced kayaker is able to right himself without serious inconvenience. Seals are captured by means of a wooden harpoon, with a detachable head of bone or metal. An inflated skin is tied to the harpoon head by a long rawhide line, and, as the seal dives, serves to show in what direction he goes. The walrus and polar bear are killed with harpoons and spears. Their flesh is used for food and their skins for rugs, beds, and tents. Walrus tusks are of value for harpoon heads. Fish and birds are caught with nets and small darts.

For clothing the Eskimos add animal skins to their own. Bird skins with the feathers turned inward form comfortable underclothing. Jacket, trousers, and boots of seal skin, single or double, are worn by men and women. For housing, the Eskimos make use of the materials which are most abundant, snow and ice, and find them admirably adapted to their needs. An *igloo*, or snow hut, can be built by three men in an hour. Two men cut half-frozen snow into blocks and carry them to a third man, who, standing in the center, lays up a circular wall, the circumference of which is gradually diminished until a dome is completed at about his own height. A small opening is made at the bottom and protected by a covered passage, through which the occupants crawl in. A seal-oil lamp or two burning inside soon causes some of the snow to melt; the water, soaking outward, freezes, and the walls of the hut become so solid that a bear cannot break into it. Permanent winter houses are built of driftwood, stones, and turf, and in summer skin tents are used. Men, women, and children consume great quantities of flesh and fat; and lighting, heating, and cooking are done by burning oil in an open lamp made from a piece of soft stone, a bit of twisted moss serving for a wick.

The Eskimo has but one friend and helper, his dog. The Eskimo dog is a domesticated wolf admirably adapted to the conditions of Arctic life. He is strong, hardy, impervious to cold, and can live upon one frozen fish a day. He curls up on the snow, lays his bushy tail over his nose, and sleeps in any weather. He is almost indispensable in an attack upon a bear, and is an efficient draft animal. A sledge is made of driftwood and whale or walrus bones bound together with thongs of hide or sinew, and capable of carrying a load of several hundred pounds. A team of ten dogs, each attached to the sledge by a separate thong, will draw the hunter over a good ice or snow surface seventy miles a day. Dog driving is as much of an art as kayaking. The driver controls his team by words of command enforced with a whip short in the handle, but having a lash long enough to reach the farthest dog, and wielded with great skill.

The men fish, hunt on sea, ice, and land, make harpoons and spears, drive when traveling, and build the huts. The women cut up and cook the game, dress and prepare the skins, which they render soft and pliable by persistent chewing, make clothing with bone needles and sinew threads, construct kayaks and large open boats for family use, and take care of the children. Family life is generally happy and children are kindly treated. The feast which follows a successful hunt is shared by all the neighbors. The Eskimos are naturally peaceable, honest, and truthful, and crime is almost unknown. They roam about a good deal, because they are compelled to use the resources of a large territory. They "live upon the farthest edge of things," and their life is so nicely adjusted to their environment that any interference with it is apt to disturb the balance to their detriment. The introduction of firearms, steel knives, and other civilized weapons and utensils should be of great benefit to them, but a fixed abode, "white men's" clothing, and wooden houses warmed with coal stoves, often prove disastrous. Native habits of life are extremely unsanitary according to civilized standards, but departure from them and contact with white men render the Eskimos less hardy, and have introduced lung diseases which prove very fatal. Civilization is likely to result in the decline and perhaps final disappearance of the race. Destruction of the seal by white hunters threatens to destroy the economic basis of Eskimo life.

Greenland belongs politically to the kingdom of Denmark, and a few Danish officials and missionaries, with their families, reside on the west coast. Greenland has been used as a station and point of departure by many Arctic explorers, and it was only by help of the Eskimos and their dogs that Admiral Peary was enabled to make so many journeys in that region and finally to reach the North Pole.

The Antarctic Province. — Since 1898 a number of exploring expeditions have visited the Antarctic regions. The first winter passed on the continent by human beings was in 1899. In 1901–1904 Captain Scott spent two winters in land travel. In 1908 Sir Ernest Shackleton located the position of the south magnetic pole and reached a point 113 miles from the geographical South Pole. On December 16, 1911, Captain Amundsen, after a sledge journey of 870 miles, attained the South Pole. A few days later, on January 7, 1912, Captain Scott also reached the South Pole. As a result of these explorations, the Antarctic province is now known to contain a continental land mass, covered with snow and ice and bordered in most places by a barrier of floating ice several hundred feet thick. South of New Zealand a gulf of open water extends nearly to 80° S. Lat. and is bordered by a high plateau. At 85° S. Lat. a mountain range, with peaks 15,000 feet high, extends toward South America. The pole is situated upon a plateau at a height of 10,500 feet. The climate, even at that elevation, was not found to be very severe. Land life is more meager than in Greenland. The shores are occupied by penguins (Fig. 211) and other sea birds.

THE ECONOMIC STANDING OF THE PRINCIPAL COUNTRIES OF THE WORLD.

(Statistics based chiefly on Statistical Abstract of the United States for 1918 and the Statesman's Year Book for 1919.)

Country.	Area, Sq. Mi.	Population.	Density.	Railways, Miles.	Foreign Commerce.
North America.					
United States	3,088,519	105,000,000	35.	266,381	$ 8,784,217,000 †11,827,000,000
Alaska	590,884	64,000	......	455	131,000,000
Porto Rico	3,435	1,246,000	363.	340	137,683,000
Canada	3,729,665	8,361,000	2.24	37,434	2,502,550,000
Mexico	767,323	15,502,000	20.	15,840	222,971,000
Central America	208,339	5,747,000	27.6	2,179	88,819,000
Cuba	44,218	2,628,000	59.4	2,359	611,936,000
Haiti and Dominican Republic	30,397	3,225,000	100.	548	68,053,000
Other West Indies	13,973	2,188,000	156.	......	60,872,000
South America.					
Argentina	1,153,419	8,284,000	7.	21,880	883,967,000
Bolivia	514,155	2,890,000	5.6	1,354	45,856,000
Brazil	3,280,905	26,542,000	8.	17,477	507,998,000
Chile	289,796	3,870,000	13.36	5,105	380,333,000
Colombia	435,278	5,473,000	12.57	708	59,677,000
Ecuador	118,627	1,323,000	11.5	365	19,930,000
Guiana	167,540	455,000	2.7	......	72,385,000
Paraguay	165,000	1,000,000	6.	255	9,181,000
Peru	683,321	4,620,000	6.7	1,724	156,440,000
Uruguay	72,172	1,379,000	19.	1,601	112,073,000
Venezuela	393,476	2,828,000	7.2	533	45,353,000
Europe.					
United Kingdom	121,438	46,089,000	379.5	23,709	7,404,706,000
France	212,822	41,000,000	192.5	31,958	6,478,384,000
Belgium	11,760	7,575,000	644.	5,451	1,691,775,000
Netherlands	13,199	6,583,000	498.75	2,113	1,551,745,000
Denmark	* 16,585	*2,987,000	180.	2,556	422,238,000
Sweden	173,008	5,758,000	33.28	9,303	722,245,000
Norway	124,675	2,509,000	20.12	1,979	624,210,000
Switzerland	15,945	3,880,000	243.4	3,660	931,460,000
Italy	*123,000	*37,000,000	300.	11,891	1,928,368,000
Spain	195,057	20,730,000	106.28	9,354	517,537,000
Portugal	35,501	5,958,000	167.83	1,854	104,195,000
Germany*	179,500	60,000,000	335.	35,000	....
Austria*	31,700	6,500,000	205.	5,300	....
Hungary*	36,500	8,500,000	232.	5,400	....
Czechoslovakia*	54,700	13,500,000	247.	10,700	....
Jugoslavia*	95,000	11,000,000	115.7	5,000	....
Roumania*	113,900	16,000,000	140.	9,100	....
Bulgaria*	39,100	4,300,000	110.	1,824	....
Albania*	8,450	620,000	73.3	......	....
Greece*	57,400	6,300,000	109.7	1,500	....
Constantinople*	275	1,040,000	......	......	....
Russia in Europe*	1,598,000	81,000,000	50.7	30,000	....
Ukraine*	197,000	30,000,000	152.2	3,400	....

* Estimated. † 1919.

Country.	Area Sq. Mi.	Population.	Density.	Railway, Miles.	Foreign Commerce.
Europe — Continued					
Poland*..............	150,000	30,000,000	200.	6,100	....
Finland*.............	128,000	3,140,000	24.5	2,527	....
Esthonia*......... ...	19,750	1,395,000	70.6	......	....
Letvia*....	20,000	1,550,000	77.5	......	....
Lithuania*......	18,500	2,200,000	119.	......	....
Danzig*..............	730	300,000	......	......	....
Asia.					
China................	4,278,352	325,000,000	76.	6,467	1,031,000,000
Japanese Empire......	245,551	78,622,000	308.6	9,101	1,462,718,000
British India..........	1,802,657	315,156,000	174.8	36,333	1,241,672,000
Other British Asia.....	169,826	9,305,000	54.	1,847	1,171,120,000
Siam.	195,000	8,820,000	45.2	1,210	81,176,000
French Indo-China.....	256,196	17,250,000	70.	......	161,000,000
Afghanistan*..........	240,900	6,000,000	25.	......	....
Persia*..............	612,000	9,000,000	15.	34	74,737,000
Turkey*..	160,000	8,000,000	50.	3,260	....
Russia in Asia*........	6,656,096	29,694,000	4.5	10,000	....
Philippines............	115,026	9,010,000	78.8	757	200,378,000
Dutch East Indies.....	739,545	47,956,000	64.8	1,730	454,470,000
Syria and Palestine*...	114,530	3,675,000	33.	......	....
Mesopotamia*..... ...	143,250	2,000,000	9.	......	....
Hedjaz*..............	96,500	300,000	3.	......	....
Arabia*..............	954,000	1,700,000	1.8	......	....
Armenia*............	103,500	3,500,000	34.	......	....
Africa.					
Egypt................	383,900				
Inhabited area.......	12,013	12,569,000	1000.	3,916	335,069,000
Sudan................	984,520	3,400,000	3.45	1,500	24,468,000
Union of South Africa..	792,340	6,068,000	7.6	10,021	294,631,000
British East Africa*....	786,500	14,509,000	18.4	1,618	43,560,000
British West Africa*...	451,500	19,608,000	43.5	1,567	149,469,000
Kongo Free State*.....	913,127	15,000,000	16.4	1,020	22,033,000
Morocco*.............	169,576	6,000,000	33.4	550	51,979,000
Algeria and Tunis......	270,432	7,517,000	28.	4,025	214,915,000
Madagascar...........	228,600	3,512,000	15.4	245	44,795,000
Other French Territory*	3,691,000	21,385,000	5.8	......	102,358,000
Portuguese Africa......	927,292	7,734,000	8.3	1,155	....
Liberia...............	36,834	1,500,000	40.	......	2,523,000
Libia................	406,000	530,000	1.3	......	....
Abyssinia............	350,000	8,000,000	23.	......	....
Australasia.					
Australia.............	2,974,581	4,981,000	1.67	24,769	794,971,000
New Zealand.........	104,751	1,170,000	11.1	3,012	277,791,000
British Islands.........	109,073	571,000	5.2	......	....
French Islands........	9,194	81,000	9.	......	11,600,000

* Estimated.

RANK OF LEADING COUNTRIES OF THE WORLD.

(Including their colonies, dependencies, etc.)

	In Area.	Square Miles
1	British Empire	13,500,000
2	Russia	8,254,000
3	Chinese Republic	4,278,000
4	United States	3,797,000
5	French Republic	3,662,000
6	Brazil	3,281,000
7	Argentina	1,153,000
	The Land	57,156,000

	In Population.	
1	British Empire	451,000,000
2	Chinese Republic	325,000,000
3	United States	115,000,000
4	Russia	111,000,000
5	French Republic	82,000,000
6	Japanese Empire	77,000,000
7	Germany	60,000,000
	The World	1,678,400,000

	In Railroad Mileage.	
1	United States	266,387
2	British Empire	150,000
3	French Republic	50,000
4	Russia*	40,000
5	Germany*	35,000
6	Argentina	22,000
7	Brazil	17,500
	The World	730,000

	In Foreign Commerce.	
1	British Empire	$16,292,600,000
2	United States	11,827,000,000
3	French Republic	6,875,000,000
4	Italy	1,928,368,000
5	Belgium	1,691,775,000
6	Netherlands	1,551,745,000
7	Japanese Empire	1,462,718,000
	The World	52,781,000,000

*Estimated.

INDEX

INDEX OF REFERENCE MAPS

CONTOUR MAPS (U. S. G. S.)